SEX CHROMOSOMES

SEX CHROMOSOMES

Ursula Mittwoch

THE GALTON LABORATORY
UNIVERSITY COLLEGE LONDON
LONDON, ENGLAND

1967

ACADEMIC PRESS   New York • London

ACADEMIC PRESS, INC.
111 Fifth Avenue, New York, New York 10003

United Kingdom Edition published by
ACADEMIC PRESS INC. (LONDON) LTD.
Berkeley Square House, London W.1

LIBRARY OF CONGRESS CATALOG CARD NUMBER: 66-29672

PRINTED IN THE UNITED STATES OF AMERICA

PREFACE

During the present renaissance of chromosome studies, the sex chromosomes occupy a place of paramount importance. Thus, among human chromosomal abnormalities, there are more cases affecting the sex chromosomes than all the other chromosomes put together. On a more theoretical level, the frequently outstanding behavior of the sex chromosomes in dividing and nondividing cells is giving a lead to current thinking on the behavior and function of chromosomes in general.

Recent developments in the field of human chromosomes are unprecedented. Within the past ten or fifteen years research into this subject has progressed from a difficult undertaking, attempted from time to time by a few individual investigators, to a flourishing discipline with worldwide application, which has, moreover, a direct bearing on the medical sciences. As a corollary, an interest in the subject is no longer confined to the traditional specialists in cytogenetics; the new findings must be intelligible to all students of biology and medicine, as well as to physicians, and to others whose work brings them into contact with diseases of the sex chromosome mechanism. In addition, knowledge of the role of the chromosomes in normal sex determination has reached a stage of scientific achievement where an understanding is satisfying for its own sake.

A large proportion of present-day literature is of necessity unintelligible to nonspecialized readers who may lack the necessary cytogenetic background. In the present work, the discussion of recent discoveries of normal and abnormal sex chromosomes in man and in other mammals is preceded by a description of the basic discoveries relating to the sex chromosomes in diverse organisms which form the foundations supporting the rapidly growing superstructure of modern work. The historical approach has been adopted because it provides a natural framework for the growth of a science and thus helps in an understanding of the subject. Since the amount of teaching provided in cytogenetics is so variable, this approach should also help to make this monograph useful to people with different levels of attainment in the subject, for, confronted with scientific discovery all—from the doyen to the novice—are equal.

Obviously, in a work of so wide a range none of the topics could be treated exhaustively. It has been my intention to include those aspects from the earlier literature which are most closely related to recent work, and from this, in turn, I could select only what appeared to be most relevant.

I owe a debt of gratitude to all authors and publishers who gave me permission to include their illustrations; I am especially grateful to a number of scientists who went to the trouble of providing me with original material. They are all acknowledged in the text. Chapter 10 is based on an article which was published in *The Journal of Medical Genetics*, and appears through the courtesy of the editor. Dr. J. R. Ellis, Dr. C. E. Ford, F.R.S., and Dr. G. R. Fraser very kindly read parts of the manuscript and suggested valuable improvements. Needless to say, they are in no way responsible for any errors which may remain. All the drawings, whether original or copies, were done by Mr. A. J. Lee and, though they speak for themselves, I should like to thank him for the combination of artistic skill with care for scientific detail which he employed. I also wish to thank Mrs. Anne Ginger for her patient cooperation in preparing the typescript, and Academic Press for skillful help in producing the finished product.

January, 1967   URSULA MITTWOCH

CONTENTS

Chapter 10. Sex Chromatin

Chapter 11. Heterochromatin

Chapter 12. The Function of the Sex Chromosomes

CHAPTER 1

THE CHROMOSOMAL
BASIS OF SEX DETERMINATION

I. Introduction

It was in 1908 that Edmund B. Wilson gave an address to the American Association for the Advancement of Science. The subject was: "Recent researches on the determination and heredity of sex," and in this talk he asked the following two questions: "Does sex arise, as was long believed, as a response of the organism to external stimuli? Or is it automatically ordered by internal factors, and if so, what is their nature?" He concluded that in all probability sex was controlled by internal factors of the germ cells, and that the male or female condition does not arise primarily as a response of the developing organism to corresponding external conditions (Wilson, 1909a).

This answer was by no means self-evident. Twelve years before, Wilson himself had held that "the determination of sex is not by inheritance, but by the combined effect of external conditions" (Wilson, 1896). At the close of the nineteenth century the view prevailed that the embryo was at first sexually undifferentiated and that sex was subsequently determined by such agents as temperature and nutrition (Wilson, 1896; Doncaster, 1914). Let us therefore retrace some of the landmarks which caused this fundamental change in outlook.

II. The Development of the Cell Theory

During the course of the nineteenth century the role of the cell as the basic unit of organisms became gradually understood. The detailed study of cells required the existence of optically advanced microscopes, and such instruments became available in the second quarter of the century. The introduction of achromatic lenses at that time paved the way for new investigations and discoveries (Nordenskiöld, 1927), while conversely a renewed interest in microscopic observations encouraged

1

improvements in the instruments and their production in larger numbers (Hughes, 1959).

In 1833 the Scottish botanist Robert Brown published his discovery that cells contain a nucleus as an essential component. A few years later, the cell theory was put on its feet by Schleiden (1838) and by Schwann (1839), in Germany. They established that animals and plants are organized into basic units of comparable structure, which have an individual life and yet coordinate to form the organism as a whole. The tissues of the body are composed either entirely of cells, or of cells plus products which originated in cells.

As regards the origin of new cells, Schleiden and Schwann had thought that this might come about by either one of two processes. Cells might arise either from a parent cell, or they might be formed by a process of free cell formation, crystallizing from a material which was not itself composed of cells. Gradually it became clear that the idea of free cell formation had to be abandoned. In his book on cellular pathology, published in 1858, Rudolph Virchow insisted that every cell must be the offspring of a preexisting cell, just as an animal arises only from an animal or a plant from a plant; and gradually the concept of the continuity of cells from generation to generation was established.

III. Mitosis

Although the principle that cells arise only from preexisting cells has become the foundation of modern biology, when Virchow wrote this, evidence was, as yet, unavailable. Indeed, the mechanism by which cells divide eluded investigators for another 20 years. Then, during the 1870s began an era of intense investigations into the problems of cell division and fertilization. The introduction of techniques for fixation and staining made it possible to study the different processes in considerable detail; and new discoveries followed each other in close succession. In 1873, Schneider announced that during cell division the nucleus does not disappear, as had hitherto been assumed, but undergoes a complicated process of metamorphosis. By the end of the decade, four investigators reported that they had succeeded in following the process of cell division in living cells. Flemming (1879) saw it in epithelial cells of salamander larvae, Peremeschko (1879) in epithelial cells of newt larvae (*Triton cristatus*), and Schleicher (1879) in cartilage cells of amphibian larvae, while Strasburger (1880) described it in the staminal hairs of the spiderwort (*Tradescantia virginica*). Thus, the sequence of events could be verified, and it became clear that essentially the same process of cell division occurs in animals and in plants (Flemming, 1882a; Strasburger, 1884).

The last decade of the nineteenth century saw the introduction of apochromatic lenses, which removed the residual chromatic aberration inherent in the achromatic combinations (Hughes, 1959); and thus, the resolving power of the microscope had reached the highest degree possible with visible light.

Schleicher (1879) called the process of cell division "karyokinesis" (nuclear movement), a term which is still sometimes used; it is of interest because it recognizes the kinetic nature of the nucleus, in which stages of quite different appearance give rise to one another. Flemming (1879, 1880) made the all-important discovery that the threads, into which the nucleus resolves itself prior to cell division, divide lengthwise, and van Beneden (1883) and Heuser (1884) showed that in both animals and plants one member of the two newly formed threads went to each daughter cell. Flemming also introduced the word "mitosis" (1882a), as well as the term "chromatin" to denote the substance in the cell nucleus which takes up the color from nuclear dyes (1880). The word "chromosomes" is due to Waldeyer (1888): "I should like to permit myself the suggestion that those bodies, which Boveri has called 'chromatic elements' and in which occurs one of the most important acts of karyokinesis, i.e. Flemming's lengthwise division, be given a special technical term, 'chromosomes.'"[*]

IV. Fertilization

Once the fundamental aspects of the cell were appreciated, it was at last possible to understand the facts of fertilization, and its significance. Oscar Hertwig (1876) observed, among others, the eggs of the sea urchin, *Toxopneustes lividus*, which are particularly favorable objects for study, since they are transparent and can be artificially inseminated. He discovered that during fertilization two nuclei unite, one of which is derived from the egg and the other from the spermatozoon, and he concluded that fertilization consists in the fusion of sexually differentiated cell nuclei. Having established this, Hertwig went one important step further: Since fertilization must be the act during which the qualities of the father are transmitted to the offspring, he concluded that the nuclear material must be the bearer of those qualities which are inherited from parents to children (Hertwig, 1885).

These conclusions were confirmed by the work of van Beneden (1883)

[*] Author's translation.

on the fertilization of the threadworm, *Parascaris equorum,* (formerly *Ascaris megalocephala*), which lives as a parasite on the horse. In *Parascaris,* the eggs are transparent, and the organism has the further advantage of having a small number of large chromosomes; van Beneden was able to observe that in the variety which he studied the sperm and the egg nucleus each resolve themselves into two chromosomes and that the four chromosomes then divide longitudinally, so that each daughter nucleus receives equal amounts of paternal and maternal chromosomes. Thus, it became clear that the male and the female germ cells are equivalent from the point of view of the hereditary material which they contain and that each germ cell contributes one-half of the chromosomes that are present in the offspring.

Van Beneden's results on *Parascaris* were confirmed by Boveri (1890), who also extended them to a number of other animals; he showed that in the sea urchin *Echinus microtuberculatus,* each parent contributed 9 chromosomes, in the worm *Sagitta bipunctata,* 9, in the medusa *Tiara,* 14, and in the mollusc *Pterotrachea,* 16 chromosomes. By comparing the position of the chromosomes in nuclei which had just begun to divide with that found at the end of the previous division, Boveri concluded that the chromosomes retain their individuality in the nondividing nucleus, even though, at that time, they are not visible.

V. Meiosis

Since it was shown that the germ cells contain one-half of the number of chromosomes contained in the body cells, it followed that at some time during the formation of the germ cells the chromosomes had to be reduced to one-half of their original nunber (Boveri, 1890). This assumption was first made by Weismann (1887) on purely theoretical grounds, and it was he who introduced the term "reduction division." In the following year, Strasburger (1888) observed that in flowering plants the chromosome number is halved during the formation of pollen grains and embryo sacs.

The sequence of events which results in the halving of the chromosome number was described in 1905 by Farmer and Moore. They had observed that during the first division the chromosomes form into pairs and that each daughter cell receives one member of each pair. This is followed by a second division, which resembles an ordinary mitosis, except that the cells contain only half the number of chromosomes. To these two cell divisions they gave the name "maiosis"; the spelling was later changed to "meiosis."

VI. The Beginning of Mendelian Genetics

Although it took some time until the mechanism which brought about the halving of the chromosome number during meiosis became understood, it is clear that by the end of the nineteenth century the basic phenomena of the cell were largely known.

The bodies of all higher animals and plants are composed of cells, which have originated by the repeated division of the fertilized egg. The characters of the parents are transmitted to the offspring by means of the chromosomes which are situated in the nuclei of the egg and the spermatozoa (or the pollen grains of flowering plants). Prior to the formation of the gametes the number of chromosomes which are present in the body cells of the parents is reduced by one-half, and the original number is restored at fertilization. Henceforth, the process of mitosis ensures that all newly formed cells receive the same complement of chromosomes.

Thus, by the beginning of the present century the stage was set for the rediscovery of Mendel's laws of heredity, and this in fact happened in the year 1900.

As is well known, Mendel (1866) used the garden pea, *Pisum*, for his experiments. By crossing inbred lines differing in one unit character, such as tall and short stems, he obtained a hybrid, or F_1, generation, all of which had tall stems; and on selfing the hybrids, obtained an F_2 generation in which plants with long and short stems segregated in a three-to-one ratio (Fig. 1.1). The character for tallness, which was manifest in the hybrid, was called "dominant" and the character for shortness, which became apparent only after breeding from the hybrid, was called "recessive."

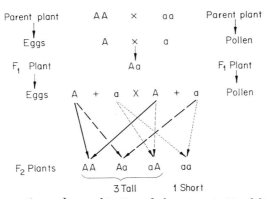

FIG. 1.1. Segregation and recombination of characters in Mendelian inheritance.

Underlying these results is the concept of unit characters, which are present in pairs, but of which only one enters the gametes. The combination of gametes in pairs results in the segregation of characters in the offspring.

Mendel's second law states that if two pairs of contrasting characters are considered, each pair segregates independently prior to the formation of the gametes. Thus, peas may be either yellow or green, and either round or wrinkled, and one pair of characters has no influence on the segregation of the other.

These ideas made little impact in 1865, but in the year 1900 they fitted into the scientific picture. In that year, three investigators independently reported their results on crossing experiments, Correns with pea plants and maize, Tschermak with pea plants, and de Vries with a number of plants. They found not only that Mendel had anticipated their results, but that he had also explained them in the same way.

But Mendel's results were not merely in agreement with breeding experiments in progress at the turn of the century; the striking similarity shown in the behavior of Mendel's factors and that of the chromosomes was decisive in establishing the theory that the chromosomes are the bearers of the hereditary material. In 1902, Sutton, working on the spermatogenesis of the "lubber grasshopper," *Brachystola magna*, suggested the probability that the association of paternal and maternal chromosomes in pairs and their subsequent separation during the reduction division may constitute the physical basis of the Mendelian laws of heredity. He pointed out that the phenomena observed in the division of the germ cells and in heredity have two essential features in common, namely the purity of units (chromosomes, characters) and the independent transmission of them.

Mendel's factors were called "genes" by Johannsen (1909), and from that time the science of genetics produced rapid and far-reaching results.

VII. Linkage

A few years after the rediscovery of Mendel's papers, Bateson *et al.* (1908) in England reported that certain characters of the sweet pea, *Lathyrus odoratus*, did not seem to obey Mendel's second law of the independent segregation of characters. When plants with purple flowers and long pollen grains were crossed with others having white flowers and round pollen grains, the combinations, purple and long, and white and round, were found among the offspring more often than would be expected on the theory of independent assortment. Bateson and co-workers tried to explain their finding by assuming a repulsion between the characters, purple flowers and round pollen grains and white flowers and long pollen grains. The phenomenon underlying this observation was worked out in great detail by Thomas Hunt Morgan and his school in America, and it was here that the union between genetics and cytology was completed. As their experimental animal they used the fruit fly, *Drosophila melanogaster*, (its specific name at that time was *D. ampelophila*), which is a fast breeder—a generation can be completed in 10 days—and has only four pairs of chromosomes. Over the years during which this fly was bred in the laboratory it acquired a large number of new characters which, arising as changes in the genes (or mutations) were, henceforth, inherited. As a result of many crossing experiments it was found that only those genes that were located on different chromosomes assorted independently. Genes which were situated on the same chromosome tended to stay together when the gametes were formed and were described as being linked. Thus, in *Drosophila melanogaster* the characters fall into four linkage groups. Linkage implies that any two characters which come in together from a parent tend to stay together in the offspring, but this association does not generally hold in 100% of the cases for it may be broken as a result of a crossover. The further away two genes are situated from each other on a chromosome, the more likely it is that a crossover will occur, and conversely, genes which are very close to each other rarely cross over (are tightly linked). By making many crosses between different genes and observing the number of recombinants among them, T. H. Morgan (1912) was able to ascertain the relative positions of the genes on the chromosomes and the distances between them. In this way, the principles of formal genetics were laid down.

The physical basis underlying these phenomena began to become clear with Janssens' theory of the chiasmatype, which was first elaborated in 1909. According to this theory, the chiasmata, or crosses, which are visible in the paired chromosomes during the prophase of meiosis are a result of an interchange between paternal and maternal chromosomes. Morgan and his colleagues (T. H. Morgan *et al.*, 1925) incorporated this theory into their own, namely, that crossing-over between linked genes involves an exchange between large pieces of chromosomes.

VIII. Nondisjunction

Genetics has always benefited from apparent exceptions to its rules and the chromosome theory of heredity received strong additional support in 1916, when Bridges discovered that in *Drosophila* a pair of chromosomes may fail to separate at meiosis, so that both chromosomes go into the same egg. As a result, flies are formed which have the wrong number of chromosomes and at the same time show an abnormal type of inheritance of the genes borne on these chromosomes.

In 1926, T. H. Morgan's book "The Theory of the Gene" was published, and thus, within a quarter of a century, classic genetics had become established.

IX. The Discovery of Sex Chromosomes

Genetics is based on an analysis of segregating characters. Of such characters, sex is undoubtedly the most striking and the one that is most widely spread among living organisms. Nevertheless, at the beginning of the century, the genetic basis of sex was by no means obvious. An understanding of the mechanisms which determined sex came only gradually, for it required a special knowledge of the behavior of chromosomes, which in due course emerged from studies on the cell divisions leading to the formation of the gametes in insects.

In 1891 Henking studied the cell divisions of the spermatocytes (p. 31) in the plant bug, *Pyrrhocorus apterus,* and observed that during the first division of the spermatocyte there was a peculiar chromatin body, which was more intensely stained than others and frequently lagged behind other chromosomes. In the second division of the spermatocyte, this chromosome passed undivided into one of the daughter nuclei. Henking did not form any clear idea about this chromosome and, perhaps, for this reason, labeled it X. Nevertheless he observed two characteristic phenomena about it: (1) its differential staining behavior and (2) its lack of synchronization with the rest of the chromosomes. Other authors, among them Montgomery (1904), confirmed that during the spermatogenesis of insects, one of the chromosomes differed from the rest by remaining visible during the early stage of the spermatocyte and passing undivided to one of the daughter cells during one of the meiotic divisions. McClung was the first to suggest that this chromosome might be concerned with the determination of sex: Since two classes of spermatozoa, one of which contained the accessory chromosome and one of which lacked it, were formed in equal numbers, it followed that the offspring also would be of two types; and "we know that the only quality which separates the members of a species into these two groups is that of sex" (McClung, 1901). This view received some support from Sutton (1902) from his studies on the lubber grasshopper, *Brachystola magna,* even though Sutton, like McClung himself, believed the accessory chromosome to be male-determining. On the other hand,

Montgomery (1904) regarded the accessory chromosomes as degenerating chromosomes, which were in the process of disappearance in the evolution from a higher to a lower chromosome number. It is obvious that the problem was bedeviled not only by the ideas current at the time as to how sex was determined, but also by the singular behavior of the accessory chromosomes, which may assume entirely different shapes in different types of cells and in the two sexes.

Stevens (1905) studied spermatogenesis in a number of insects. In one of them, the common meal worm, *Tenebrio molitor*, she found two classes of spermatozoa, which differed from each other in the size of the chromosomes, while the eggs were all the same. In the same year, Wilson (1905), who had studied the chromosomes in a number of insects belonging to the group Hemiptera (bugs, lice, etc.), came to the following conclusion; "The sexes of Hemiptera show constant and characteristic differences in the chromosome groups, which are of such a nature as to leave no doubt that a definite connection of some kind between the chromosomes and the determination of sex exists in these animals." Wilson (1906) further observed that in these insects two types of sex determination may occur: Either the males have an unequal pair of chromosomes, whose members pass into different daughter cells at one of the meiotic divisions (in a few instances these two chromosomes are not visibly differentiated), or the males have only one such chromosome while the females have two (Fig. 1.2). In these species, therefore, the males have one chromosome less than the females. These chromosomes, which differ in the two sexes, have been called "heterochromosomes" by Montgomery (1904), and the rest of the chromosomes, which are the same in both sexes, "autosomes" (Montgomery, 1906). The terms "sex chromosomes," as well as "X-" and "Y-chromosomes," are due to Wilson (1909b,c, 1911).

We have thus arrived at two types of sex determination. If an X- and a Y-chromosome are present, the scheme is as in Fig. 1.2a. If only one sex chromosome is present, sex determination will be as in Fig. 1.2b (the O representing absence of a sex chromosome).

In both cases, the male produces two types of gametes and was therefore called the "digametic" or "heterogametic" sex; as the female gametes are alike insofar as each carries one X-chromosome, the female was called the "homogametic" sex.

Genetic evidence that sex is inherited was brought forward by Correns (1907) from his work on a flowering plant, *Bryonia* (see Chapter 3). As a result of crossing two different species and observing the sex of the reciprocal hybrids he concluded that half the male germ cells have a tendency towards male development, while the other half have a tendency to female development, whereas the eggs do not differ in this tendency. These conclusions were a great surprise at the time.

One of the difficulties was that at that time the relationship between genes and chromosomes was not yet worked out. Originally it was thought that sex was inherited like any other ordinary pair of Mendelian characters, and it was not until the second decade of the century that Morgan and his associates demonstrated that the genes are mere points situated along the length of the chromosome, like the stations along a railway line.

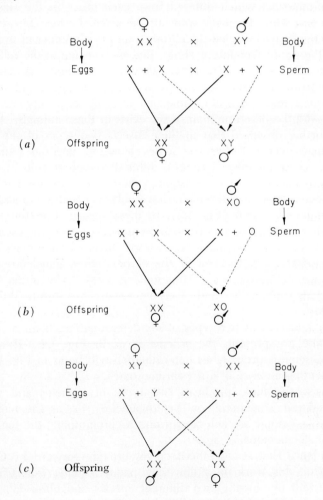

FIG. 1.2. Inheritance of sex: (a) male heterogamety, XY-type; (b) male heterogamety, XO-type; (c) female heterogamety, XY-type.

A second obstacle to an understanding of the cytological basis of sex determination turned out to be a historical accident. Just as the cytotological facts were being worked out which indicated that the male is the heterogametic sex, the first genetic experiments carried out on the currant moth, *Abraxas* (Doncaster and Raynor, 1906), seemed to show that it was the eggs of the female which contained two different types of sex determinants. In 1908 Stevens showed that in certain flies of the order Diptera, to which *Drosophila* belongs, the male has an unequal pair of sex chromosomes and is heterogametic, while the female has two X-chromosomes and is homogametic. But the first instance of sex-linkage in *Drosophila* was not published until 1910, when T. H. Morgan showed that the gene for white eye color was carried on the X-chromosome and thus provided genetic evidence that the female has two of these and the male only one. Thus, the period between 1901 and 1910 was one of confusion. As Bateson (1909) put it: "It is not a little remarkable that on this point . . . there should be diametrical opposition between the results of breeding experiments and those derived from cytology. . . . At first sight it seems difficult to suppose that a feature apparently so fundamental as sex should be differently constituted in different animals, but that seems at present the least improbable inference."

Bateson's inference proved to be right. Seiler (1914) obtained cytological evidence that in the ruby tiger-moth, *Phragmatobia fuliginosa,* the eggs fall into two classes with respect to the presence of sex chromosomes; and almost at the same time Doncaster (1914) discovered that although in most stains of *Abraxas* the chromosomes of the male and the female cannot be distinguished cytologically, the females of some strains have one chromosome less than the males. In these strains the males have 56 chromosomes and the females have 55 chromosomes; the latter produce two types of eggs containing 28 and 27 chromosomes, respectively. In other words, the females are XO and the males XX, while in the majority of strains the females are presumably XY, although the X- and the Y-chromosomes are not morphologically distinguishable. As Doncaster (1914) pointed out: "These observations have thus provided a rather remarkable confirmation of the hypothesis that the presence of an unpaired or unequally paired chromosome is connected with sex-limited transmission, for the hypothesis was founded on cases in which such a chromosome existed in the male, and thence it was inferred that in *Abraxas* and other moths it should theoretically be found in the female . . . and the condition which had been predicted was found."

In order to avoid confusion between this type of sex determination and that found in *Drosophila*, where the male is the heterogametic sex, a different type of terminology is sometimes employed: the chromosome which is present in duplicate in the male *Abraxas* is called Z, while the chromosome which occurs singly in the female is called W. A male would therefore be ZZ and a female WZ. However, as the latter terminology appears to be at least equally confusing, the names X- and Y-chromosome will be used in the present text for both types of sex determination. Accordingly, in *Drosophila* the male is XY and the female XX, whereas in *Abraxas* the male is XX and the female XY (Fig. 1.2c). The XY terminology, regardless whether the male or the female is heterogametic, is in accordance with the usage of Winge (1932). If it should later be found that the sex chromosomes act in fundamentally different ways in animals with male and female heterogamety, the terminology may have to be altered accordingly. At present the simpler XY terminology appears to be adequate.

In the years which followed, evidence in favor of the chromosomal basis of sex determination accumulated. In 1916 T. H. Morgan's and Bridges' monograph "Sex-Linked Inheritance in *Drosophila*" appeared. By that time over 30 genes carried on the X-chromosome had been found, and the mode of inheritance of the characters produced by them proved that the female of *Drosophila* has two X-chromosomes, while the male has one X-chromosome and a Y-chromosome, which does not take part in sexual differentiation.

On the cytological side, Mohr in 1916 published a detailed study on gametogenesis in *Locustu viridissima*. He found that whereas in the spermatocytes the single X-chromosome stained differently from the autosomes, in the oocytes of the female the two X-chromosomes could not be distinguished from the autosomes, thus adducing evidence that the X-chromosome may be morphologically different, according to whether it is present in the single or paired state.

In 1925, a year before Morgan's "Theory of the Gene," Wilson's monumental work, "The Cell in Development and Heredity" was published, and thus, at the first quarter of the century, classic cytology, too, was firmly established. The chapter entitled "Chromosomes and Sex" describes the sex chromosome mechanisms in a large variety of animals and plants. In addition to the usual XX/XY or XX/XO types of sex chromosomes, some more complicated arrangements had been discovered in certain organisms. For instance, the X-chromosome may consist of more than one chromosome and thus form a compound. Sex determination in organisms which reproduce by parthenogenesis had also been worked out.

It thus became established that in higher organisms sex is determined by a difference in chromosome constitution. As a rule this is established at fertilization; one of the sexes produces gametes of two kinds, which in turn give rise to offspring of either sex. In the majority of cases, the male is the heterogametic sex, and the eggs are sexually undifferentiated until they are fertilized either by a male- or a female-producing spermatozoon; but the opposite situation also occurs.

Regarding the part played by the sex chromosomes in genetic theory, Wilson (1925) wrote: "Nature here offers us, indeed, a series of experiments, systematically carried out on a grand scale, that afford crucial evidence concerning the causal relation between chromosomes and heredity." Sex chromosomes continue to be in the forefront of cytogenetic research today.

CHAPTER 2

MITOSIS, MEIOSIS, AND THE
FORMATION OF GAMETES

I. Introduction

The chromosomes as morphological units are generally visible only during cell division, that is during mitosis and during meiosis. Since the appearance of the chromosomes may be quite different in different stages of division, a knowledge of what happens during mitosis and meiosis is essential for an understanding of chromosome morphology. Detailed reviews of the physiology of mitosis and of meiosis have been published by Mazia (1961) and Rhoades (1961), respectively. The present description presents only a few essential facts concerning the morphology of the chromosomes during cell division.

II. Mitosis

The function of mitosis is to make two cells where there was one before, ensuring at the same time that each daughter cell has an identical set of chromosomes to the parent cell. In order to fulfil both functions, it is clear that two processes must be involved: (1) a doubling of the material of the chromosomes in the parent cell, and (2) the distribution of identical halves of the doubled chromosomes among the daughter cells.

The chromosomes consist of nucleic acids and proteins. The nucleic acids are themselves composed of large numbers of nucleotides, each of which consists of four chemical entities: a pentose sugar, phosphoric acid, one purine, and one pyrimidine base. There are two types of nucleic acids, deoxyribonucleic acid and ribonucleic acid, which are chemically distinguished in two ways. Deoxyribonucleic acid (DNA) contains deoxyribose as its sugar part, while ribonucleic acid (RNA) contains ribose as its sugar and one different pyrimidine base. Present day theories postulate that DNA is the seat of the genetic information, that is the biological instructions which are handed down in the reproductive cells from parents to offspring and which subsequently determine the function of the cells and their role in the organization of the body. The synthesis of DNA leading to a doubling of its quantity is therefore a phenomenon of primary importance in relation to the division of chromosomes.

It used to be assumed that DNA was confined to the cell nucleus, but in recent years evidence has accumulated that some DNA may be localized in the cytoplasm (See J. N. Davidson, 1965; Gahan and Chayen, 1965). Nevertheless, the amount of cytoplasmic DNA is so small compared with the DNA in the nucleus that for practical purposes of chromosome study the cytoplasmic DNA may be ignored.

Nuclei which are not in mitosis are variously described as "resting," "metabolic," "interkinetic," or in "interphase." There is now conclusive evidence that this is the time when the doubling of the DNA takes place (Mazia, 1961). Thus, from the point of view of cell division, the interphase nucleus is productive, while the nucleus in mitosis is distributive; and the fact that the chromosomes become visible during mitosis may be interpreted as the result of packaging the chromosomal material into compact dimensions, which are capable of orderly distribution.

Interphase nuclei generally contain one or more nucleoli. In contrast to the rest of the nuclear material, nucleoli consist mainly of RNA. Although not chromosomal in nature, nucleoli are probably formed by special chromosomes, with which they often seem to be associated (Chapter 2, Section III). Most nucleoli disappear during mitosis, but occasionally they persist (Thomas and Revell, 1946).

Living cells tend to be colorless and transparent. Although it is possible to observe them with special optical devices, such as dark field illumination, and phase contrast and interference microscopy, most of our knowledge of chromosomes has been gained from studying fixed and stained preparations. The purpose of fixatives is to kill the cell and preserve its contents during further treatment. Fixation also makes the cells receptive to the action of stains, whose purpose it is to render the different components of the cells in contrasting colors.

A considerable number of dyes are used for staining the cell nuclei and chromosomes, including orcein, thyonin, and crystal violet. Of particular importance is basic fuchsin ("Feulgen"). This reaction was introduced by Feulgen and Rossenbeck (1924) as a specific test for DNA. The fixed tissues are treated with normal hydrochloric acid at 58°–60°C, as a result of which the deoxyribose sugar part of the DNA releases aldehydes; and these combine with decolorized fuchsin (Schiff's reagent) to produce a purple color. This method gives excellent cytological preparations and in addition acts as a cytochemical test since a positive reaction may be regarded as indicating the presence of DNA (Pearse, 1960).

Although mitosis is a continuous process, it is generally divided into four stages with characteristic landmarks. The stages are (1) prophase; (2) metaphase; (3) anaphase; (4) telophase (Figs. 2.1, 2.2). All these terms date from the nineteenth century (Wilson, 1925).

A. PROPHASE

The interphase nucleus is bounded by a nuclear membrane. The chromatin may stain more or less evenly, or part of it may form aggregates of deeply staining clumps, separated by lightly staining areas. At the beginning of prophase the nuclear material resolves itself into darkly staining threads, the chromosomes. When first visible, the chromosomes

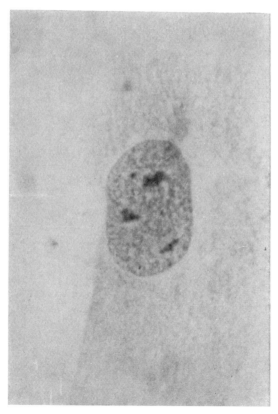

(a)

FIG. 2.1.

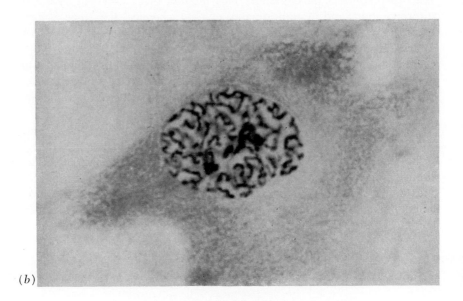

(b)

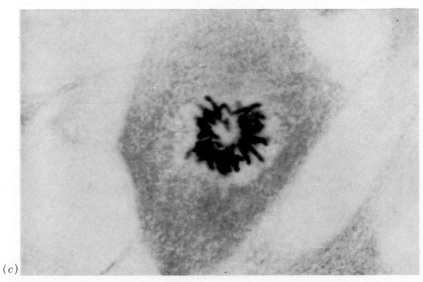

(c)

FIG. 2.1. Mitosis in cultured human cells, without special treatment to show up chromosome morphology (cf. Fig. 8.1). (a) interphase; (b) prophase; (c) metaphase; (d) anaphase; (e) telophase. (May-Grunwald Giemsa × 2200.)

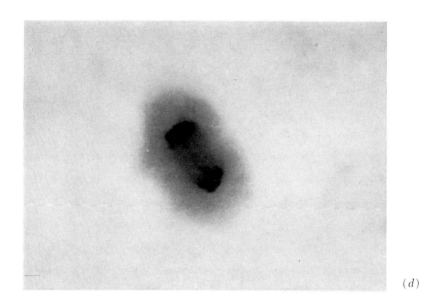

(d)

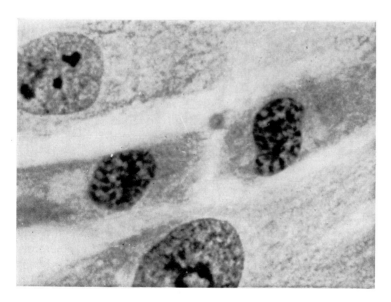

(e)

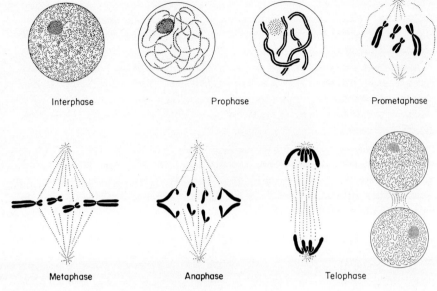

Interphase   Prophase   Prometaphase

Metaphase   Anaphase   Telophase

FIG. 2.2. Stages of mitosis.

are long and thin, and they seem to be in the form of a network, in which it is impossible to perceive the ends of the individual chromosomes. Nevertheless it is assumed that even at this stage each chromosome is a separate unit.

As prophase proceeds, the chromosomes become shorter and thicker. The shortening of the chromosomes is regarded as the result of progressive spiralization (Swanson, 1958). In favorable material it can be seen that the chromosomes are longitudinally double, being composed of two "chromatids." The chromatids are held together at the centromere. This structure was first described 70 years ago and since then has been given at least 27 names (Hughes, 1952a). The term "centromere," which was proposed by Darlington (1936) is commonly used in Great Britain, while the name "kinetochore" (proposed by J. A. Moore; see Sharp, 1934) is frequent in the U.S.A. This organ is best seen at metaphase, when it appears as an unstained constriction at some point along the length of the chromosome. Although the structure of the centromere has not yet been elucidated, it is clear that it plays a role of paramount importance in regulating the movement of the chromosomes during mitosis. A single circumscribed centromere is present in the chromosomes of most organisms. So-called diffuse centromeres, which appear to be distributed along the whole length of the chromosome, are much rarer; however, they appear to be characteristic of the insect order Hemiptera (plant bugs) (Schrader, 1935; Hughes-Schrader, 1935 and Ris, 1941; Hughes-Schrader, 1948). In these species, the processes of mitosis and meiosis are modified.

Apart from the contraction of the chromosomes, three other processes occur during mitosis. The nuclear membrane loses its rigidity or disappears altogether, so that the difference between nucleus and cytoplasm becomes less distinct; the cell becomes polarized; and the mitotic spindle is formed.

The spindle consists of fibers which enclose a considerable part of the cell from one pole to the other. The spindle does not contain DNA and does not stain with nuclear dyes. It is largely composed of proteins, although other substances, such as RNA and polysaccharide may also be present (Mazia, 1961).

B. METAPHASE

At this stage the chromosomes, which have until now been dispersed inside the nucleus, move toward its center. In fact, all the centromeres take up a position on the plane which is circumscribed by the equator of the spindle and known as the metaphase plate ("or equatorial plate").

C. ANAPHASE

At the beginning of anaphase the centromere divides lengthwise, and thus the longitudinal division of the chromosomes is at last completed. Henceforth the two chromatids of each chromosome move away from each other in opposite directions. According to Darlington (1937, 1940a), this movement is caused by the mutual repulsion of split centromeres. Oestergren (1950, 1951) believes that the anaphase chromatids are attracted by the poles. Whatever the mechanism of anaphase may be, the result is that sister chromatids of all the chromosomes arrive at the two opposite poles. The cytoplasm between the two chromosomes becomes furrowed and divides, and each chromosome set becomes associated with its own cytoplasm.

D. TELOPHASE

The last stage of mitosis, telophase, is in many ways the reverse of prophase. When the two sets of halved chromosomes have reached their destination, the spindle disappears and the nuclear membrane is formed around each new nucleus. The chromosomes elongate either by despiralization or by swelling (Mazia, 1961) and disappear from view. The two interphase nuclei resemble that of the parent cell from which they were formed except that they are smaller. They grow by synthesizing nuclear material during interphase.

The shape of individual chromosomes is an important aspect of descriptive cytology. But since it is a feature of cell division that the chromosomes undergo cycles of condensation followed by decondensation, it is evident that when describing chromosomes it is necessary to specify the stage in cell division in which they occur; and moreover, since fixation and other kinds of treatment will affect the morphology of the chromosomes, the method by which the preparation was made is also of importance.

For many purposes it is usual to choose metaphase chromosomes, since this is the stage when the chromosomes have reached their maximum degree of condensation and are therefore best suited to be studied individually.

In order to facilitate the dispersal of chromosomes inside the cell and to minimize overlapping, it is now usual, particularly in the study of mammalian chromosomes, to immerse the unfixed cells in a hypotonic salt solution, which causes them to swell by imbibition of water (Hsu, 1952). It is also common practice to expose the cells to the drug colchicine, which inhibits the formation of the mitotic spindle, with the result that the chromosomes, unable to pass into anaphase, accumulate in metaphase. The presence of colchicine also adds further to the contraction of the chromosomes and it spreads the two chromatids of a chromosome away from each other (see Clarke, 1962).

Another prerequisite for obtaining clear preparations of chromosomes is to ensure that all the chromosomes lie in one plane. In modern practice, one of two methods is usually used to achieve this. One method is to squash the cell between the slide and the cover glass by applying pressure. This method was used by Boveri in 1890, but during the early part of the twentieth century it became superseded by the practice of cutting thin sections. The squash technique was reintroduced by Heitz (1935b). The second method consists of flattening the cells to the glass slide by means of drying them in a current of air. This method has been only recently introduced for the study of chromosomes (Tjio and Puck, 1958) but has previously been used for making preparations of blood cells.

An illustration of human chromosomes in mitotic metaphase, prepared by modern techniques, is shown in Fig. 8.1. A comparison with Fig. 2.1c which shows a similar cell which was simply allowed to grow on the cover glass, makes it clear that although the effect of colchicine, the hypotonic salt solution, and the squashing is to destroy the structure of the cell, this greatly facilitates the study of the individual chromosomes.

Such a preparation is an artifact in the best sense of the word, a true work of art. As a result, the chromosomes can be counted and their individual shapes compared. The method of analysis of human chromosomes has been described by Turpin and Lejeune (1965).

The most obvious difference between individual chromosomes is that of size, although it must be kept in mind that the size of the chromosomes is a relative concept, comparing the lengths of the chromosomes within the same cell. As mentioned before, the actual size of the chromosomes varies not only in different stages of cell division, but may also be different in the same stage in different cells. But the relative size of the chromosomes is a constant characteristic, which is of primary importance in the task of identifying the individual chromosomes. The shape of the chromosomes is further determined by the position of the centromere.

There has been a great deal of discussion regarding the position of the centromere and the nomenclature to be used (see Levan et al., 1964). Some of this is concerned with the question whether a centromere may be situated at the extreme end of a chromosome, or whether there is always a short arm which may or may not be visible. From a practical point of view, however, the most important distinction is whether the centromere is somewhere near the middle of the chromosome, thus dividing it into two arms, or whether the centromere is so close to one end that the second arm, if present, can be virtually neglected. White (1945) called the latter type of chromosome "acrocentric" and used the term "metacentric" for chromosomes having two arms. These terms will be used in this book. Many authors confine the term "metacentric" to those chromosomes in which the centromere is exactly in the middle and use "submetacentric" for those two-arms in which the centromere is nearer one end. This term will not be used because with increasing accuracy of measurements, there will be fewer chromosomes in which the centromere will be found to be exactly in the middle, and thus the large majority of chromosomes would have to be given the more cumbersome term "submetacentric." In order to distinguish further between different types of metacentric chromosomes, quantitative measurements of relative arm lengths should be given, although the error inherent in such measurements must, of course, be kept in mind. Levan et al. (1964) use a more complicated terminology based on such measurements, but the simple division into "acrocentric" and "metacentric" is preferred here. Clearly, whatever terminology is used there must be borderline cases where a decision as to which category is applicable must be made. In the present instance, the question may sometimes arise whether a short arm may be regarded as negligible or whether it should rank as a short arm in its own right.

In the older type of preparation, the two chromatids of a chromosome could generally not be distinguished, and consequently acrocentric chromosomes in metaphase appeared to be rod-shaped, while metacentric chromosomes were V- or J-shaped. With modern techniques, however, the two chromatids are usually clearly separate, and the chromosome is held together only at the centromere. Consequently acrocentric chromosomes are V-shaped, and metacentric chromosomes are in the form of a cross.

On the basis of these two characteristics, length of the chromosomes and position of the centromere, the chromosomes may be arranged in order, as shown in Fig. 8.1. When this is done, it becomes evident that there are as a rule two chromosomes which are similar in size and in the position of the centromere. Such chromosomes form a homologous pair. The sex chromosomes of the heterogametic sex provide an exception to this rule.

III. Meiosis

The purpose of meiosis is to divide the cell in such a way that the daughter cells receive only one of a pair of homologous chromosomes. In animals, meiosis occurs just prior to fertilization.

Meiosis consists of two cell divisions, which take place consecutively (Fig. 2.3). The prophase of the first meiotic division is lengthy and complicated. It is usually subdivided into the following phases: leptonema, zygonema, pachynema, diplonema, and diakinesis (the ending in "-tene" is sometimes used in place of "-nema"; "tene" is the correct ending for adjectives). All these terms date either from the end of the last or the beginning of the present century (see Wilson, 1925).

Leptonema

At the beginning of meiosis the chromosomes are very long and thin. There has been some controversy whether leptotene chromosomes are composed of a single or of two chromatids. The present day evidence seems to suggest that replication of DNA occurs before the chromosomes become visible in meiosis (Rhoades, 1961).

Zygonema

During zygonema the two members of a homologous pair of chromosomes come to lie next to each other. Pairing is said to take place in a zipperlike fashion, and as a result the two members of a pair become intimately associated. The process is often referred to as "synapsis."

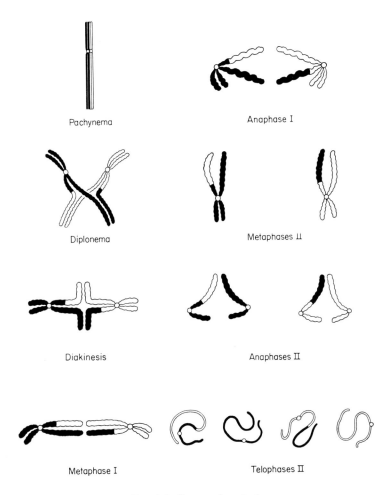

Fig. 2.3. Stages of meiosis.

Pachynema

At pachynema pairing is completed and the paired chromosomes are known as bivalents. As in mitotic prophase, the prophase of meiosis is also characterized by a gradual shortening and thickening of the chromosomes. As a result of this it can be seen that the bivalents in pachynema are not in the form of an even thread but that all along their length darkly staining knobs of varying sizes alternate with lightly staining gaps. The darkly staining knobs are known as chromomeres (see Wilson, 1925). It is believed that the relative size and position of the individual chromomeres is characteristic for each pair of chromosomes and that the chromomeres pair specifically with their partners in the homologous chromosomes.

Diplonema

At this stage the paired chromosomes fall apart and the bivalents are held together only at certain points, which are known as chiasmata (singular, chiasma). The number of chiasmata which are present determines the shape of the bivalents at diplonema and later stages. The number of chiasmata is not constant for any given bivalent, but there is a rough rule that the longer the bivalent the more chiasmata there are likely to be, and vice versa (Darlington, 1937). Thus, very short chromosomes generally have only one chiasma.

Chiasmata were first described and named by Janssens in 1909, and it was he who proposed the theory that the chiasmata are the visible expression of an exchange between paternal and maternal chromosomes, before the genetic facts of linkage and crossing-over were known. The relationship between chiasmata and genetic crossing-over has been widely accepted, although not every visible chiasma may result in such crossovers (Sturtevant, 1951). Each chiasma involves only two of the four paired chromatids. Although the formation of chiasmata has been the subject of intense research and much speculation, the mechanism by which they are produced is still not clear. The possible mechanisms of chiasma formation have been discussed by Rhoades (1961), by Westergaard (1964), and by Whitehouse (1965).

Diplonema is often a difficult stage to study, since the chromosomes may be rather diffuse and relatively unfixable.

Diakinesis

At diakinesis the bivalents are shorter and thicker than at the preceding stage, and they have a more definite outline. In many species there seem to be fewer chiasmata than at diplonema. According to Darlington (1929) this is probably due to a tendency of the chiasmata to move towards the ends of the bivalent, a process which he called "terminalization." This process may continue until metaphase; as a result, the number of visible chiasmata becomes progressively reduced.

At late diakinesis, the nuclear membrane disappears and the spindle is formed.

Metaphase I

At the first metaphase of meiosis, the bivalents move towards the equatorial plane of the spindle; when metaphase is complete, the two centromeres of each bivalent lie opposite each other on either side of the equatorial plate.

Anaphase I

At anaphase I, the two centromeres of each bivalent move towards opposite poles, carrying with them the two chromatids attached to them. Chromatids in which no exchange took place will be either of paternal or of maternal origin; but if chiasmata were formed between them, the resultant chromatids will be of mixed paternal and maternal composition.

Telophase

Having reached their respective poles, the chromosomes may prepare for a brief interphase, or they may continue almost immediately into the prophase of the second meiotic division.

Second Meiotic Division

The prophase of the second meiotic division is of short duration. The nuclear membrane, if formed, disappears. The spindle is formed and the centromeres move towards the equatorial plate, where they take up their position. The cell is now in metaphase II.

At anaphase II the centromeres divide, and the two halves, each with a single chromatid attached to it, move to opposite poles. The telophase resembles that of an ordinary mitosis, apart from the fact that only half the number of chromosomes are present.

Thus the first meiotic division results in two cells, each of which has half the original number of chromosomes, but with the same total number of chromatids as in a mitotic telophase cell. The second meiotic division results in the formation of four cells, each with half the number of chromosomes and half the number of chromatids compared with an ordinary product of cell division.

The number of chromosomes present in cells after meiosis is known as the "haploid" number and the chromosomes in cells subsequent to fertilization are present in the "diploid" number. Both terms originated with Strasburger (1908).

IV. Special Characteristics of Sex Chromosomes

According to the theory put forward by Darlington (1931, 1937, 1939b), the paired chromosomes during the first meiotic metaphase are held together by chiasmata, and orderly segregation of bivalents cannot occur unless they contain at least one chiasma. This clearly represents a problem in the case of the sex chromosomes of the heterogametic sex, for unless the chromosomes are strictly homologous, pairing and chiasma formation cannot take place. As a way out of this dilemma, Darlington postulated that the X- and the Y-chromosome each consist of two parts, (1) a pairing segment, in which chiasmata are formed and (2) a differential segment, in which there is neither pairing nor chiasma formation. There has been a considerable amount of controversy over this theory particularly as regards mammalian sex chromosomes, and for many years the cytological evidence for the presence of chiasmata between the X- and the Y-chromosomes seemed to be unconvincing. However, in recent years the existence of chiasmata between the X- and Y-chromosomes has been incontrovertibly demonstrated in a number of mammalian species (Chapter 9, Section VII), and a pairing segment between the X- and the Y-chromosomes of man has been postulated on theoretical grounds (Chapter 10, Section XV). Thus, recent results have confirmed Darlington's theory, at least in some species.

V. Some Abnormalities of Cell Division

While the majority of cell divisions go on in a normal manner, accidents may occasionally occur which give rise to cells with chromosomal abnormalities. Some of these errors are of particular interest in relation to sex chromosomes.

A. NONDISJUNCTION

Normally during the first meiotic division homologous chromosomes pair and separate at anaphase. If the bivalents fail to disjoin and both go to the same pole, one of the daughter cells will contain both the members of a homologous pair of chromosomes while the other cell contains neither. A somewhat similar result may occur at the second meiotic division, if the two chromatids of a chromosome fail to separate at anaphase. In either case, gametes may be formed which contain one chromosome too many or too few; and on fertilization such gametes will give rise to individuals each of whose cells contain an additional chromosome, or alternatively lack a chromosome.

In individuals of this type, which are themselves the products of nondisjunction, meiosis is of necessity abnormal and secondary nondisjunction frequently occurs. Nondisjunction was first described by Bridges (1913), who obtained a fly whose sex-chromosome constitution was XXY. In *Drosophila*, such an individual is a female. It produces the following types of eggs: X, XY, XX, and Y, the second and third classes being the result of secondary nondisjunction. On fertilization such eggs will produce further XXY- as well as XXX- and XYY-individuals. This will be further described in Chapter 4.

A process which is somewhat analogous to nondisjunction may occur during mitosis, if the two chromatids of a chromosome fail to separate at anaphase. This may result in certain cells of an individual containing one chromosome too many or too few. Cells from which one chromosome is missing may also arise if one of the chromosomes at anaphase fails to reach its pole and is lost.

B. INVERSION

A chromosomal abnormality in which a piece of a chromosome has been turned around so that it is present in the reverse order is called an "inversion." If the inversion is on one side of the centromere only, it is referred to as "paracentric" and if it involves the centromere, it is called a "pericentric" inversion.

An inversion was discovered by Sturtevant (1921) as a result of the changed behavior of linked genes. Cytologically, inversions are only rarely recognizable in mitosis but are more likely to be seen in meiosis. This is because pairing takes place strictly between homologous portions of chromosomes; therefore, if one chromosome carries an inversion and its partner the normal sequence, pairing fails to take place along the length of the inversion and a loop is formed. Failure of pairing also causes a characteristic appearance of heterozygous inversion in salivary gland chromosomes (Chapter 4, Section VII). If present in the homozygous state, inversions can here be recognized by the changed pattern of banding.

C. TRANSLOCATIONS

A translocation results if a break occurs in two different chromosomes and the broken ends rejoin reciprocally. This is known as a reciprocal translocation and is the most common type of translocation. If present in the heterozygous state, translocations will give rise to characteristic associations in meiosis and in salivary gland chromosomes (see Swanson, 1958). If a translocation alters the shape of the chromosomes, it can also be recognized in mitosis. A translocation was first described by Bridges (1919) as a result of a changed linkage arrangement in *Drosophila*.

D. DUPLICATION

An additional piece of chromosome belonging to the normal set, which is present in the nucleus, is known as a duplication. A duplication in *Drosophila* was described by Bridges in 1919.

E. DELETION (DEFICIENCY)

A chromosome from which a piece is missing is said to carry a deletion or a deficiency. Some authorities (e.g., Darlington, 1937; Sturtevant and Beadle, 1939) restrict the term "deletion" to cases where a terminal piece is missing and apply the term "deficiency" if an interstitial piece of chromosome has been lost. The latter occurs more commonly. It may originate by two breaks occurring on the same side of the centromere and the two broken ends joining up. A deficiency of the X-chromosome in *Drosophila* was described by Bridges (1917).

F. RING CHROMOSOMES

If two breaks occur on opposite sides of the centromere, the ends of the piece containing the centromere may fuse to form a ring chromosome. The two fragments lacking the centromere will be lost, and a ring chromosome is therefore a deleted chromosome. The occurrence of an X-chromosome in the shape of a ring has been described in man (Chapter 8).

G. ISOCHROMOSOMES

An isochromosome is a chromosome in which two homologous arms are joined at the centromere. Isochromosomes are therefore perfectly metacentric. Compared with normal chromosomes, they represent a duplication of one arm and a deficiency of the other arm. The origin of isochromosomes has been described by Darlington (1939, 1940b) on the basis of his studies on *Fritillaria,* as follows. The centromere, instead of dividing longitudinally as in an ordinary mitosis may occasionally divide transversely, and in a proportion of such cases the sister chromatids rejoin at the centromere.

Presumed isochromosomes of the X-chromosome have been described in man (Chapter 8).

VI. The Formation of Gametes

As a result of meiosis, the chromosomes are present in the single, or haploid set. Fertilization of haploid gametes ensures that the diploid condition is restored.

In animals, meiosis occurs immediately prior to the formation of gametes. In plants, however, this is not so. In some of the lower plants (algae and fungi) meiosis occurs immediately after fertilization, so that the organism is haploid. In higher plants, the products of meiosis, known as spores, divide by mitosis for a varying length of time before the gametes are formed. Here, therefore, a diploid generation, known as the sporophyte, alternates with a haploid generation, known as the gametophyte. In some of the less highly evolved plants, such as the mosses, the gametophyte constitutes the leafy plant. In the flowering plants, on the other hand, the gametophyte is reduced to a few cells.

Boveri in 1892 described the production of gametes by meiosis in animals (nematode worms) and showed that the nuclear phenomena are essentially the same in the male and the female. His basic scheme for spermatogenesis and oogenesis is still valid. Meiosis in flowering plants was described by Strasburger (1894).

A. SPERMATOGENESIS

In animals the male gametes, or spermatozoa, are formed in the testis. The process by which the primitive germ cells multiply and are transformed into spermatozoa is known as spermatogenesis (Fig. 2.4). The

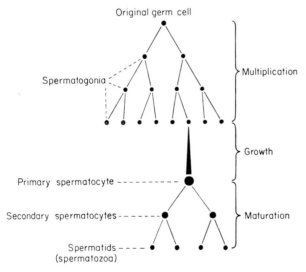

FIG. 2.4. Stages in spermatogenesis. (After Boveri, 1891.)

initial germ cells are called spermatogonia and they divide mitotically for many generations. Following the last mitosis the spermatogonia duplicate their DNA, grow in size, and their chromosomes associate in pairs. The cells are now called primary spermatocytes. Since they contain the duplicated amount of DNA they may technically be regarded as tetraploid. The primary spermatocyte then undergoes the first meiotic division and gives rise to two secondary spermatocytes. Then the second meiotic division occurs, giving rise to four spermatids, each containing the haploid number of chromosomes. Each spermatid is transformed into a spermatozoon, usually without further division.

B. OOGENESIS

The female gametes, eggs, or ova, are formed in the ovary by the process of oogenesis. The details of this process differ in different animals (see Beatty, 1957), but the general principle is as follows (Fig. 2.5). The ancestors of the egg cells are known as oogonia and they divide mitotically. The last generation of oogonia duplicate their DNA content, grow

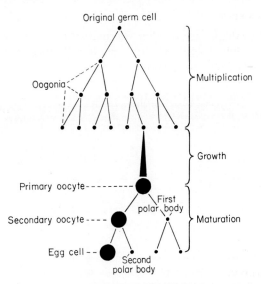

FIG. 2.5. Stages in oogenesis. Division of polar body is not obligatory.

in size, and pairing of chromosomes take place. The cells are now primary oocytes. The primary oocytes have already undergone the initial stages of the first prophase of meiosis preceding diplotene. The cells may remain in this stage for a very long time. Just before the egg is about to mature, the first meiotic division is completed and each primary oocyte gives rise to two cells of unequal size, a large secondary oocyte and a small cell which is called first polocyte, or polar body. As a result of the second meiotic division the secondary oocyte gives rise to another pair of unequal cells, a large ovum or egg, and a small second polar body. The first polar body may or may not also undergo the second meiotic division, and either give rise to two haploid polar bodies, or remain undivided. All the polar bodies degenerate. An important difference, therefore, between gametogenesis in the male and in the female is that each primary spermatocyte gives rise to four functional spermatozoa, whereas a primary oocyte produces only one egg.

As a result of fertilization of an egg by a spermatozoon a zygote is produced.

In plants the products of meiosis are not directly transformed into gametes. In liverworts and mosses the spores, which are the products of meiosis, give rise to a haploid green plant, the gametophyte. The gametophyte forms eggs and spermatozoids in organs which are known as archegonia and antheridia, respectively. In some species, both types of gametes are borne on the same plant, which is then said to be homothallic, or monoecious. In other species, which are heterothallic or dioecious, eggs and spermatozoids are borne on different plants. Since the gametophyte is haploid, both eggs and spermatozoids are formed as a result of mitosis, followed by growth and differentiation. As a result of fertilization, a zygote is produced. This germinates and gives rise to the diploid generation, the sporophyte. The sporophyte does not usually contain chlorophyll and lives parasitically on the gametophyte. The sporangia of the sporophyte contain certain cells known as sporocytes; each one undergoes two meiotic divisions and gives rise to four spores. The spores then germinate to produce haploid gametophytes (for further details on this and the following, see Sharp, 1934).

In the flowering plants, also, meiosis gives rise to four spores, but here the spores are of two kinds, namely, microspores and megaspores. Both types of spores germinate to form the gametophyte generation, which is of short duration and is parasitic on the sporophyte.

The male organs are the stamens, each one of which is composed of an anther borne on a filament. The cells destined to become microspores divide by mitosis and eventually enter the first prophase of meiosis. They are now known as microsporocytes or pollen mother cells. Each one undergoes two meiotic divisions, which result in the formation of four haploid microscopes, or pollen grains.

A microspore undergoes two mitotic divisions and thus forms a very simple male gametophyte. The first division separates a tube cell from a generative cell, and the latter divides again to form two male gametes.

The egg cells develop inside the pistil, which comprises one or more carpels. Each carpel consists of an ovary, surmounted by a style and stigma. The future egg cell is contained in the ovule inside the ovary. In the ovule, one cell enlarges and enters the prophase of the first meiotic division; this cell is known as the megasporocyte. As a result of the two meiotic divisions four megaspores are formed. Three of these generally disintegrate and the remaining cell divides by three mitotic divisions to form the female gametophyte. Of the eight nuclei thus produced, the largest one is the egg, and two others are known as polar cells.

At fertilization one of the male gametes fuses with the egg to form the embryo, and in addition the other male gamete fuses with the two polar cells, thus giving rise to the endosperm, which is triploid.

VII. Sexual Differentiation

Meiosis and gametogenesis result in the formation of two types of gametes, which, although equivalent as regards their nuclear material, are functionally differentiated to play specialized parts in fertilization. The male gamete is essentially a nucleus, which, unencumbered by large amounts of cytoplasm, is capable of movement. Female gametes, on the contrary, contain considerable quantities of cytoplasm, which serve in the nourishment and differentiation of the embryo. During fertilization the male gamete delivers its nuclear contents to the female gamete.

Although there is no biological definition of the term "sex," the differentiation of male and female gametes must be regarded as a basic requisite. It is undesirable to extend the term to any mechanism which brings about outbreeding by preventing the fusion of gametes from the same individuals. It is true that in those species in which male and female gametes are produced in different organisms—this comprises the majority of animals—sexual reproduction usually leads to outbreeding between individuals of different genetic constitutions. But if both types of gametes are produced in the same individual, as in the majority of flowering plants, sexual reproduction could result in perpetual self-fertilization. If this is to be avoided, another mechanism must intervene. Thus, the large majority of flowering plants in Great Britain are bisexual, which means that ovules and pollen grains are borne on the same plant; but in many of them self-fertilization is prevented by a system of incompatibility genes, which prevent the pollen grains from reaching ovules of the same genetic constitution (D. Lewis, 1942, 1954). In bisexual organisms, the differentiation into male and female gametes is not determined by a difference in genes or in chromosomes, but is due to developmental processes, by which different organs are formed within the same individual.

The flowering plants clearly illustrate the essential difference between sexual reproduction and incompatibility, since both mechanisms occur side by side. In many of the lower organisms, however, the distinction is less easy, since sexual organs may not be present. In the absence of sexual organs, a primitive type of sexuality may be exhibited when fusion can take place only between different strains of cells, which show some degree of differentiation. For instance, in the bacterium *Escherichia coli* there are two types of cells known respectively as "donor bacteria," which transfer genetic characteristics, and "recipient bacteria," which receive genetic characteristics. Because of their different behavior during conjugation, donor bacteria may be considered analogous to males and recipient bacteria to females (Jacob and Wollman, 1961). While this type of differentiation may be called "sexual" by courtesy, there can be no advantage in extrapolating the concept still further by including under the heading "sex" incompatibility mechanisms, such as are found, for instance, in fungi belonging to the Basidiomycetes, in which there is no trace of sexual differentiation. For a stricter definition, there is much to be said for Darlington's statement (1937) that "sexual differentiation demands the fusion of gametes which are morphologically different." In this way the term "sex" in its stricter meaning is confined to multicellular organisms producing specialized germ cells. In such organisms, the young embryo, nourished originally by the female gamete, grows and develops new organs.

It is clear, however, that even if one accepts this strict definition of the term "sex," sexual differentiation will affect different organisms in entirely different ways. Thus, in animals, the entire organism is involved, an individual being either male or female according to whether it is adapted for the production of spermatozoa or ova. On the other hand, in a moss plant the diploid sporophyte is sexually undifferentiated. In dioecious mosses, maleness and femaleness are attributes of the haploid gametophyte, which may bear either spermatozoids or eggs. By contrast in dioecious flowering plants, it is the sporophyte which is differentiated into two classes, one of them bearing male flowers, which form the microspores and ultimately male gametes, and the other one bearing female flowers which produce megaspores giving rise to female gametes. The sexual differentiation of an organism depends on the stage in the life cycle at which the gametes are formed.

In this book we are concerned with the chromosomal mechanisms, which bring about the divergence of organisms within the same species into two kinds, male and female, which differ in the gametes which they produce and generally also in many other characteristics. This type of sexual differentiation, brought about by sex chromosomes is the rule among animals—though exceptions are known (see Crew, 1965; Bacci, 1965)—and occurs less commonly among plants.

CHAPTER 3

SEX CHROMOSOMES IN PLANTS

I. Introduction

In spite of the fact that the differentiation of organisms according to sex is primarily a characteristic of animals, the inheritance of sex was first demonstrated in a plant. In 1907 Correns provided definite evidence that in the white bryony, *Bryonia dioica*, the sex of the plant is determined by the pollen grains. These, he found, were of two classes, male-producing and female-producing, while the eggs were all the same in this respect. At the same time it was also shown that sex in mosses and liverworts is genetically determined. The determination of sex in liverworts and mosses will be described first.

II. Liverworts and Mosses

Slightly over 50% of species of liverworts and mosses are dioecious (Correns, 1928). The liverwort *Marchantia* is strictly dioecious. Noll showed in 1907 that the spores consist of two classes, those which grow into male plants and those which grow into female plants. Both types of spores are produced in the same sporangium. The plants can be asexually propagated by buds, but these always grow into plants of the same sex as the parents (Fig. 3.1.)

Similar experiments performed by the Marchals (1907, 1909, 1911) showed that the same phenomenon applies to dioecious mosses such as *Bryum caespiticum*. The sex of a haploid plant was rigorously preserved among the products of continued vegetative propagation. When pieces of the sporophyte were vegetatively propagated, the resultant plants looked like leafy gametophytes, but they were monoecious. These gametophytes were found to be diploid. They could be propagated indefinitely, but they were sterile. On the other hand, by propagating the sporophyte of a normally monoecious moss, such as *Amblystegnium serpens*, diploid gametophytes were produced which were monoecious and fertile. They gave rise to tetraploid sporophytes, and by vegetative reproduction tetraploid gametophytes were obtained.

As a result of these experiments, which were confirmed and extended by von Wettstein (1924), it became clear that the sporophyte contains the potentialities of both sexes, and that these were separated during meiosis, when the spores are formed. Thus the sporophyte is sexually

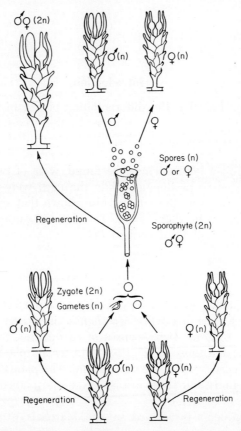

FIG. 3.1. Determination of sex in dioecious mosses. (From Wilson, 1925. Redrawn by A. J. Lee.)

undifferentiated, and only the haploid gametophyte bears the genetic constitution of either sex.

The actual proof that the factors for sex are segregated during meiosis was brought by Lorbeer (1927). He succeeded in isolating the tetrads of four spores, which are the result of the two meiotic divisions, in species of *Sphaerocarpus*. He found that whenever all four spores germinated and survived—which was the case in the majority of tetrads—two spores gave rise to male plants and two to female plants. Since this result was obtained from over 200 tetrads, this is strong evidence that the sexes in the spores are strictly segregated into two males and two females.

In 1917 Allen demonstrated a chromosomal difference between male and female gametophytes in the liverwort *Sphaerocarpus*. There are eight chromosomes in both sexes. The female has a large X-chromosome, and the male has a small Y-chromosome. These results were confirmed by Lorbeer (1927), by Heitz (1927, 1928), and by Tatuno (1936) for *Sphaerocarpus* and other liverworts. Sex chromosomes have also been demonstrated in mosses (Kurita, 1937, Tatuno and Yano, 1953). In the liverwort *Pellia* Heitz showed that the sex chromosomes do not become invisible at the end of the mitotic division but retain their characteristic shape during interphase. Because of its different staining behavior Heitz called this type of chromosomal substance "heterochromatin." This topic is further discussed in Chapter 2.

The size of the spores in liverworts and mosses often varies considerably. Correns (1928) examined the possibility that male and female spores might be distinguished by this criterion. He found that the frequency distributions for the size of the spores of some dioecious mosses showed two slight peaks, but similarly, two-peaked curves were obtained for some monoecious species. Correns concluded that male and female spores could not be distinguished by their size. Dening (1935/1936) found that in four species of dioecious mosses the frequency distribution for spore size contained only a single peak. The subject was studied in detail by Ernst-Schwarzenbach (1939). She found that among tropical mosses the size of the spores of some species, for instance *Macromitrium fasiculare*, all fell into one class, while in other species, for instance *M. salakanum*, the spores fell clearly into two classes which differed in size and also in color. The large spores are green and the small spores are yellow. However, in many species of liverworts the males are smaller than the females, and in *M. salakanum* the males are actually dwarfs, which grow epiphytically on the much larger female plants. Ernst-Schwarzenbach was able to show that the small spores of *M. salakanum* give rise to dwarf males, while the large spores form female plants. Thus, although we have here a clear difference in size between male- and female-determining spores, this is not a direct result of a difference in the amount of sex chromosomes, but should be regarded as a secondary sexual characteristics. The male-determining spores are small and yellow and give rise to dwarf males, while the female-determining spores are large and green and give rise to large plants.

Knapp (1936) and Lorbeer (1936) independently succeeded in changing female plants of *Sphaerocarpus Donnellii* into males by irradiation of spores or growing points of gametophytes. Knapp and Hoffmann (1939) believed that this change was caused by the loss of a piece of the X-chromosome, whereas Lorbeer (1938) favored the view of a gene mutation. The experiments were repeated by Heitz (1942), who also favored the latter explanation as the basis of the change from female to male.

III. Flowering Plants

In the majority of flowering plants male organs (stamens) and female organs (carpels or pistils) are present in the same flower, and such plants are said to be hermaphrodites. If the stamens and carpels are found in separate flowers on the same plant, the species is monoecious; and if the two types of flowers are present on separate plants, the species is dioecious. Both hermaphrodite and monoecious plants are also called "bisexual," while dioecious plants are "unisexual," and from the point of view of genetics, this division is the more important, since it separates the plants into two groups, those in which stamens and carpels are produced in separate organisms and those in which they are formed in the same organism.

Female flowers often have rudimentary stamens, and rudimentary pistils are often present in male flowers (Allen, 1940). Again, in structurally hermaphrodite flowers one or the other sex may predominate, so that there is almost a continuous gradient between hermaphrodite flowers and those which are strictly unisexual. The bryony, *Bryonia*, and the red and white campion, *Silene* (previously known as *Melandrium* or *Lychnis*—see B below), belong to the latter group.

A. *Bryonia dioica*, THE COMMON BRYONY

After the rediscovery of Mendel's papers the common bryony, *Bryonia dioica* (a member of the cucumber family, Cucurbitaceae), became the first organism in which the inheritance of sex was worked out genetically. This was done by Correns (1907), who made use of the fact that a related species, *B. alba*, is hermaphrodite. Female plants of *B. dioica* fertilized with pollen from the same species result in offspring in which males and females occur in roughly equal numbers. Similarly, if female plants of *B. alba* were crossed with pollen from *B. dioica*, the hybrids, although sterile, consisted of equal numbers of males and females. On the other hand, when female flowers of *B. dioica* were fertilized with pollen from *B. alba*, the hybrids consisted entirely of female plants.

These experiments showed not only that sex is determined at fertilization but they clearly demonstrated that in B. *dioica* the pollen is of two kinds, male-determining and female-determining, whereas the eggs all have the same tendency regarding sex determination. This difference in the behavior of male and female gametes had been quite unexpected. It proved to be the first genetic counterpart to Wilson's findings on the spermatozoa of insects, which differed in their chromosome constitution, whereas the eggs were all the same in this respect (Chapter 1). Correns' experiments were repeated by Heilbronn (1949) with the same results regarding the proportion of sexes present in the hybrids. The hybrids, however, were not as sterile.

Attempts to find sex chromosomes in plants failed at first. Strasburger (1909, 1910) was unable to find a heteromorphic pair of chromosomes either in dioecious liverworts or in flowering plants, and the subject appeared to be decided in a negative way. It was therefore a surprise when Allen (1917) reported the presence of sex chromosomes in the liverwort *Sphaerocarpus*. Then in 1923 appeared no fewer than four publications describing sex chromosomes in flowering plants. Santos found a heteromorphic pair in the Canadian pondweed, *Elodea canadensis*, Blackburn (1923) and Winge (1923a) independently described sex chromosomes in the campion, *Silene*, and in the hop, *Humulus*, and Kihara and Ono (1923) in the sorrel, *Rumex acetosa*. After this, discoveries followed one another in rapid succession in what Correns (1928) described as "a hunt for sex chromosomes in the plant kingdom." The subject has been reviewed by Westergaard (1958), who concluded that the evidence for the presence of sex chromosomes is not always convincing. In most cases this has been based on the observation of a heteromorphic pair of chromosomes in one sex during the first meiotic division. Westergaard considers that the presence of sex chromosomes can be considered conclusive only if the following criteria are fulfilled: (*a*) demonstration of an unequal XY-pair during the meiotic cycle of the heterogametic sex; (*b*) the absence of an unequal pair in the homogametic sex; (*c*) the identification of sex chromosomes in the somatic cells of both sexes. On the basis of these criteria, the presence of an unequal pair of sex chromosomes has been established in the hemp, *Cannabis sativa*, in hop, *Humulus* spp., in the sorrel, *Rumex* spp., and in the campion, *Silene*.

B. *Silene*, RED, AND WHITE CAMPIONS

The red and white campions, *Silene dioica* and *S. alloe*, have proved to be particularly favorable for the purpose of elucidating the sex-determining mechanism among flowering plants. The plants are easy to cultivate, the flowers (Figs. 3.2 and 3.3) are sufficiently large to handle with comfort, and the sex chromosomes are clearly recognizable (Fig. 3.4).

The nomenclature is somewhat confusing because of frequent changes on both the generic and the specific level (Clapham *et al.,* 1962). Although *"Silene"* is the current generic name, the genus was

FIG. 3.2. Male and female flowers of *Silene.* (From Warmke and Blakeslee, 1940.)

previously known as "*Melandrium*" and as "*Lychnis.*" The red- and the white-flowering forms are generally given separate specific ranks as *Silene dioica* (*Lychnis dioica, Melandrium rubrum*) and *S. alba* (*L. alba, M. album*), respectively, but according to D. Löve (1944) the two forms merit only subspecific rank and should both be included within a single species.

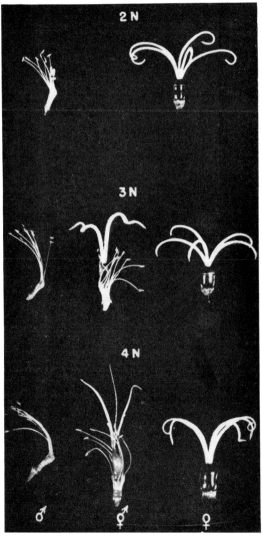

Fig. 3.3. Sex organs of male, female, and hermaphrodite flowers of *Silene*. (From Warmke and Blakeslee, 1940.)

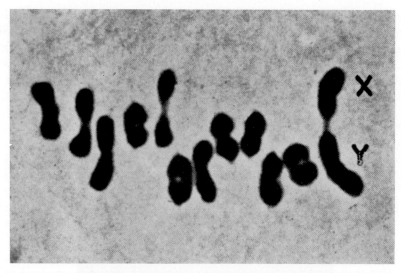

Fig. 3.4. Chromosomes of first meiotic metaphase of pollen mother cell of *Silene*. (From Warmke, 1946.)

The sex chromosomes of *Silene* were discovered independently by Winge (1923a) and by Blackburn (1923). Both investigators found that an unequal pair of chromosomes was present in the male. Genetic evidence that the male was the heterogametic sex had already been provided by Correns (1907), and by Baur (1912), and by Shull (1914). The sex chromosomes are the largest of the complement, and the Y- is larger than the X-chromosome (Fig. 3.4).

Silene is normally diploid, with eleven pairs of autosomes plus two X-chromosomes in female plants and an X- and a Y-chromosome in male plants. Polyploids have been artificially produced, by soaking the seeds in solutions of colchicine (Warmke and Blakeslee, 1940; Westergaard, 1940; Ono, 1939; Warmke, 1946). Meiotic chromosomes were obtained by squashing the anthers in aceto-carmine on a slide. Mitotic chromosomes were prepared from sectioned root tips.

Doubling the chromosomes of a female plant results in a tetraploid with four sets of autosomes and four X-chromosomes, while a male plant will be transformed into a tetraploid with two X- and two Y-chromosomes. Such tetraploids continue to be female and male, respectively.

By crossing tetraploid XXXX-females with XXYY-male plants an F_1 generation was obtained in which the males were far more numerous than the females (Table 3.I). The large majority of the males proved to be XXXY and only a very few XXYY (Fig. 3.5).

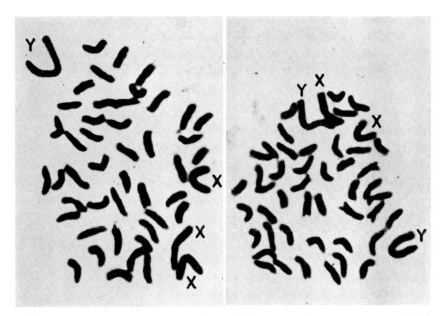

Fig. 3.5. Mitotic chromosomes of tetraploid male *Silene* plants. (*a*) XXXY; (*b*) XXYY. (From Warmke and Blakeslee, 1940.)

The XXXY-tetraploid males clinched the supposition that the Y-chromosome was the larger of the two sex chromosomes, since the occurrence of plants with an XYYY-constitution would have been wholly unexpected.

The large preponderance of male plants suggests a preferential formation of XY-gametes compared with XX- and YY-gametes. On a purely random hypothesis, one would expect four XY-gametes to each XX- and YY-gamete. The assumption that the XY-class is, in fact, more numerous, was borne out by direct observation of meiotic chromosomes. Out of 100 pollen mother cells which were examined by Warmke and Blakeslee, no less than 89 contained configurations of the X- and the Y-chromosomes, either as two bivalents or one quadrivalent, which were interpreted as yielding exclusively XY-gametes. Only 7% would have resulted in XX- and YY-gametes, while 4% of the cells had associations which would be expected to undergo nondisjunction and thus give rise to aberrant types. The majority of XXXY-males were indistinguishable from XXYY, but about 10% of the plants produced a few hermaphrodite flowers in addition to male ones.

Second generation tetraploids are obtained by crossing F_1 female and male plants. Since there are two types of males, XXY and XXYY, two types of crosses are possible, but since the XXYY-class is so much in the minority, it tends to be eliminated. By crossing XXXX-females to XXXY-males, a second generation of tetraploid plants is obtained which consists of approximately equal number of XXXX-females and XXXY-males; and thus a tetraploid race is obtained in which males and females occur in approximately equal numbers.

By crossing tetraploid plants to diploids of the opposite sex, triploid offspring were produced. Plants of the constitution 3A + XXX were female, as expected, and of those with an (3A + XXY)-constitution the majority were male, but a minority contained also a few hermaphrodite flowers.

The sexes of the various diploid and polyploid plants containing a Y-chromosome are shown in Table 3.I. It is clear that the Y-chromosome must be strongly male-determining. In Warmke's strains, a few hermaphrodite blossoms could be found in addition to the male ones, whereas in Westergaard's material all such flowers were entirely male. It is possible that the male-determining potency of the Y-chromosome in

TABLE 3.I

RELATION OF AUTOSOMES, X- AND Y-CHROMOSOMES TO SEX IN *Silene*[a]

Chromosomes constitution	Ratio X/Y	Sex
2A XYY)	0.5	Male
2A XY) 3A XY) 4A XY) 4A XXYY)	1.0	Male
4A XXXYY	1.5	Male
2A XXY) 3A XXY) 4A XXY) 4A XXXXYY)	2.0	Male (occasional hermaphrodite blossom)
3A XXXY) 4A XXXY)	3.0	Male (occasional hermaphrodite blossom)
4A XXXXY	4.0	Hermaphrodite (occasional male blossom)

[a] From Warmke (1946).

these plants was slightly stronger. Moreover, the X-chromosome must have a certain, although weaker, female-determining power, since as the ratio of X- to Y-chromosomes increases, so does the proportion of hermaphrodite flowers. On the other hand, the autosomes do not seem to take any considerable part in the determination of sex.

Plants with defective Y-chromosomes have arisen spontaneously on several occasions. Westergaard (1953) distinguishes three such defective Y-chromosomes, Y^1, Y^2, and Y^3 (Fig. 3.6). Y^1 and Y^3 are probably simple deletions, but Y^2 is interpreted as a translocation between the Y- and the X-chromosome. Plants containing a Y^1- or a Y^2-chromosome are hermaphrodites with normally developed stamens and pistils and are fertile. On self-pollination they give rise to females lacking the defec-

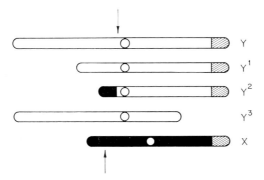

FIG. 3.6. Normal (Y) and defective (Y^1, Y^2, Y^3) Y-chromosomes in *Silene*. Arrows indicate points of breakage resulting in translocation. (From Westergaard, 1953.) See also Fig. 3.7.

tive Y-chromosome and to hermaphrodites containing it, but normal males are not found. It is therefore concluded that the distal end of the Y-chromosome (i.e., the end away from the homologous part), which is lacking in the Y^1 and Y^2-chromosomes, normally suppresses the formation of the female organs.

Plants containing a Y^3-chromosome, which lacks the homologous and part of the differential segment, are male but sterile. The stamens are formed normally and the two meiotic divisions take place, but then development stops and the pollen grains do not mature. It appears therefore that this segment controls the last stages of pollen formation. Thus the differential segment of the Y-chromosome may be divided into three parts (Fig. 3.7): one suppresses the female organs, one is concerned with the maturation of the pollen, while the middle portion, which also contains the centromere, controls the formation of stamens.

There is, however, one exception to the rule that the presence of a Y-chromosome is necessary for the production of male flowers. It was known to Strasburger (1900) and has been confirmed many times, that female *Silene* plants which are infected with the smut fungus *Ustilago violacea* develop stamens of normal external morphology. The anthers, however, do not contain pollen but are filled with the spores of the fungus (Westergaard, 1953). The pistil also becomes sterile. No explanation for this strange phenomenon has yet been found.

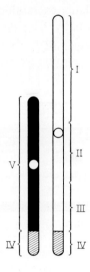

FIG. 3.7. Possible subdivisions of the sex chromosomes in *Silene* according to effect on sex determination. I, II, III, differential segments of Y. IV, homologous segment of X and Y; V, differential segment of X-chromosome. (From Westergaard, 1953.)

Under normal conditions of fertilization when there is an abundance of pollen *Silene* produces slightly more female plants than male ones. Correns (1928) found that when plants are pollinated with very small amounts of pollen, the proportion of males among the offspring increases. This he explained on the assumption that in the competition for fertilization the male-determining pollen grains are at a slight disadvantage. If, however, only very few pollen grains are present, competition is reduced and the male-determining pollen grains are able to reach their destination. The proportion of male plants is also increased by treating pollen with alcohol vapor, or by using old pollen which has been kept for a period of 80–100 days.

C. *Humulus*, THE HOP

The sex chromosomes in hops were first studied by Winge (1923a), who found an XY mechanism in the two species, *Humulus lupulus* and *H. japonicus*. However, Kihara (1929) reported that the male of *H. japonicus* contains two different Y-chromosomes, and is therefore of the constitution XY_1Y_2 (see p. 82). These results were confirmed and extended by Jacobsen (1957), using improved techniques of pretreatment and squashing. He found an XY-mechanism in *H. lupulus*, the X-chromosome being the larger of the two and of medium size compared with the autosomes. *Humulus japonicus* has an XY_1Y_2-mechanism, and all three sex chromosomes are longer than the autosomes. Both Y-chromosomes are heteropycnotic, i.e., the intensity of staining differs from that of the autosomes (see Chapter 11).

D. *Rumex acetosella*, THE SHEEP'S SORREL

Rumex acetosella, the sheep's sorrel, has been classified as a subgenus containing four species which are diploid, tetraploid, hexaploid, and octoploid, respectively. The haploid chromosome number is 7. The sex-chromosome mechanism has been elucidated by A. Löve (1943).

The male is the heterogametic sex. In the first meiotic metaphase of the male in the diploid species, the sex chromosomes can be distinguished, as they form an unequal bivalent. Studies on mitotic chromosomes in both sexes have shown that the Y-chromosome is larger than the X; the Y-chromosome is in fact the largest of the chromosome complement.

In the tetraploid species, the female is XXXX and the male XXXY. The Y-chromosome must therefore be strongly male-determining. During meiosis, the Y-chromosome usually associates with one X-chromosome, and the other two X-chromosomes form a bivalent together. The configurations of the sex chromosomes were studied in 298 cells, with the following results: 245 XX + XY; 27 XXXY; 26 XXX + Y.

In the hexaploid species, the female has six X-chromosomes and the male five X- and one Y-chromosome. The association of the sex chromosomes in meiosis was studied in 169 cells and found to be as follows: 131 XY; 31 XXXY; 7 XXXXXY.

The sex chromosomes in the octoploid species have not been studied.

The sex chromosome constitution of the polyploid species shows that the Y-chromosome in *Rumex* ssp. *acetosella* must be strongly male-determining. The same appears to be true for *R. paucifolius*, which belongs to the subgenus *Acetosa*. A. Löve and Sarkar (1956) have shown that this species is tetraploid with 28 chromosomes, of which four are the sex chromosomes. The female has four X-chromosomes and the male three X- and a Y-chromosome. On the other hand, in *R. acetosa* the male has one X-chromosome and two Y-chromosomes and is of the constitution XY_1Y_2, while the female is XX (Westergaard, 1958). Here it appears that the male-determining factors are located mainly in the autosomes, and that sex is determined by the ratio of X-chromosomes to autosomes, as in *Drosophila* (see Chapter 4).

E. *Fragaria*, THE STRAWBERRY

The genus *Fragaria* contains diploid, tetraploid, hexaploid, and octoploid species. All the diploid species are hermaphrodite, but the polyploid wild species are nearly all dioecious. A great deal of work has been done in crossing different species and varieties; this has been summarized by Westergaard (1958).

The results of many crosses between dioecious and hermaphrodite forms agree with the assumption that in the strawberry the female is the heterogametic sex. Evidence for the presence of heteromorphic sex chromosomes has been presented by Kihara (1930) in the female of *F. moschata* (previously *F. elatior*) a hexaploid species with 42 chromosomes. It would be of great interest if this could be confirmed with modern techniques of chromosome preparation, particularly since the presence of heteromorphic sex chromosomes in the female has not otherwise been established in plants.

F. THE ORIGIN OF SEX CHROMOSOMES

In a large number of dioecious flowering plants sex chromosomes have been looked for but could not be found. A list of these was published by Allen (1940). In one of these species, the spinach (*Spinacia oleracea*), Ellis and Janick (1960) were able to show that the longest pair of chromosomes was concerned with sex determination. This was accomplished by the cytological examination of a strain which was known from its breeding behavior to be trisomic for the sex chromosomes. Later, Iizuka and Janick (1963) localized the sex-determining part to a region which might represent a single locus. Here, then, we have a likely example of sex being determined by a single pair of allelic genes situated on chromosomes which are not otherwise differentiated. Since chiasmata will be freely formed between these chromosomes, the sex genes will pass from one chromosome to the other. It is likely that a similar situation occurs in other dioecious plants which do not have heteromorphic sex chromosomes. An attempt to explain the genetic data on sex determination in flowering plants in physiological terms was recently made by Köhler (1964).

It is generally agreed that in higher plants dioecism has arisen from a condition in which both sexes are present in the same organism (Westergaard, 1958). A possible scheme for the evolution of dioecism with differentiated sex chromosomes from monoecious (or hermaphrodite) ancestors has been described by Darlington (1932).

1. Origin of a gene-pair (the sex differentials) whose segregation determines the opposite sexes.
2. Genotypic suppression of crossing-over in the region of the sex differentials.
3. Structural and gene changes in this region, making it into a differential segment.

The first step has been observed by Emerson (1932) and by Jones (1932, 1934) in maize (*Zea mays*), although here two pairs of genes are involved. Maize is normally monoecious; the apical flower (tassel) is male, having functional stamens and a rudimentary pistil, while the lateral flowers (silks) are female, with a functional pistil and rudimentary stamens. A recessive gene, called *tassel seed*, causes the female organs of the tassel to develop and to form seeds and suppresses the development of the stamens. A plant which is homozygous for this gene, ts_2/ts_2, is therefore functionally a female. Another gene, *silkless*, which is located on a different chromosome, suppresses the development of the female organs in the lateral flowers. Plants of the genetic constitution sk/sk are therefore functional males. When the two genes are combined as in $ts_2/ts_2\ sk/sk$ the plants are female, because the *tassel seed* gene predominates when present in double (homozygous) dose. However, in single (heterozygous) dose, it is unable to do this, and plants of the constitution $Ts_2/ts_2\ sk/sk$ are male. By crossing these two types of plants a permanently dioecious line of maize is established, in which the male may be regarded as heterozygous for the sex gene, while the female is homozygous.

This scheme, followed by the differentiation of the chromosome pair involved, may be regarded as a model of the mechanism by which dioecism determined by sex chromosomes may evolve from an original bisexual state.

CHAPTER 4

SEX CHROMOSOMES IN *DROSOPHILA*

I. Introduction

The sex chromosomes of the fruit fly *Drosophila* are of particular interest because the wealth of knowledge about this fly, which has been derived both from breeding experiments and from the direct observation of the chromosomes, has made a fundamental contribution to our understanding of cytogenetics in general and of the genetics of sex determination in particular.

The fruit fly, which has also been called vinegar fly or pomace fly, became etsablished as a laboratory animal in America during the first decade of this century. It proved an ideal experimental subject for breeding experiments since it breeds prolifically in milk bottles, and 25 generations can be obtained within a year. Although small, a great wealth of anatomical detail can be observed in individual flies. This became of great use to genetics when, one by one, and at first unexpectedly, mutations began to appear in the laboratory. A mutation was defined (T. H. Morgan *et al.*, 1925) as a transmissible change in the germ plasm, producing a detectable change in the characteristics of the individual, which is called a "mutant." As a result of mutation, flies are distinguishable from the normal or wild-type by such characteristics as the color or the shape of the eye, the color of the body, the shape of the wings, or the arrangement of its veins, or the form of its bristles.

In *D. melanogaster*, the males are easily distinguished from the females by a number of secondary sexual characteristics. In the females, which are slightly larger than the males, the abdomen is elongated and contains five separate dark grey bands. In the males the abdomen is rounded off and has only two separate dark bands in front, while the tip is entirely dark grey. The males are also distinguished by their sex combs, a row of bristles situated on the first pair of legs (Fig. 4.1).

The chromosomes of *D. melanogaster* were first described by Stevens (1908), who found four pairs of chromosomes in the female, including a pair of X-chromosomes. The sex-chromosome constitution of the male was established by Bridges (1914), who found that the male has an unequal pair of sex chromosomes, consisting of a "rod-shaped" (i.e., acrocentric, p. 23) X-chromosome, as in the female, and a "V-shaped" (i.e., metacentric, p. 23) Y-chromosome. Other species of *Drosophila* may have different types of sex chromosomes. For instance, in *D. miranda* multiple sex chromosomes of the type X_1X_2Y have been reported (Dobzhansky, 1935).

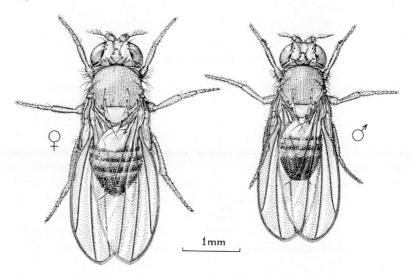

Fig. 4.1. *Drosophila melanogaster*, male and female. Drawing by A. J. Lee.

II. Sex Linkage

The first mutant found in *Drosophila* was a male, which had white eyes instead of the normal dark red ones (T. H. Morgan, 1910). When mated to his red-eyed sisters, this male produced 1237 red-eyed offspring, as well as 3 white-eyed males, which will be discussed later. By interbreeding the red-eyed F_1, the following offspring were obtained: 2459 red-eyed females, 1011 red-eyed males, 782 white-eyed males. No white-eyed females appeared in the F_1 generations. However, it was shown by the following experiments that such individuals could exist. A white-eyed male was mated to his red-eyed daughter, with the following result: 129 red-eyed females, 132 red-eyed males, 88 white-eyed females, 86 white-eyed males.

All these results can be explained on the assumption that the gene for white eye is situated on the X-chromosome (Fig. 4.2).

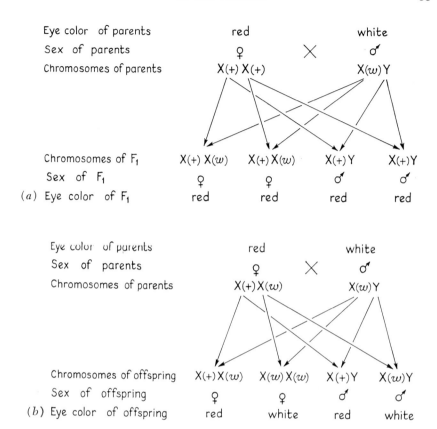

FIG. 4.2. Mode of inheritance of a sex-linked gene. (a) mutant father and homozygous wild-type mother. (b) mutant father and herterozygous mother. Wild-type alleles shown as (+).

This type of inheritance was originally called "sex limited." This was in accordance with experiences in human heredity, in which such characteristics as color blindness and hemophilia are, in most families, confined to males. Similarly, in the moth *Abraxas*, with female heterogamety, the variety *dohrnii* is met with in the wild only in females (Chapter 5, Section 2). It soon became clear, however, that as a result of inbreeding, such characters can also exist in the opposite sex. Thus, the first white-eyed *Drosophila* found was a male, and in the F_2 generation also the character was confined to males. However, by crossing a white-eyed male with a female which is heterozygous for eye color, white-eyed females are produced. Clearly, the reason this character is more frequently encountered in males is that a male requires only one gene to show it, whereas a female requires two. Accordingly, Morgan and his school soon changed the term "sex limitation" to "sex-linkage." "Sex limitation," in modern terminology, implies that the genic expression differs in males and females, as in the case of baldness in man.

Some recent authors have preferred the term "X-linkage" rather than sex-linkage, in order to distinguish genes carried on the X-chromosome from those on the Y-chromosome (which are found in fishes and to a lesser degree in *Drosophila*). Strictly speaking, such genes are either X-borne or Y-borne, whereas the term "linkage" refers to the relationship of two or more genes which are situated on the same chromosome. "This term (sex-linked) is intended to mean that such characters are carried by the X-chromosome" (T. H. Morgan and Bridges, 1916), and its use was based on the assumption that the X-chromosome carried one or more sex factors, to which the other genes would be linked. It will be shown later (Section IV) that the X-chromosome as a whole in *Drosophila* is female-determining but detailed analysis of this chromosome has failed to reveal the existence of either one or several separate female-determining genes. In other organisms, such as man, it is not even certain that the X-chromosome is female-determining, so that there is even less reason to believe in the existence of sex genes on the X-chromosome. Thus neither the term "sex-linked" nor "X-linked" is strictly accurate. In the circumstances, there seems to be little harm in retaining the old established "sex-linked," meaning a gene which is carried on the X-chromosome; while the much rarer instances of genes being carried on the Y-chromosome will be referred to as "Y-borne."

The different genes which are located on the X-chromosome are linked to one another and, indeed, the phenomenon of linkage was first discovered from results obtained with X-borne genes. In 1913 the first chromosome map, consisting of six genes located on the X-chromosome, was published (Sturtevant, 1913).

The fact that two genes are linked is deduced from the observation that among the offspring of individuals which are heterozygous for both genes the parental arrangements of genes outweigh the new combinations. Linked genes, therefore, are an exception to the rule of independent assortment of characters required by Mendel's second law. The new recombinations are the result of crossing-over between the chromosome pairs.

Linkage between two sex-linked genes, *miniature* wing and *yellow* body color, is illustrated by an early experiment of Sturtevant (1913, see Fig. 4.3). A female with long (normal) wings and yellow body was crossed to a male with miniature wings and grey (normal) body. The F_1 generation consisted of normal females and yellow males. The F_1 females formed four types of gametes, two being original and two new recombinations. The female F_2 offspring consisted of yellow and normal flies, but from this type of cross they cannot be sorted out into products of original and crossover chromosomes. This, however, can easily be done in the case of the males: the yellow and miniature groups are original, whereas the miniature yellow and normal flies are recombinants. Out of 270 F_2 males, 99 were recombinants, giving a crossover value of $99 \times 100/27 = 36.7\%$. More detailed and extensive work has later modified this value to 36.1% (Bridges and Brehme, 1944).

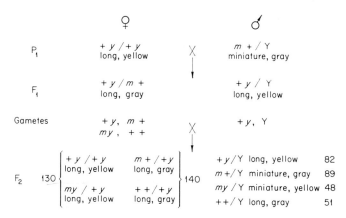

FIG. 4.3. Mode of inheritance of two sex-linked genes.

In order to establish the linear order of the genes on the chromosome, crossing-over between at least three pairs of genes must be considered. This may be illustrated from an early experiment by Sturtevant and Muller (see T. H. Morgan and Bridges, 1916). A female carrying the genes for yellow body and white eyes on one of its X-chromosomes, and the gene *bifid*, causing an abnormality of the veins of the wings, on the other, was mated with a male which was homozygous for all three genes (Fig. 4.4). As can be seen from the diagram, both male and female offspring can immediately be scored as having received an original or a crossover chromosome. Out of a total of 506 flies, 3 resulted from crossing-over between yellow and white, giving a crossover value of 0.6%. Similarly, 16 flies resulted from crossing-over between white and bifid, giving a crossover value of 3.2%. The total number of breaks between yellow and white were 19, which gives a crossover value of 3.8%.

These values have later been modified as follows: distance between *yellow* and *white* 1.5 units; between *white* and *bifid* 5.4 units; and between *yellow* and *bifid* 6.9 units. It is evident that the distance between *yellow* and *bifid* is made up of the sum of the distances between *yellow* and *white* and *white* and *bifid*. If data had been available merely for crossover values between individual pairs of genes, it could not have been ascertained whether *yellow* or *white* should be in the middle.

The distance between two genes on a chromosome is measured in map units, or centimorgans. A crossover unit is defined as a length of

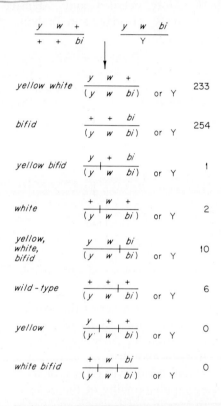

Vertical line represents point of crossing-over

FIG. 4.4. Result of crossing female heterozygous for three sex-linked genes with hemizygous male.

chromosome along which, on an average and under standard conditions, one crossover occurs among 100 gametes. In order to calculate map units, the proportion of double crossovers must also be known.

In the experiment illustrated in Fig. 4.4, the genes *yellow* and *bifid* are sufficiently close together so that no double crossing-over occurred between them. If it had occurred, it would have been detected, owing to the presence of the intermediate gene, *white*. However, if this gene had not been present, the occurrence of a double crossover would have gone undetected, for the two outside genes would have been present in their original arrangement. It follows from this that unless a large number of genes are taken into account, any two of which are fairly close together, map distances derived from crossing-over values will be somewhat too small, since the occurrence of double crossovers will be missed. It also follows that, regardless of the length of the chromosome and the total number of crossover breaks that may occur, the total amount of crossing-over observed between any two genes does not exceed 50%. In *Drosophila*, the length of the X-chromosome is 66 map units, but the amount of crossing-over observed between genes situated at either end, *yellow* and *bobbed* (causing a shortening of bristles) is just under 50% (Bridges and Brehme, 1944).

The relative positioning of genes is thus determined as a result of linkage experiments, while the actual order from right to left is arbitrarily fixed for the sake of uniformity. Thus, in the X-chromosome of *Drosophila melanogaster*, the gene *yellow* is placed at the extreme left end, and the gene *bobbed* on the right; the centromere is situated close to the right end.

The amount of crossing-over which occurs is somewhat dependent on the temperature at which the flies are kept as well as on the age of the mother, but crossing-over on the X-chromosome is least subject to these external conditions. However, the genetic constitution as well as treatment with X-rays may affect crossing-over also on the X-chromosomes (T. H. Morgan *et al.*, 1925). Since the relative positioning of the genes is based on the assumption that the amount of crossing-over is proportional to the length of the chromosomes, it follows that adding up the result from isolated linkage experiments, carried out under different conditions, may lead to erroneous conclusions.

By piecing together the results of crossover experiments, the relative position of about 150 genes situated on the X-chromosome has been established. In *Drosophila*, linkage maps based on cytological observations of metaphase chromosomes and particularly of salivary gland chromosomes are also available (Sections VI and VII). Whether based on genetic or cytological evidence, the maps are basically similar, the points of divergence being relatively minor.

III. Nondisjunction of the X-chromosome

The phenomenon of nondisjunction of the X-chromosome in *Drosophila* is of particular interest, first because it provides direct proof that the sex-linked genes are borne on the X-chromosome; and second because it is now known that it occurs in man and is responsible for abnormalities in sexual development.

In the typical course of sex-linked inheritance a recessive gene carried by the mother gives rise to affected sons and unaffected daughters, whereas a sex-linked gene borne by the father is transmitted to his daughters and to none of his sons. Occasionally in *Drosophila* this criss-cross pattern is broken: Some exceptional daughters bear their mother's sex-linked character, while the sons resemble the father.

Bridges (1913, 1914, 1916) found that on mating a female with normal eye color to a white-eyed male, about 5% of the daughters were like the mother and about 5% of the sons were like the father. He explained this anomaly on the assumption that a small proportion of the mother's sex chromosomes failed to disjoin at meiosis, thus producing some eggs with two X-chromosomes and some with none (Fig. 4.5). Nondisjunction of

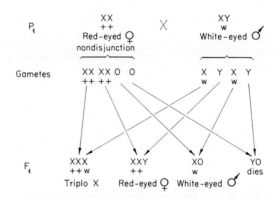

FIG. 4.5. Nondisjunction in *Drosophila*.

the sex chromosomes had previously been observed cytologically by Wilson (1909d) in the spermatocytes of *Metapodius* and Frolowa (1912) had found exceptional eggs containing two X-chromosomes or no X-chromosome in *Parascaris equorum*. The correctness of the supposition that the exceptional daughters were of XXY-chromosome constitution was confirmed by analysis of the chromosomes in their oogonia (Bridges, 1916). The formation of XXX-zygotes was assumed on hypothetical grounds; such individuals were not actually found until several years later (Bridges, 1921).

The incidence of nondisjunction in ordinary stocks of *Drosophila* is of the order of one in 2000 individuals, but among the offspring of non-disjunctional mothers the incidence of abnormal offspring due to secondary nondisjunction is about one in twenty (T. H. Morgan *et al.*,

1925). Clearly, the separation of the sex chromosomes in the oogenesis of an XXY-individual is bound to be abnormal. Either the two X-chromosomes stay together and the Y-chromosome goes to another cell, or the X- and Y-chromosomes disjoin as a pair from a single X (Fig. 4.6). Bridges (1916) found that in *Drosophila* the latter alternative happens more frequently. Fertilization by an X-bearing sperm will give rise to XX- and XXY-daughters, while a Y-bearing sperm will result in XY and XYY-sons. All these individuals will be unexceptional as regards the inheritance of sex-linked characters, since the daughters receive an X-chromosome each from their mother and their father, while the sons receive their single X from their mother. By contrast, eggs containing two X-chromosomes or a single Y-chromosome will give rise to exceptional

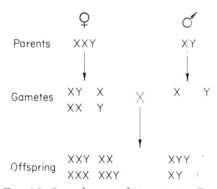

FIG. 4.6. Secondary nondisjunction in *Drosophila*.

sons and daughters. The daughters, of chromosome constitution XXY, have received both X-chromosomes from their mother and therefore express their mother's sex-linked characters; and the sons, though of normal XY-constitution, have received the Y-chromosome from their mother and the X-chromosome from their father, and thus resemble their father as regards sex-linked characters. In addition, two other classes of zygotes may be expected from these types of nondisjunctional eggs: those with three X-chromosomes and those with two Y-chromosomes and no X. The latter type have never been found, and it may be concluded that the presence of at least one X-chromosome is essential for viability (this is not so in organism's in which the sex chromosomes are little differentiated, e.g., fishes, see Chapter 7, Section II). In *Drosophila,* the early development of eggs lacking an X-chromosome has been found to be very abnormal, with an oxygen consumption no higher than that of unfertilized eggs (Poulson, 1945). Individuals with three X-chromosomes were found (Bridges, 1921) as a result of nondisjunction as well as among the offspring of triploid females. Such individuals are very inviable; the survivors are abnormal sterile females. Owing to the excessive number of X-chromosomes which they contain they have been called "super-females" (Bridges, 1921), in spite of the fact that the ovaries are underdeveloped. Stern (1959) proposed the term "meta-female," implying that the phenotype is beyond femaleness. Many authors, particularly in human cytogenetics, prefer the term "triple X-female."

Stocks exist in *Drosophila* in which two X-chromosomes are joined by their centromeres; in addition, the females carry a Y-chromosome. In such "attached-X" stocks, the two X-chromosomes always disjoin as a pair from the Y, and consequently all the offspring will be aberrant with respect to the inheritance of sex-linked genes: the females receive both X-chromosomes from the mother and a Y-chromosome from the father, whereas the males receive their X-chromosome from the father and their Y-chromosome from their mother.

Nondisjunction in *Drosophila* females was recently studied by J. R. Merriam and Frost (1964); they confirmed, from the distribution of exceptional offspring of experimental crossings, that nondisjunction, is, in fact an error of meiosis. In *Drosophila,* nondisjunction is not affected by maternal age (Kelsall, 1963), but an increase occurs after X-irradiation (Mavor, 1921; A. M. Clark and Clark, 1963).

Nondisjunction has been defined as primary, when the mother is of XX-sex chromosome constitution, and as secondary, when the mother is XXY (T. H. Morgan *et al.,* 1925). In *Drosophila,* secondary nondisjunction is always a very much more frequent event.

Primary nondisjunction in the male is more difficult to detect, since it does not usually result in offspring with phenotypes contrary to the rules of sex-linked inheritance. That this phenomenon occurs was shown by Kelsall (1961) from the offspring of flies with a special type of chromosome constitution and containing markers both on the paternal and maternal X-chromosomes. In addition to the usual type of nondisjunction, this mating gave rise to XXY-females containing one paternal and one maternal X-chromosome, which must therefore have arisen from an XY sperm. In addition, XYY-males with a maternal X-chromosome were found, which probably arose from a YY-sperm.

IV. Sex Determination

We have seen that in diploid fruit flies an individual with two X-chromosomes is a female, an individual with an X- and a Y-chromosome is a male, XXY is female, and a single X-chromosome (XO) is male. The last two premises rule out the possibility that the Y-chromosome is male-determining, while all the data are consistent with the assumption that the X-chromosome is female-determining. In diploid flies, two X-chromosomes result in a female, and a single X-chromosome in a male individual; but in triploid flies the situation is different. The existence of triploid flies was discovered by Bridges (1921) on the basis of cytological studies as well as by the fact that these flies carry in triplicate a large number of genetic markers on the second and third chromosomes. Triploid flies with two X-chromosomes turned out to be intersexes: sex combs were present, but the abdomen was intermediate between male and female; the gonads were typically rudimentary ovaries, though not infrequently one was an ovary and the other a testis, and ovotestes were sometimes present. All intersexes were sterile. The sterility could not be due to the triploid condition, since triploid flies with three X-chromosomes were fertile females (Bridges, 1925).

The existence of these intersexes gave rise to the idea that sex in *Drosophila* is determined by a balance of the number of X-chromosomes with that of the autosomes. Thus, the autosomes in *Drosophila* are also sex-determining, and moreover, they are male-determining. With this idea in mind, other combinations of X-chromosomes and autosomes were looked for and found (Table 4.I). Tetraploid individuals with four X-chromosomes proved to be fertile females. Thus, in *Drosophila*, female individuals result when the number of X-chromosomes is the same as the number of homologous autosomes, and if the number of X-chromosomes is half that of homologous autosomes, the individual is male. Other types of chromosome combinations result in sterile individuals. According to

TABLE 4. I

RELATIONSHIP OF CHROMOSOMES TO SEX IN *Drosophila melanogaster*[a]

Sex	Number of X-chromosomes: autosomes (A)
"Superfemale"	3:2
Female	2:2
	3:3
	4:4
Intersex	2:3
	3:4
Male	1:2
	2:4
"Supermale"	1:3

[a] After Bridges, 1939.

Bridges' terminology, individuals with ratios of X-chromosomes to autosomes which are intermediate between that for normal males and females
are called "intersexes," if the ratio is higher than that of a normal female,
the individual is a "superfemale," while a ratio below that for normal
male results in a "supermale." Frost (1960) found that a minority of
triploid females with four X-chromosomes are partially fertile.

Dobzhansky and Schultz (1934) attempted to find out whether any
genes for femaleness could be localized more precisely on the X-
chromosome. For this purpose they used triploid intersexes containing two
X-chromosomes and in addition different fragments of the X-chromosomes
for which the flies were therefore triploid. The fragments were produced
by X-irradiation, and their length and position relative to the whole
X-chromosome were determined both cytologically and genetically. They
found that there was no single sex gene on the X-chromosome; but that
all duplications studied—and between them they covered the whole of
the X-chromosome—increased the female characteristics of the intersexes.
The extent of the shift in the female direction was on the whole proportional to the cytological length, and the addition of sufficiently long
sections converted the intersexes into fertile females. Only the part of
the X-chromosome near the end which is regarded as genetically "inert"
had no effect on the intersexes. Thus, the X-chromosome as a whole,
rather than individual genes on it, appears to be female-determining;
and, similarly, the whole of the large autosomes 3 and 4 appear to be
male-determining (Pipkin, 1960).

The Y-chromosome does not determine whether a fly becomes a male
or a female, but its presence is necessary to ensure the motility of the
sperm. Stern (1929) has shown that only a certain portion of the Y-
chromosome is required for this purpose.

Although the sex of *Drosophila* is determined by the totality of the
X-chromosome as well as the autosomes, a number of individual genes
are known which affect the development of sex organs and secondary
sexual characters. Probably the most striking is the gene "transformer,"
which is located on the third chromosome and transforms females into
individuals which appear to be normal males (Sturtevant, 1945). They
have fully developed sex combs, male-colored abdomens, and male external and internal genitalia. The testes, however, are small, and although the flies mate with females, they are sterile, even if a Y-
chromosome is present. Although indistinguishable from normal males
except by the size of their testes, the transformed males resemble females
in size, rate of development, and the expression of some sex-limited
characters (Sturtevant, 1945); however, with regard to the expression
of the gene *lozenge-clawless,* which is carried on the X-chromosome,

and the expression of which differs in males and females, the transformed individuals behave like males (Anders, 1948). This example illustrates that maleness and femaleness represent two alternative developmental systems, the components of which may be laid down at different stages of embryogenesis.

V. Gynandromorphs

Gynandromorphs, or individuals with both male and female parts of the body, occur from time to time in cultures of *Drosophila*. The distribution of male and female parts is variable; the most striking gynandromorphs are the bilateral types, in which one longitudinal half is male and the other half female (Fig. 4.7). The frequency of gynandromorphs

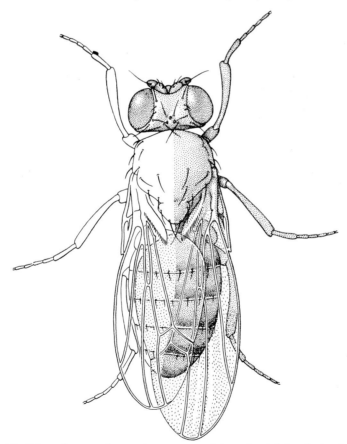

Fig. 4.7. Bilateral gynandromorph in *Drosophila*. The left-hand (male) side shows the gene for yellow body.

has been estimated as one in about 2000 flies (T. H. Morgan and Bridges, 1919); and in an organism such as *Drosophila* an incidence of this magnitude is amenable to experimental procedure.

With a view to elucidating the origin of gynandromorphs, T. H. Morgan and Bridges (1919) set up matings involving sex-linked as well as autosomal genes. They studied the distribution of these genes on the male and female parts of the gynandromorphs which emerged and concluded that most gynandromorphs in *Drosophila* arise from an XX-zygote, in which one of the X-chromosomes is lost. If the loss occurs during the first cleavage division, a lateral gynandromorph will result; otherwise the distribution of male and female parts will be more variable. More recently it has been shown by a number of authors (see Mainx, 1957, 1964) that gynandromorphs in *Drosophila* may also arise by a process of double fertilization. This implies the simultaneous fusion of two spermatozoa, in this case an X- and a Y-bearing one, with the nuclei of the egg and a polar body and the subsequent development of the products into a single individual.

The male and female parts of gynandromorphs in *Drosophila* are always self-determining as regards the expression of sex-linked genes. A male part containing a sex-linked recessive gene always shows this, regardless of the genetic constitution of the cells surrounding it; the expression is in no way influenced by the gonads. These, in fact, are generally of the same kind, either testes or ovaries, on both sides of an individual gynandromorph. If testes are present, the individual is sterile, which may be due to the lack of a Y-chromosome, but gynandromorphs having ovaries are sometimes fertile.

VI. Cytological Investigations

The chromosomes of *Drosophila* were first studied by Stevens (1908), and the exact situation as regards the sex chromosomes was discovered by Bridges (1914, 1916) and by Metz (1914). These studies were carried out on oogonia and spermatogonia. The cells of both sexes contain three pairs of autosomes, of which two are large and metacentric (Chapter 2, Section II) (these are called chromosomes 2 and 3), while the fourth pair of chromosomes is very small and in the shape of a dot. In addition, the female has a pair of acrocentric chromosomes; these are the X-chromosomes. In the cells of the males there is only one X-chromosome and in addition another chromosome, which is somewhat larger than the X: it is also metacentric, though its centromere is nearer one end; this is the Y-chromosome. In accordance with the positioning of the centromeres, the X-chromosome appears in the shape of a rod, while the Y-chromosome is hook-shaped.

The chromosomes in dividing cells of *Drosophila* are small and not favorable for cytological investigation. This is only partly offset by two redeeming features, namely, the small number of chromosomes per nucleus and the fact that homologous chromosomes tend to lie side by side, which undoubtedly helps in their identification.

Attempts have been made to construct cytological maps of the X-chromosomes by locating genes on visible parts of the chromosome and correlating the phenotypic effect of genes carried on cytologically visible chromosomal abnormalities (Painter, 1931; Dobzhansky, 1932). Dobzhansky treated wild-type males with X-rays, in order to induce fragmentation of the X-chromosome, and subsequently mated them to attached X-females, which were homozygous for the sex-linked genes *yellow, apricot, echinus,* and *forked*. Most of the female offspring carried the mother's sex-linked genes but some failed to show some or all of these genes; these females had received an additional fragment of the X-chromosome from the irradiated father. The genes carried on the duplicated piece were ascertained by appropriate genetic crosses. A comparison of the cytological and genetic distances separating the genes showed that the order of genes was the same, but that genes which appeared to be crowded on the genetic map may be less closely spaced on the cytological map, and vice versa. This must mean that the susceptibility to crossing-over varies in different portions of the X-chromosome.

An important point emerging from these studies is that a third of the X-chromosome as seen in metaphase carries only a single gene, *bobbed*. This gene, which is located on the extreme right end of the genetic linkage map, also occurs on the Y-chromosome (Stern, 1927, 1929). Painter suggested that in this region the X- and Y-chromosome are homologous.

The paucity of genes on the right-hand side of the X-chromosome, as well as on the whole of the Y-chromosome (which, it will be remembered, is larger than the X-chromosome during metaphase) has given rise to the notion that these regions are composed of heterochromatin. The significance of this substance will be discussed later (Chapter 11).

VII. Salivary Gland Chromosomes

The work which has just been described brought cytogenetic studies based on metaphase chromosomes in *Drosophila* to the limit beyond which no further information on the relationship between genes and chromosomes could be expected. Henceforth a new line of investigation was required—and was duly found in the giant chromosomes present in the nuclei of the salivary glands of *Drosophila* larvae.

In 1881, Balbiani had described similar structures in the salivary gland nuclei of another fly, the midge *Chironomus*—a coiled string, which was transversely striated, with dark bands alternating with light ones—but their significance was not appreciated until 50 years later. In 1930, Kostoff described these chromosomes in *Drosophila melanogaster* and suggested that the alternating bands were an expression of the linear arrangement of the genes. Heitz and Bauer (1933) described the salivary gland chromosomes in *Bibio*, but the realization that the study of salivary gland chromosomes could add a new dimension to the cytogenetical analysis of *Drosophila* came particularly through the work of Painter (1933). Painter found that each chromosome has a characteristic morphology and contains a characteristic pattern of bands so that any chromosome or part of a chromosome can easily be recognized in different cells. Steffensen (1963) has recently produced evidence based on autoradiography (Chapter 11, Section IV) that the DNA of salivary gland chromosomes is confined to the bands, and that no appreciable amounts are present in the regions between the bands.

In salivary gland nuclei there appear to be six chromosome arms—five large ones and one tiny one—which are attached to a common substrate, known as the "chromocenter." As a result of the somatic pairing, the two X-chromosomes of a female are represented by a single chromosome; the two large pairs of autosomes are each represented by two arms, corresponding to the two arms on either side of the centromere, while the fourth chromosme is represented by the very short arm of the salivary gland chromosomes.

A further remarkable fact about salivary gland chromosomes is that the banded structures appear to represent only the genetically "active" portions of the metaphase chromosomes. Thus, about a third of the length of the X-chromosome in metaphase, which does not carry any genes, is not represented on the X-chromosome in salivary gland nuclei. However, detailed investigations of the chromocenter (Muller and Prokofyeva, 1935) have shown that faint cross-striations can be recognized and have led to the conclusion that this part of the X-chromosome, as well as the entire Y-chromosome of the male, is present inside the chromocenter. Owing to the differential cytological behavior of these regions, as well as the paucity of the genes carried by them, these regions are regarded as made up of "heterochromatin" (Heitz, 1934). The chromocenter also contains the centromeres of all the chromosomes, together with their adjacent chromosomal regions, which are also regarded as composed of heterochromatin (see Chapter 11).

In some cells enlarged regions of salivary gland chromosomes are found. These are known as "chromosomal puffs" and the larger ones as "Balbiani rings." It is believed that in these regions the chromomeres are relatively uncoiled. Puffs and Balbiani rings tend to be rich in ribonucleic acid, which is probably produced by the genes. Recently definite evidence has been presented correlating the presence of a Balbiani ring and the activity of a gene located at that site (Beermann, 1961).

It was pointed out earlier that good correlation was obtained between genetic linkage maps in *Drosophila* and so-called cytological maps based on the presence of supernumerary chromosomal fragments; but the crowning glory of *Drosophila* cytogenetics was undoubtedly achieved with the mapping of salivary gland chromosomes. The discovery that genetic loci can be marked within these patterns was made by Painter (1933, 1934a,b,c,). After making a careful investigation of the patterns made by the cross bands and thus being able to recognize the individual chromosomes, Painter studied the salivary gland chromosomes in female flies heterozygous for the "forked-Bar" break, which was known, from metaphase preparations, to break the X-chromosome into approximately equal parts. One of the six elements of the salivary gland chromosomes also showed a break, and this was therefore known to be the X-chromosome. There was, however, only one X element in the cell, and the break was not in the middle but well towards one end. From these facts, Painter drew two conclusions, namely, (1) that in salivary glands, the homologous chromosomes show extremely close side-by-side pairing, and (2) that it is the relatively active genetic parts which form the bands. By using other chromosomal aberrations, such as deficiencies, duplications, translocations, and inversions, all the chromosomes were identified and their genes mapped.

The map of the X-chromosome of *Drosophila* constructed by Painter was improved upon by Bridges (1938). On his revised map, the X-chromosome is 414 μ (0.414 mm.) long and is divided into twenty main divisions. In Fig. 4.8 the first three divisions of this map are illustrated, together with the corresponding portion of the genetic linkage map.

The detailed correspondence between these two maps is one of the triumphs of cytogenetics, and information of this order of magnitude is not available for any other organism. Nevertheless, recent progress in the cytogenetics of vertebrates has been equally significant. The advance in our knowledge of the sex chromosomes of man and other mammals has come at such a pace as to be truly revolutionary. Among non-mammalian vertebrates, progress has been somewhat slower, but here, too, much important knowledge has already been gained and more can be expected in the near future.

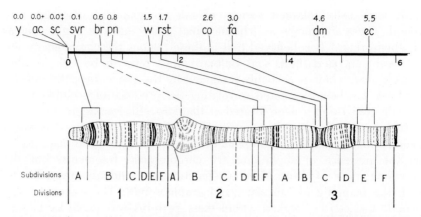

Fig. 4.8. Part of the salivary-gland linkage map of the X-chromosome in *Drosophila melanogaster*. The total X-chromosome measures 20 divisions. The corresponding position of the genetic linkage map is shown above. (From Bridges, 1938.)

Before these new advances will be discussed, brief mention will be made of the more basic findings on the sex chromosomes of Lepidoptera, in which the female is the heterogametic sex, as well as of some other groups which show yet further differences from the basic pattern of sex determination.

CHAPTER 5

SEX CHROMOSOMES IN LEPIDOPTERA

I. Introduction

The Lepidoptera comprise an order within the class of insects. The larger part of the Lepidoptera is further subdivided into eight super-families, of which the butterflies are one, while all the rest are moths. Most of the experimental work on Lepidoptera has been confined to moths.

In the Lepidoptera the female is the heterogametic sex. Although some cytological evidence for this exists (Seiler, 1914), the bulk of our knowledge on sex determination in this group stems from genetic work based on breeding experiments. A vast body of data on sex determination in the gypsy moth, *Lymantria dispar*, has been accumulated (R. B. Goldschmidt, 1934), and the theories evolved have some bearing on sex in other organisms. A great deal is also known about the genetics of the silkworm (*Bombyx mori*). Unfortunately the wealth of genetic data cannot be matched by cytological findings, for which so far the Lepi-doptera have proved to be very unfavorable. The chromosome number tends to be large, while the individual chromosomes are small and do not show much variation.

II. *Abraxas grossulariata*, the Currant Moth

The currant moth, *Abraxas grossulariata* L., which is a pest on currant and gooseberry plants, was the first organism in which the occurrence of sex-linkage was discovered (Doncaster and Raynor, 1906; see Chapter 1). The currant moth has a rare variety *A. dohrnii* (formerly *A lacti-color*) which is of a paler color than the normal (Fig. 5.1). Specimens of *dohrnii* taken by collectors are almost always female. When such a female is bred to a *grossulariata* male, all the offspring are *grossulariata*, indicating that the gene for this character is dominant over *dohrnii*. Males showing the *dohrnii* variety can be produced by mating a *dohrnii*

71

female with one of her sons (Fig. 5.2). Such a mating results in four classes of offspring, *grossulariata* males and females, and *dohrnii* males and females. If, however, a *dohrnii* male is mated to a *grossulariata* female, all the male offspring are *grossulariata* and all the females are *dohrnii*. It is clear that the male transmits the color factor to both his sons and his daughters, but the female transmits it exclusively to her sons. The female must therefore produce two types of eggs, those which carry the color factor and produce sons, and those which lack the color factor and give rise to daughters.

Fig. 5.1. Top: currant moth, *Abraxas grossulariata*. Bottom: pale variety, *A. dohrnii*. (From Doncaster, 1914.)

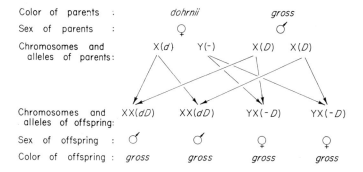

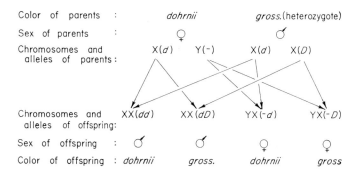

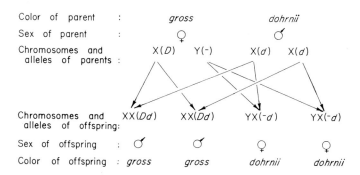

FIG. 5.2. Mode of inheritance of *dohrnii* variety in *Abraxas*.

The majority of currant moths appear to have a diploid number of 56 chromosomes in both sexes and sex chromosomes cannot be distinguished. In one strain, however, Doncaster found that mitotic cells in the ovary contained only 55 chromosomes and that after the first meiotic division some eggs contained 28 and others 27 chromosomes. From this he inferred that in the majority of strains an X- and a Y-chromosome must be present in the female, and that the Y- was absent in this particular strain.

Occasionally gynandromorphs are found in the currant moth, and they may occur with a high frequency in some strains. It is likely that, as in *Drosophila,* gynandromorphs in moths may originate by one of two mechanisms (E. B. Ford, 1955). On the one hand the sex chromosomes may be incorrectly distributed in the early embryo, thus giving rise to tissues with male- and female-determining sex chromosomes. If the mistake occurred during the first mitotic division of the embryo, the result would be a bilateral gynandromorph, one side of which is male while the other side is female. Gynandromorphs may also arise through double fertilization, caused by the exceptional entry of two spermatozoa into an egg. If one of the spermatozoa fuses with a polar body nucleus bearing a different sex chromosome from that of the egg nucleus, an embryo may result with male and female parts.

III. *Lymantria dispar,* the Gypsy Moth

Goldschmidt's monumental work on the gypsy moth, *Lymantria dispar* was specifically undertaken in order to analyze the mechanism of the X- and the Y-chromosomes in sex determination. The gypsy moth was chosen because crosses between different races frequently result in offspring with abnormal sexual development. Normally the males are dark brown and the females whitish. Increasing degrees of female intersexuality gradually change from whitish to dark brown, but in male intersexes light color patches appear on the wings (E. B. Ford, 1955).

The diploid chromosome number appears to be 62 in both sexes. The sex chromosomes cannot be distinguished.

Early on in this work it became clear that apart from gynandromorphism there was another type of abnormality in sexual development, which was called an intersex. Whereas a gynandromorph is a mosaic of male and female cells, each with the appropriate sex chromosome constitution, an intersex has the same chromosome constitution throughout. According to Goldschmidt's theory, an intersex starts its development as one sex and then at some point change to the opposite sex. A female intersex is thought of as beginning as a female and later changing toward the male direction, while a male intersex starts as a male which subsequently turns into a female.

Goldschmidt has described gynandromorphs as mosaics in space and intersexes as mosaics in time. The earlier the occurrence of the turning point from one sex to the other in development, the more extreme will be the intersexuality. Different organs will be affected in the reverse order to that in which they are laid down in embryo. For this reason the wings of an insect will be affected most often and the gonads least often.

Intersexes of *Lymantria dispar* may appear as the result of crossing different geographic races or strains. Thus, whereas a cross between a Japanese female and a European male resulted in a normal F_1 the reciprocal cross gave rise to normal males and intersexual females. On the other hand, the F_2 from the cross Japanese female by a European male resulted in normal females and a proportion of intersexual males. From these and many other crosses Goldschmidt concluded that female intersexes arose in the progeny of European, but not of Japanese mothers, whereas male intersexes tended to appear in crosses where the mother was Japanese, provided the father was not pure Japanese. For these reasons the Japanese race appeared to be strong in sex-determining factors, while the European race appeared to be weak. Thus an intersexual female arises from the combination of weak maternal sex factors with strong paternal ones. Regarding the weak maternal factors, no difference was observed whether they were present in the homozygous or the heterozygous state, and Goldschmidt regarded them to be present in the cytoplasm. On the other hand, the female offspring of a "strong" homozygous male (in conjunction with a weak female) was exclusively intersexual, whereas if the father was heterozygous only half the daughters were affected. Thus the paternal factors appear to be chromosomal in nature, and Goldschmidt was of the opinion that they are carried on the X-chromosome, which a female moth receives exclusively from her father. Winge (1937) agreed that the X-chromosome in *Lymantria* is male-determining (strongly so in the Japanese strain and weakly in the European strain), but criticized the theory of cytoplasmic female determination. According to Winge, the Y-chromosome is female-determining, strongly so in the Japanese and weakly in the European strain. In addition, Winge postulates male and female sex-determining genes on the autosomes; in the Japanese strain, the net effect of the autosomes should be markedly female-determining, and only slightly female-determining in the European strain.

Whatever their precise location may be, the sex of an individual is the result of a balance between male- and female-determining factors. In any given strain, an individual with two X-chromosomes will have two doses of male-determining factors which will outweigh the female-determining factors in the cytoplasm, resulting in a male. On the other hand, in an individual with only one chromosome, the female-determining factors will outweigh the single set of male-determining factors, thus forming a female. Calling the female-determining factor *F* and the male-determining factor *M*, a female will be *FM* and a male *FMM*. But in an *FM* individual, which is a hybrid between two geographically isolated strains, the male-determining factors may be too weak to overrule the female-determining factors, thus giving rise to a male intersex. Conversely, if the female-determining factors in an XY-individual are insufficient to outweigh the male-determining ones, a female intersex results. This interpretation makes it clear that the idea of a turning point at which sexual differentiation is reversed should not be interpreted too rigidly. As was pointed out by Bridges (1939), an *FM* or *FMM* individual in which the *F* and *M* factors are not properly balanced cannot be regarded as a normal female or male, but is genetically an intersex from the beginning. The development of such an organism will undoubtedly be influenced by the relative strength of the opposing sex factors at a given time.

The analysis of intersexuality in *Lymantria* is of interest because it serves as a model of sex determination, in which male- and female-determining factors are balanced in such a way that one set of factors normally outweighs the effect of the other. An intersex, on the other hand, results from an incorrect balance between the opposing sets of factors.

The distinction between an intersex and a gynandromorph is clearly a valid one in insects, in which organs develop male or female characteristics according to their own sex-chromosome constitution. As will be shown later (Chapter 12) this is not so in vertebrates, because here the sex chromosomes act by remote control rather than directly. Accordingly, there is no direct correspondence between sex chromosomes and the phenotypic expression of the tissues containing them, so that a different terminology has to be applied to abnormalities of the sexual development in vertebrates.

IV. The Silkworm, *Bombyx mori*

The domestic silkworm, *Bombyx mori*, is a member of the moths. A great deal of work has been done on its genetics, for which it has proved a very suitable organism; while the fact that the silkworm is of economic importance has been an additional incentive to research. The genetics of the silkworm has been reviewed by Tanaka (1953) and by Tazina

(1964). Unfortunately its chromosomes, like those of other moths, are not favorable for study. The diploid chromosome number is 56 and the chromosomes, being small, do not show much individual variation. The sex chromosomes have not been distinguished morphologically; however, Kawaguchi (1928, 1933) found that during oogenesis one bivalent remained associated with the nucleolus and condensed later than the other bivalents, and he regarded this pair as the sex chromosomes.

At least five genes are known in the silkworm which show sex-linked inheritance. The first one described manifests itself by a translucent skin of the larvae and is derived from an Italian strain, *Giallo puro indigeno*. This gene was investigated by Tanaka (1922), who found a few females exhibiting this trait. By mating these females to their brothers, some of which must have been heterozygous, Tanaka obtained translucent males. The mode of inheritance of this gene was like that of *dohrnii* in the currant moth. In addition to this sex-linked gene causing translucent skin, Tanaka found seven others which were similar in phenotypic effect but which were inherited like autosomal genes. The other four sex-linked genes also appear to be inherited as in *Abraxas,* indicating that the female is heterogametic and the male homogametic. A number of sex-linked lethal genes have also been described. Dominant lethals bring about the death of all organisms which carry them, whereas recessive lethals will kill all female silkworms but cause the death of males only if the lethal gene is on both X-chromosomes. In the silkworm as in *Drosophila,* crossing-over occurs only in the homogametic sex.

Tanaka (1953) described a strain with disturbed sex ratio, into which he introduced the sex-linked recessive gene *elongate.* This resulted in some aberrant individuals, which were interpreted as XO-males, being the result of nondisjunction in the mother. On this interpretation, the Y-chromosome must contain female-determining tendencies. Nondisjunction of the sex chromosomes would be expected to result in XXY-individuals in addition to XO-males, but the fate of the former has not been established. The XO-males in the silkworm were considerably smaller than normal ones, and relatively inviable.

Occasionally in the silkworm an egg may develop parthenogenetically. Such larvae are also weak and less viable than normal ones. Parthenogenesis in the silkworm appears to arise through a number of mechanisms, for some give rise to both males and females, while others result in all female offspring.

CHAPTER 6

SEX-CHROMOSOME MECHANISMS
WHICH DIFFER FROM THE CLASSIC TYPE

I. Introduction

In the classic type of sex-chromosome mechanism, one sex has two X-chromosomes, while the other has either an X- and a Y-chromosome or a single X-chromosome (so-called XO-type). In most organisms the heterogametic sex (XY or XO) is male, but in a minority of groups the females are heterogametic. Other types of sex-chromosome mechanisms are occasionally found. Of these, multiple sex chromosomes represent a variation on the classic theme; by contrast, sex determination by parthenogenesis and male haploidy appears to be entirely different from the other types.

II. Multiple X-Chromosomes

Multiple X-chromosomes occur rather sporadically in different animal species. The subject has been reviewed by White (1940b, 1954), and a list of species in which multiple sex chromosomes have been recorded is given by K. R. Lewis and John (1963). If two X-chromosomes are present, the heterogametic sex, i.e., generally the male, will have a sex-chromosome constitution which is either X_1X_2 or X_1X_2Y, while the homogametic sex is $X_1X_1X_2X_2$. Clearly, with multiple X-chromosomes, the homogametic sex will have a higher chromosome number than the heterogametic sex. More than two different X-chromosomes may be present.

Multiple sex chromosomes were first described in an insect, the "toad-bug" *Gelastocoris* (*Galgulatus*) *oculatus* by Payne (1909). During the first meiotic division of the spermatocyte he found five univalents, of which four went to one pole and one to the other. The female had three more chromosomes than the male, and the interpretation of the sex chromosome constitution of this insect is, therefore, $X_1X_2X_3X_4Y$ in the male and $X_1X_1X_2X_2X_3X_3X_4X_4$ in the female. In the nematode worm, *Ascaris incurva*, eight multiple X-chromosomes have been reported (see White 1940b), and Darlington (1940a) found up to fourteen different X-chromosomes in some specimens of the insect, *Cimex lectularius*; however, there is some doubt whether all these can be regarded as true sex chromosomes.

Much of our knowledge of multiple sex chromosomes has been acquired by the use of conventional techniques, but Boyes (1954) demonstrated multiple sex chromosomes in a root maggot, *Hylemya fugax* (Diptera), with the aid of an improved method, which gave excellent chromosome preparations in males and females. The X_1-chromosome is a medium-sized acrocentric chromosome, the Y is somewhat shorter and metacentric, and the X_2 is a very short chromosome.

Multiple sex chromosomes in two other groups of insects have attracted particular interest, namely those in earwigs (order Dermaptera: W. P. Morgan, 1928; Callan, 1941; Bauer, 1947; E. Goldschmidt, 1953) and in mantids (order Orthoptera: reviews by Hughes-Schrader, 1950, 1953; and see White 1940b, 1962, 1965). In the mantids, 23 genera have been described with an XO/XY-sex chromosome mechanism and in 15 genera multiple sex chromosome of the type $X_1X_2Y/X_1X_1X_2X_2$ have been found.

It is assumed that whenever multiple sex chromosomes are present, they have originated from a simple sex-chromosome mechanism. According to White (1940b), the multiple sex chromosomes of mantids have arisen from the original XO/XY-mechanism by a reciprocal translocation of the X-chromosome with an autosome (Fig. 6.1). Thus the

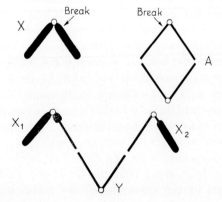

FIG. 6.1. Hypothesis to account for origin of multiple X-chromosome in mantids. (From White, (1940b.)

X_1- and the X_2-chromosomes each contain one arm of the original X-chromosome as well as one arm of a former autosome; while the homologous partner of the autosome now pairs with the "new" arms of the X_1- and the X_2-chromosomes at meiosis, and has thus become a Y-chromosome. Since the Y-chromosome in different species of mantids shows considerable variation, it would seem that it has undergone a great deal of evolutionary change since its formation from an autosome. Originally White assumed that all multiple sex chromosomes in mantids had arisen as the result of a single event, but in a later publication (White, 1965) evidence was presented that the multiple sex chromosomes in the genus *Compsothespis* must have had an independent origin from that found in other mantids.

White considers that a second method of multiple sex-chromosome formation has occurred in those groups, such as the insect orders Heteroptera and Neuroptera, in which the sex chromosomes of the heterogametic sex do not pair at meiosis. In such species he assumes that the multiple sex chromosomes have arisen by duplication of an original single X-chromosome.

Bauer (1947) as well as E. Goldschmidt (1953) have postulated that the multiple sex-chromosome mechanism in earwigs may have originated through polyploidization. This assumption is based on the observation that earwig species with low diploid chromosome numbers have an XX/XY-sex chromosome mechanism, while most species with high chromosome numbers have multiple sex chromosomes of the $X_1X_2Y/X_1X_1X_2X_2$ type. However, the existence of widely differing chromosome numbers in related species is not by itself proof that polyploidy has occurred, for it is a well-established concept in cytology that two acrocentric chromosomes may give rise to a metacentric one by a process known as "centric fusion" (see White, 1954). Centric fusion implies that a break has occurred in each of two acrocentric chromosomes close to the centromere, in the long arm of one and in the short arm of the other chromosome. The two long arms fuse, forming a metacentric chromosome, and the two short arms form a centric fragment which is subsequently lost. Accordingly a species with metacentric chromosomes often has a lower diploid chromosome number than a related species with acrocentric chromosomes. Therefore, to establish polyploidy, accurate morphological analysis of the chromosomes is essential. Another useful technique for this purpose is the measurement of DNA by photometry of Feulgen-stained nuclei. Clearly, if polyploidy has occurred, the amount of DNA in the chromosomes would be doubled, whereas centric fusion would cause hardly any difference in DNA contents. Wahrman and O'Brien (1956) studied the DNA contents in the nuclei of different species of mantids (genus *Ameles*), which show wide differences in chromosome numbers. The DNA content of the different species was remarkably similar, thus giving no evidence of polyploidy, and this finding was in agreement with chromosomal morphology. Similarly, Hughes-Schrader (1958) found no evidence of polyploidy in mantid species belonging to the genus *Liturgousa*, although its occurrence in the more remote evolutionary history of mantids could not be excluded. Modern studies of photometry combined with studies of chromosomal morphology should be able to give a definite answer to the question whether multiple sex chromosomes can arise through polyploidy.

Multiple X-chromosomes are now known to occur in some mammalian species (see Chapter 9).

III. Multiple Y-Chromosomes

Multiple Y-chromosomes seem to occur much more rarely than multiple X-chromosomes. The table compiled by White (1940b) contains over fifty examples of multiple X-chromosomes and only three with more than one Y-chromosome. However, in recent years, clear examples of multiple Y-chromosomes have been discovered in a number of mammalian species (Chapter 9). If the sex chromosome constitution of the male is XY_1Y_2, the diploid chromosome number is of course higher in the male than in the female.

IV. Sex Determination by Haploid Parthenogenesis

In animals with haploid parthenogenesis the chromosome number of the males is originally one-half that of females. This type of sex determination is probably the least understood. Although chromosomes are clearly involved, there is no convincing evidence that heteromorphic sex chromosomes are present.

Parthenogenesis is a common phenomenon among animals as well as plants; it is particularly widespread among insects. In the absence of fertilization, an egg may develop into an embryo by three different cytological processes (see Vandel, 1931; Schrader and Hughes-Schrader, 1931; Whiting, 1945; White, 1954, 1964). (1) The egg may fail to undergo or complete meiosis and so give rise to a diploid embryo; (2) meiosis of the egg cell may be normal, but subsequently two haploid nuclei fuse and produce a diploid embryo. Animals produced by this or the previous mechanism are generally female; (3) the egg cell undergoes normal meiosis and, without nuclear fusion, develops into a haploid embryo. Such embryos always develop into males, while the same eggs, if fertilized, give rise to diploid females. This type of facultative parthenogensis is known as "arrhenotoky" ("giving birth to a male child") and, though little understood, the chromosomal mechanism underlying this phenomenon is clearly of great interest for the problem of sex determination.

The best known example of sex determination through haploidy in the male comes from the honey bee (whose scientific name is generally given as *Apis mellifera* in English-speaking countries and *A. mellifica* in countries of the European continent). The theory that queen bees lay two types of eggs, namely, fertilized ones which give rise to females, i.e., workers and queens, while unfertilized ones produce males or drones, was put forward over a hundred years ago by Dzierzon (1848), a curate and beekeeper in Silesia, which is now part of Czechoslovakia. Dzierzon's theory accounts for the well-known facts that, normally, only fertilized queens can give rise to both male and female offspring, whereas a queen which has not been fertilized, or worker bees, which are probably never fertilized, produce only drone broods. This theory has been much attacked (see Nachtsheim, 1913) but is now universally accepted. It is supported both by genetic and cytological evidence, though neither is as extensive as one might wish.

Since a drone bee receives all his chromosomes from his mother, all the genes should behave like those borne on the X-chromosome of heterogametic animals, i.e., all the genes should show sex-linkage. For instance, American-Italian bees are yellow, while Swiss-Nigra bees are black. A yellow queen fertilized by a black drone will have all yellow offspring, but the reciprocal cross results in yellow queens and workers and black drones. Aberrant results have sometimes been obtained and these may be due to the fact that the queen was not of a pure strain or to the possible occurrence of drones derived from fertilized eggs (see below). In recent years, quite a number of mutant genes have become known in the bee (Rothenbuhler, 1958) and it appears that, so far as is known, they show satisfactory agreement with the hypothesis of sex-linked inheritance. In general, however, it must be admitted that in spite of the long association between bees and men, much less is known about the genetics of bees than of many other domestic animals, let alone *Drosophila*. Controlled mating of bees was impossible until the introduction of artificial insemination. Now that success in this technique has been achieved, it is to be hoped that the genetics of the honey bee will be put on a firmer foundation.

Turning to the cytological evidence, Nachtsheim, (1913) concluded that the diploid chromosome number was 32, and that this number was present in the nuclei of young female embryos, while the cells of male embryos had only 16 chromosomes. The same chromosome numbers were found by Sanderson and Hall (1948). An interesting variant of this scheme was reported by Manning (1952) and by W. E. Kerr (1951). These authors described the presence in the male of a chromosome with a somewhat different staining capacity from the others, which they called "X"-chromosome. This chromosome is eliminated during telophase of the second spermatocyte, so that it is absent from the sperm. It was assumed that the female has one such X-chromosome and 30 autosomes (giving a total of 31 rather than 32 chromosomes), and that the eggs have 15 autosomes as well as the X. Such eggs would give rise to males in the absence of fertilization and, if fertilized, they would produce females. Subsequently, however, Ris and Kerr (1952), although confirming the presence of a body which lagged behind the others during the second meiotic metaphase, were unable to stain it by the Feulgen reaction and concluded that it cannot be a chromosome. There is no doubt that the chromosomes of the honey bee are very much in need of reinvestigation by modern techniques.

Although male bees originate from haploid eggs, the majority of the developing cells do not remain haploid. They first become diploid and a large proportion reach stages of polyploidy of varying degrees (Risler, 1954; R. W. Merriam and Ris, 1954). Mittwoch et al. (1966) studied the amount of DNA in Feulgen-stained nuclei by means of microphotometry and found that in drone larvae a few hours after hatching only a minority of the cells were haploid, while the rest were diploid, tetraploid, or more highly polyploid. However, the dividing cells were haploid in young male larvae and diploid in young female larvae. Chromosome counts, therefore, might fail to detect the polyploidy. Polyploid cells, which are common in insects, arise by repeated duplication of the chromosomal material, which is not followed by cell division (Geitler, 1939, 1953); this process is known as endoreduplication. It may be that sex determination by male haploidy was able to establish itself in an entire order of insects (see below) because, since endoreduplication is so common in this class, genetically haploid individuals do not remain haploid in the majority of their body cells.

The occurrence of gynandromorph bees has been reported since the beginning of the nineteenth century. In 1864, von Siebold gave a detailed account of the so-called Eugster gynandromorphs, named after a beekeeper who drew attention to this colony. The queen gave rise to a large proportion of gynandromorph offspring in which male and female parts were arranged in different proportions in different bees, both internally and externally. To account for the origin of these gynandromorphs, two different hypotheses were put forward. Boveri (1915) thought that if fertilization were delayed, a sperm might enter an egg after its nucleus has divided. The resultant embryo would then consist of two populations of cells, a zygotic (diploid) population which would be expected to develop female characteristics, and originally haploid, purely maternal cells, which would develop into the male parts. The nuclear phenomena underlying this scheme had been observed in sea urchin eggs. By contrast Morgan (1916) postulated that the originally haploid nuclei may be derived from a supernumerary spermatozoon, so that the male parts would be paternal in origin. Recently Drescher and Rothenbuhler (1963) have succeeded in producing gynandromorphs by chilling the eggs. Using genetic marker genes, they found that in the large majority of gynandromorphs the male parts contained only the paternal gene, while in a small minority the male parts w?re of maternal origin. Thus, most of the gynandromorphs seemed to have arisen according to Morgan's theory, but Boveri's scheme also seems to apply to a few bee gynandromorphs.

The occurrence of arrhenotoky has been reported in many other families belonging to the Hymenoptera, such as wasps (Vesperinae), ants (Formicinae), gallflies (Cynipoidea), sawflies (Symphyta) and ichneumon flies (Ichneumonoidea). It is indeed frequently assumed that this type of sex determination is a general rule among the Hymenoptera. In addition, it occurs more sporadically in other insects, notably the coccids (or scale insects, belonging to the order Homoptera), as well as in Acarina (mites and ticks), which are members of the Arachnida (Schrader and Hughes-Schrader, 1931; Vandel, 1931; Hughes-Schrader, 1948; White, 1954, 1964). In recent years, male haploidy in species of ants has been demonstrated by I. C. Smith and Peacock (1957) and by Hauschteck (1961, 1962).

The underlying basis of sex determination by male haploidy constitutes a problem which has at most been only partially solved. In most organisms the formal sex-determining mechanism consists of one of two types: (1) The so-called "*Melandrium*-type" (Chapter 3, Section III), in which maleness is determined by the presence of a Y-chromosome in the heterogametic sex; this mechanism applies also in mammals including man (Chapters 9, 10). (2) the so-called "*Drosophila*-type" (Chapter 4). Here the X-chromosome is female-determining, and females have twice as many X-chromosomes compared with males. Clearly, a system in which males originate from a haploid egg and females from a diploid zygote does not appear to fit either of these schemes.

A possible scheme of sex determination has been put forward by Whiting (1945) for the ichneumoid wasp, *Habrobracon juglandis* (also called *Microbracon hebetor*). In this insect, a large number of mutant genes with recessive effect have been obtained. Unmated females which are heterozygous for such genes produce only sons, which show segregation for the alleles in question. If females which are homozygous for a recessive allele are mated to males carrying the dominant allele, the daughters show the dominant trait of the father while the sons resemble the mother. However, as a result of inbreeding, sons may be produced which show the dominant allele of the father. Such biparental sons are rather inviable and usually sterile.

By practicing inbreeding in different lines of *Habrobracon*, Whiting (1943, 1945) and co-workers have isolated nine different chromosomal regions, any one of which causes maleness if present in hemizygous or homozygous form, and which will cause femaleness if present in heterozygous or compound form. Although these chromosomal regions have sometimes been called "alleles," no crossing-over appears to take place between them; all of them show the same amount of crossing-over, about 10%, with a mutant gene *fused*, which affects the antennae, tarsi, and wings. In this scheme of sex determination, therefore, there appears to be a single sex chromosome containing a number of sex-determining regions whose function depends on whether they are present alone, or whether they are matched either by an identical or a different partner.

In an attempt to see whether a similar scheme of sex determination might apply in the honey bee, Mackensen (1951) practiced inbreeding in this species. Although he did not succeed in obtaining biparental males, the inbreeding resulted in reduced viability of the workers. Similar results were obtained by Drescher and Rothenbuhler (1964), but in addition to an increase in inviable eggs these authors also found mosaic drones with eye tissue of zygotic origin. However, Woyke (1963, 1965a,b) was able to show that some of the "inviable" eggs laid by inbred queens would result in drone larvae, provided that they were removed from the hive and reared artificially, since otherwise they would be eaten by the workers shortly after hatching. Some of these drone larvae and prepupae showed the genetic characters of the father and must therefore have been derived from fertilized eggs. They appeared to be no less viable than drones of the same brood, which on genetic evidence were assumed to be fatherless.

The possibility of obtaining males from fertilized eggs as a result of inbreeding clearly suggests that Whiting's hypothesis of differential chromosomal segments may also be applicable to the sex determination of the honey bee. There can be no doubt that the application of modern cytogenetic techniques to bees and their relatives will give further important results bearing on their unusual sex-determining mechanism, results which cannot fail to throw light on the subject of sex chromosomes in general.

V. Sex Chromosomes Which Are Not Morphologically Differentiated

Although morphologically differentiated sex chromosomes have been found in a large variety of animals and even in some plants, there are other groups of animals in which a chromosomal difference between males and females cannot be detected. In these organisms sex determination may still be under genetic control. Thus, in the mosquito (*Culex molestus*) sex chromosomes cannot be distinguished, but Gilchrist and Haldane (1947) found that maleness is due to a dominant gene, which is fairly closely linked with the gene for white eyes, carried on the same chromosome. This chromosome, therefore, acts as a sex chromosome, even though it does not exhibit any of the cytological characteristics of sex chromosomes. Such morphologically undifferentiated sex chromosomes are characteristic of fishes (Chapter 7). They occur also in various species of the insect *Chironomus* (Beermann, 1955).

In another insect belonging to the order Diptera, *Megaselia scalaris*, Mainx (1962) found that maleness is due to a dominant gene, which may be attached, by translocation, to one of several chromosomes. Thus, the genes of any chromosome which carries the sex differentiator will exhibit sex-linkage.

In Chapter 12 the possibility will be discussed that morphologically differentiated sex chromosomes, which are characteristic of man and other mammals, may function as large units and not merely through the activity of individual genes. In those organisms, however, in which sex determination appears to be based on the action of a single pair of genes, we must assume that the basis of sex differentiation is like that of other gene effects, probably through the production of alternative enzymes.

CHAPTER 7

SEX CHROMOSOMES IN FISHES, AMPHIBIA, REPTILES, AND BIRDS

I. Introduction

Turning to the vertebrates, our present knowledge of sex chromosomes in fishes, amphibia, and birds is based mainly on genetic, rather than cytological evidence. In fishes, morphologically distinct sex chromosomes have not so far been found, but examples of sex-linked inheritance are known in some species. The sex chromosomes of many frogs (amphibia) seem to be distinguished by incomplete pairing at meiosis, rather than by any obvious difference in size (Witschi and Opitz, 1963), but in some frogs heteromorphic sex chromosomes are now known to occur (Weiler and Ohno, 1962). In reptiles, a beginning in the identification of sex chromosomes has only recently been made. Cytological studies in birds are particularly difficult, owing to the large number of chromosomes present, the majority of which are small and ill-defined. The task of identifying the sex chromosomes was further aggravated by the fact that in birds the female is the heterogametic sex, which means that the unequal chromosome pair (or unpaired chromosome) occurs in the meiosis of the female, which is not easy to study. However, considerable progress has now been made in this field, and, at least in the fowl, the sex chromosomes have been unequivocally demonstrated.

In the vertebrates, sex is no longer a direct expression of the sex chromosomes, as is the case in insects. Sexual differentiation in the vertebrates is under the control of sex hormones (see Chapter 12), which are formed by the gonads, and these in their turn are presumed to develop under the influence of the sex chromosomes (Chapter 8, Section IV). Therefore, the sex chromosomes in the vertebrates carry out their tasks by remote control rather than directly. Since the hormones are carried by the blood to all parts of the body, the sexual differentiation of a tissue will not be the direct expression of its sex-chromosome constitution, as in insects but will be the direct result of the activity of endocrine organs. The relationship between sex chromosomes and sexual differentiation is therefore more complex. It will be further discussed in Chapter 12.

II. Sex Chromosomes in Fishes

Although in fishes there is no cytological evidence of the presence of sex chromosomes, genetic experiments in this class have provided interesting results on the nature of sex-linked inheritance. This is largely due to the work of Winge (1923b, 1927, 1930, 1932, 1934) in Denmark.

In the guppy, *Lebistes reticulatus,* in which the young are born alive, the females are larger than the males and are of a dull brownish color, while the males are brilliantly colored. The actual distribution of the black, red, yellow, or iridescent colorings of the males varies according to the race, or strain, to which the fish belong.

Studies of chromosomes in the testes, and to a lesser extent in the ovaries, of guppies suggested a diploid chromosome number of 46. Sex chromosomes could not be distinguished, and Winge assumed that the female has 44 autosomes and 2 X-chromosomes, while the male has 44 autosomes plus an X- and a Y-chromosome.

The Y-chromosome always contains color factors, and in certain strains the X-chromosome carries additional color factors, which are expressed in the male but never in the female. Thus the X-chromosome designated X_s (*sulfureus:* this is really a complex of two genes which may become separated by crossing-over) results in (1) sulphur yellow color in the dorsal fin (and sometimes a dark dot in the same fin); (2) sulphur yellow color in tail and dorsal fin; red color in lower edge caudal fin. On the other hand, the X-chromosome X_o is not associated with any color. A number of different Y-chromosomes have been described in the different strains. As an example, Y_m (*maculatus,* which is present in the so-called "Spot Race") results in (1) a large black spot in the dorsal fin; (2) a large red side spot below and in front of the dorsal fin; (3) a black dot at the anus (sometimes invisible).

When a female which is heterozygous for X_s X_o is mated with a male of the constitution X_o Y_m, two classes of daughters will be produced, X_s X_o and X_o X_o, but they will be phenotypically indistinguishable, all being dull brown. On the other hand, of the two types of male offspring, those of the constitution X_s Y_m will show the yellow and red spots of the *sulfureus* gene, which is not present in the X_o Y_m offspring. Both types of males, however, will show the black and red spots of the *maculatus* gene (Fig. 7.1). In the same way, the other color genes

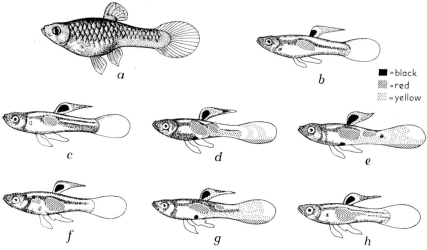

Fig. 7.1. X- and Y-borne genes in *Lebistes reticulatus*. (a) ♀ $X_s X_o$; (b) ♂ $X_o Y_m$ (Spot Race); (c)–(h) 6 sons; (c), (f), (h), $X_o Y_m$; (d), (e), (g) $X_s Y_m$. From Winge, (1922). Redrawn by A. J. Lee.

present on different Y-chromosomes are always inherited from the father to all the sons.

Thus, in *Lebistes*, we have side by side with the usual sex-linked, strictly speaking, X-borne inheritance (see Chapter 4, Section II) which operates from mother to son to daughter, the additional operation of a Y-borne inheritance, which is exclusively from father to son. This latter type, Winge called "one sided masculine inheritance." Furthermore, *Lebistes* also illustrates sex limitation, since the expression of the color genes borne on the X-chromosome is limited to the male sex, while the females carrying the same genes, even in double dose, do not show them.

However, females of certain breeds sometimes showed a tendency to produce a gonopod, the male copulatory organ, and such females also expressed the color in accordance with the genes borne on their X-chromosomes. By crossing such females to males carrying the *maculatus* gene on their Y-chromosome, Winge obtained three males which did not show the *maculatus* phenotype, though they had the colors of the X-borne genes. Since the *maculatus* gene does not cross over between the X- and Y-chromosomes (although several other genes have been shown to do so), these individuals were interpreted to be of XX-constitution when crossed with normal females. The XX-males produced a total of 314 offspring, all of which were female.

When the daughters of the XX-males were back-crossed to their fathers, the offspring were again all female, but when one of the daughters was once more crossed with an XX-male, a new XX-male resulted. This male, when crossed to his mother, produced male and female offspring in approximately equal numbers. Thus, a breed of fish with a new type of sex determination had originated. The Y-chromosome was lost, and the X-chromosome no longer took any part in the determination. Henceforth, the X-borne genes behaved like autosomal genes. Winge assumed that sex determination was taken over by a pair of alleles carried on what had previously been autosomes. Although it was not certain whether the male or the female was now heterozygous, it is clear that this change in sex determination provides an example of how male heterogamety can change into female heterogamety, and vice versa.

On another occasion, as a result of crossing experiments between different breeds, there arose some females with XY chromosomes. These females were of the genetic constitution $X_o Y_m$ and when one was mated to $X_o Y_{pa}$ male (pa = pauper, from the poverty of the coloring), it had the following kinds of offspring: 28 $X_o X_o$ females; 34 $X_o Y_m$ males; 25 $X_o Y_{pa}$ males; and 22 $Y_m Y_{pa}$ males. A point of particular interest in this cross is the occurrence of YY males. One such male, when crossed with an $X_o X_o$ female, gave rise to 17 $X_o Y_m$ males, 25 $X_o Y_{pa}$ males, and no females. The viability of YY-males is further evidence that the X- and the Y-chromosomes show very little differentiation. Apart from the sex-determining genes which they carry they resemble each other as well as the autosomes.

The unspecialized nature of the sex chromosomes is also reflected in the amount of crossing-over which takes place between them. In *Lebistes*, crossing-over takes place not only between the two X-chromosomes of a normal female, but also between the X- and the Y-chromosome of a normal male. Of seventeen genes which showed sex-linkage, Winge found that nine were confined to the Y-chromosome, three appeared to occur solely on the X-chromosome, while five crossed over from the X to the Y, and vice versa. Genes which cross over between the X- and the Y-chromosomes are said to exhibit partial sex-linkage.

Sex chromosomes of this simple type tend to function effectively in a given environment, but, as was pointed out by Winge, they are not buffered against changing external conditions. If such changes occur, the mode of sex determination too may be altered.

More recently, evidence on the nature of sex chromosomes in fishes has been obtained by Yamamoto (1961, 1963), who succeeded in reversing the genetic sex by hormone treatment. In the medaka, *Oryzias latipes*, the female has normally two X-chromosomes and the male an X- and a Y-chromosome. Both the X and the Y may contain a color gene (called R), which results in a orangey-red color, whereas the homozygous recessive condition *rr* causes absence of color. By means of estrone an XY male may be changed into a functional female, while testosterone turns an XX-female into a male. When a white female, with chromosome constitution $X^r X^r$ was mated to a testosterone-treated $X^r X^r$ white male, all the offspring were female. On the other hand, a red female resulting from hormone treatment with $X^r Y^R$ sex chromosomes mated to an $X^r Y^r$ male, produced offspring in the proportion of 1 white female: 1 white male: 2 red males, according to theoretical expectation (cf. Fig. 12.1). Thus, the combination $Y^R Y^r$ appears to be fully viable.

The fact that sex determination in fishes is of a rather labile nature is also evident from the work of Gordon (1946, 1947) on the platyfish, *Platypoecilus maculatus*. In the common aquarium strain the females are XY and the males XX, but in wild populations obtained from Mexico the situation was just the opposite. Thus a sex-linked gene, *Sb*, causing a black underside and usually known as "black bottom," was transmitted from father to son in wild populations and from mother to daughter in domesticated strains.

According to Gordon's terminology, in wild populations the female is XX and the male XY, whereas in domesticated stocks the female is WZ and the male ZZ. He suggested that the W-chromosome may have been introduced by interbreeding with the guppy, *Xyphophorus bellerii*. The Y- and the Z-chromosomes were indistinguishable in breeding, and the female could therefore equally well be written WY and the male YY. The apparent complexity of this case illustrates that the WZ terminology is basically unnecessary. In organisms in which the sex chromosomes are highly differentiated, the homogametic sex is XX, the heterogametic sex is XY, and the combination YY is generally inviable. In such organisms, sex determination may involve the action of whole chromosomes, or at least large parts thereof (Chapter 12, Section IV). In fishes, on the other hand, sex determination must be assumed to occur on the genic, rather than on the chromosomal, level. The chromosomes bearing these genes, whether they are called W, X, Y, or Z, need to be no more different from one another than any pair of autosomes, and, like autosomes, their constitution can be altered by crossing-over. The fishes illustrate sex chromosomes at their lower limit of specialization. In this they resemble spinach. (Chapter 3, Section III).

The labile nature of the sex chromosomes in fishes may be reflected in the relatively undifferentiated sexual dimorphism (a state of affairs which fishes and flowering plants also possess in common). As was pointed out by Forbes (1961), the developing gonads of most fishes pass through an indifferent and then a bisexual stage, in which both ovarian and testicular tissue are present side by side. Subsequently, one of these tissues gains the upper hand, so that the gonad becomes either an ovary or a testis. In exceptional circumstances, however, functional ovarian and testicular tissue may persist.

III. Sex Chromosomes in Amphibia

In amphibia, too, development may pass through a more or less pronounced hemaphroditic stage. In *Rana temporaria,* Witschi (1929) found that certain strains are sexually differentiated, while others are undifferentiated. In the differentiated strains, males and females differentiate on the fifteenth day of development. In the undifferentiated strains, all animals go through a female stage during the first 2 years of their life; afterwards, one-half of them turn into males.

Occasionally an adult female may turn into a male, and for a time eggs and sperm ripen at the same time, so that the individual may function in the capacity of either sex. Witschi found that normally in frogs male and female offspring are produced in equal numbers, and this also applies when a male is mated with a hermaprodite female. On the other hand, if sperm from such a hermaphrodite animal is used to fertilize the eggs of another female, only female offspring results. This indicates that in *Rana temporaria* the female is the homogametic sex and the male is heterogametic.

This situation is not, however, universal in amphibians. Experiments on sex reversal in the African water frog, *Xenopus laevis* (strictly speaking, a toad), which were performed by Chang and Witschi (1956) have shown that in this species the male is homogametic and the female is heterogametic. If male larvae are treated with estradiol, they turn into females; and when these females by hormone treatment were mated to normal males, only male offspring resulted (unless the larvae were again treated with estradiol), thus showing that the male is the homogametic sex (see Chapter 12, Section III).

Recently, Weiler and Ohno (1962) succeeded in confirming these findings cytologically. Mitotic figures from the spermatogonia of males and the spleen and liver from both sexes showed the presence of 36 chromosomes. In the male these could be arranged into 18 equal pairs, whereas the female had an unequal pair. Of these, the smaller one corresponded to the smallest pair in the male, while the larger one, which was in fact the largest chromosome in the complement, was not present in the male. Thus, it appears that the Y is the largest chromosome in the complement, while the X is the smallest. Such a striking difference between the sex chromosomes may seem surprising in an organism in

which complete sex reversal can be achieved experimentally. It is unlikely that the Y-chromosome may have arisen by a process of duplication from the X, since it is more than twice as big as the X-chromosome.
As was pointed out by Chang and Witschi, the experiments on sex reversal make it clear that the Y-chromosome in *Xenopus* function as sex
determiners only during a brief period of development. Since estradiol
need be administered to the larvae only for a short period in order to
induce full female development, it follows that during most of a frog's
life neither oogenesis nor the development of secondary sexual characters is under the control of the sex chromosomes.

IV. Sex Chromosomes of Reptiles

The reptiles include the crocodiles (order Crocodilia), the tortoises
(order Chelonia or Testudinata), as well as the snakes and lizards
(order Squamata—of which the lizards comprise the suborder Sauria or
Lacertilia, and the snakes the suborder Serpentes or Ophidia). Heteromorphic sex chromosomes are present in some groups and absent in
others. Where such sex chromosomes have been found, the female was
the heterogametic sex.

Matthey and van Brink (1956) and van Brink (1959) found the chromosomes of males and females to be the same in a crocodile, a tortoise,
five species of lizards, and one snake. In recent years, however, heteromorphic sex chromosomes have been found in some snakes. All the
snakes investigated so far contain eight pairs of fairly large chromosomes
which are known as macrochromosomes, and a number of much smaller
microchromosomes. Kobel (1962, 1963) found that in the adder *Vipera
berus,* the macrochromosomes included an unequal pair in the female.
The Y-chromosome, which did not occur in the male, was smaller than
the X and its centromere was nearer one end. Beçak *et al.* (1962, 1964)
studied seven South American species of snakes. They did not find
morphologically distinct sex chromosomes in the boa constrictor (*Boa
constrictor constrictor*) as well as another member of the family Boidae,
but found such sex chromosomes in five species belonging to the families
Colubridae and Crotalidae. The number of microchromosomes varied
between seven and seventeen pairs in different species. The metacentric
X-chromosome was always the fourth largest among the macrochromo-
some pairs; the Y-chromosome differed in size and shape in the different
species, but it was never very small. Since the X-chromosomes were so
similar in the species in which they could be distinguished, the authors
concluded that the fourth chromosomal pair represents the sex chromosomes also in those species in which they are not heteromorphic.

V. Sex Chromosomes in Birds

The discovery that in the fowl the female is the heterogametic sex stems from the early days of genetics. In the barred Plymouth Rock fowl the color of the plumage is of a black and white striped appearance. Occasionally a black bird is found, and such birds are always female. It was first pointed out by Spillman in 1908 that the mode of inheritance of *Barred* was like that of the *dohrnii* gene in the moth *Abraxas* (Chapter 5, Section II). This conclusion was confirmed by several investigators, including T. H. Morgan and Goodale (1912), who carried out extensive breeding experiments.

A barred hen mated with a black cock produced barred sons and black daughters; a nonbarred hen and a barred (homozygous) cock have offspring, all of which are barred; and a nonbarred hen mated with a heterozygous barred cock has barred and nonbarred sons and barred and nonbarred daughters (Fig. 7.2). These results indicate that the gene for barring is carried on the X-chromosome and is dominant.

In addition to barred, ten other genes are known to be carried on the X-chromosome of the fowl (Hutt, 1949). Haldane (1921) was the first to work out the linkage relationships between two of them, those for barred (B) and for silver (S). Silver inhibits yellow pigmentation, so that the feathers are white or silver rather than buff or reddish, which is known as gold. Gold is recessive to silver. Haldane mated a brown Leghorn cock of genetic constitution bs/bs to a barred Plymouth Rock hen, which genetically was BS. The male children from this mating, which must have been BS/bs, were then mated with brown Leghorn hens (bs) and produced the following types of offspring: 30 barred silver BS/bs ♂ and BS ♀; 17 nonbarred silver bS/bs ♂ and bS ♀; 10 barred gold Bs/bs ♂ and Bs ♀; and 21 nonbarred gold bs/bs ♂ and bs ♀.

There are, therefore, 27 new recombinations out of a total of 78 offspring, giving a crossover value of 34.6% with a probable error of 3.6%. The fact that barred and silver are rather far apart on the X-chromosome was confirmed by Punnett (1940), who obtained linkage data on seven genes located on this chromosome and was able to construct a tentative linkage map.

While the fowl (and to a lesser extent other domestic birds) are well known genetically, being of economic importance and at the same time small enough to permit large scale breeding experiments, the chromosomes of birds have proved very recalcitrant to cytological investigation. The karyotype of birds consists of a number of chromosomes of a normal size (macrochromosomes) and in addition a large number of very small chromosomes (microchromosomes), which are difficult to disentangle

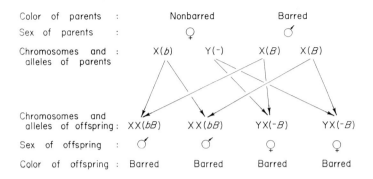

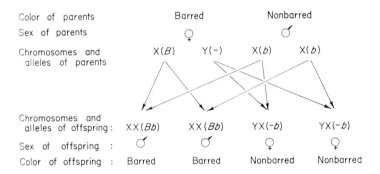

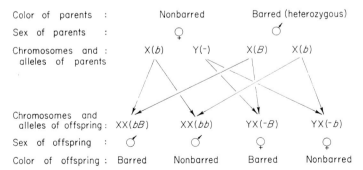

Fig. 7.2. Mode of inheritance of barred gene in the fowl.

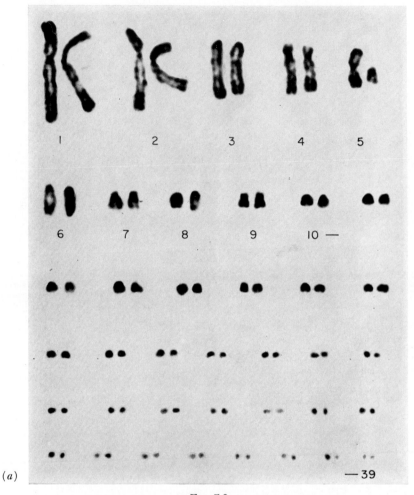

(a)   — 39

FIG. 7.3.

(Fig. 7.3). Both macro- and microchromosomes are also present in snakes but in birds the total chromosome number is much higher. The diploid chromosomes number in the domestic fowl is at least 78, as was recently shown by Owen (1965) in dividing cells derived from embryonic material. This number must be regarded as a minimum, since smaller microchromosomes, if present, might have been too small to be seen. E. H. R. Ford and Woollam (1964) have counted up to 40 paired chromosomes during meiosis in the male. There has been disagreement not only over the number and the nature of the microchromosomes, but

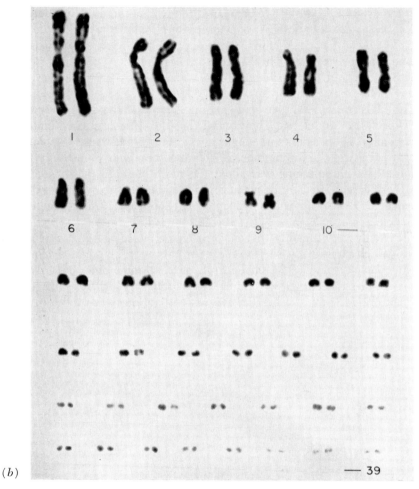

(b)   — 39

Fig. 7.3. Karyotype of fowl; (a) hen, (b) cock. (From Owen, 1965.) Contributed by Dr. Owen.

also as regards the macrochromosomes. Originally it was thought that the largest chromosome was the X-chromosome. However, Ohno (1961) and subsequently Fréderic (1961) and Owen (1965) have shown that the largest chromosome is paired in both sexes, whereas the fifth largest, a metacentric chromosome is paired in the male but is single in the female (Fig. 7.3). Whether or not there was a Y-chromosome in hens remained in doubt until its presence was demonstrated by Fréderic in 1961. This has recently been confirmed by the excellent preparations of Owen. The Y-chromosome is relatively small.

Stenius *et al.* (1963) have compared the chromosomes of the pheasant (*Phasianus coldicus*), the turkey (*Meleagris gallopavo*), and the fowl (*Gallus domesticus*). All three species appear to have a diploid chromosome number near 80. The X-chromosomes are all very similar, being metacentric and of nearly equal size. The species differ, however, in their autosomal complements.

Rothfels *et al.* (1963) have studied the chromosomes of the budgerigar, *Melopsittacus undulatus*. They found that the fifth largest chromosome was paired in the male and single in the female and must therefore be regarded as the X-chromosome. A Y-chromosome was found only in females. This chromosome was about the ninth or tenth in size and was further characterised by being fuzzy in metaphase; this was regarded as evidence for heteropycnosis (Chapter 11, Section III), a characteristic of sex chromosomes.

It is only very recently that modern techniques of chromosome cytology, which have given such excellent results with mammalian chromosomes, have been adapted for the study of the chromosomes of birds with equal success. The fowl was the first vertebrate in which sex-linkage was demonstrated. Now the best known sex chromosomes are those in man.

CHAPTER 8

SEX CHROMOSOMES IN MAN

I. Introduction

The present period of active and successful work on human chromosomes began in the second half of the 1950s. Before that time, the chromosomes of man, like those of other mammals, were regarded as unfavorable from a cytological point of view, because of their relatively large number and the consequent difficulty of isolating individual chromosomes. Human chromosomes also suffered from the additional drawback that suitable material for their study could not be easily obtained. That both these difficulties have been successfully overcome owes much to the renewed interest in the subject, which arose as a result of the discovery of sex chromatin (see Chapter 10) and its apparently anomalous behavior in patients with sexual abnormalities. While investigators had to rely on the old techniques, results were never entirely unambiguous, but, as regards the normal sex chromosome complement, the foundations laid were sufficiently accurate, so that the results of the new techniques did not come as a surprise, as they did in the case of the diploid chromosome number.

II. Findings on Human Sex Chromosomes by Traditional Techniques

Work on human chromosomes before the advent of modern techniques in the 1950s was based almost entirely on sectioned material.

Attempts to study the chromosomes of man date from the last century. Chromosomes from corneal epithelium were illustrated by Flemming in 1882 (1882b). The first investigator to give attention to the sex chromosomes was Guyer (1910) who concluded that the sex-chromosome mechanism was of the XO-type and that the total number of chromosomes was 22 in males and 24 in females. A chromosome count of that order of magnitude was generally accepted at that time. It came, therefore, as a surprise when von Winiwarter, in 1912, announced that he counted 47 chromosomes in human spermatogonia, and 24 bodies in primary spermatocytes. He, also, assumed that the sex chromosomes were represented by a single X-chromosome. Von Winiwarter's high chromosome count met with considerable incredulity, and it was not until several years later that it was confirmed, in principle, by von Winiwarter (1921) himself, by Painter (1921, 1924a), and by Oguma and Kihara (1923). The latter authors also counted 47 chromosomes in the spermatogonia and 24 bodies in primary spermatocytes, and concluded that an unpaired X-chromosome was present. On the other hand, Painter presented strong evidence for the existence of a Y- as well as an X-chromosome in man and in other mammals. He identified the XY-chromosome pair in the metaphase of first human spermatocytes and assumed that the X-chromosome was the larger of the two by analogy with findings in the opossum (Chapter 9, Section III). It should be noted that the end-to-end association of the X- and Y-chromosomes, as illustrated by Painter (1924b), is exactly as described by later authors (see below). Furthermore, Painter followed the transition of the "chromatin nucleolus," the large heteropycnotic body present in the pachytene stage of spermatocytes, to the formation of the XY-chromosome pair in metaphase, thus adding to the evidence that this heteropycnotic body represents the sex chromosomes in a heavily condensed form. This had previously been assumed on the basis of similar findings in insects. The associated X- and Y-chromosomes were clearly illustrated by Minouchi and Ohta (1934b), while a number of other authors also interpreted their findings as evidence for the existence of an X- and a Y-chromosome (see Matthey, 1949).

The presence of an X- and a Y-chromosome in human males was accepted by Koller (1937), who thought that he could detect chiasmata between parts of the X- and Y-chromosomes, and by Sachs (1954), who studied the pachytene and metaphase stages of spermatocytes in squash preparations. Sachs interpreted the heteropycnotic body in pachytene as the X- and Y-chromosomes imbedded in a less intensely staining sex vesicle. As he could see no evidence of chiasmata between the X- and Y-chromosomes, Sachs concluded that crossing-over between the X- and Y-chromosomes in the human male cannot occur. This problem will be further discussed in Chapter 9, Section XIII.

Although prior to the adoption of modern cytological techniques the findings on human sex chromosomes could not be regarded as entirely conclusive, the weight of evidence pointed to the existence of an XY-mechanism (Matthey, 1949).

III. Normal Human Sex Chromosomes

During the past years the subject of human chromosomes has been transformed from a difficult problem, tackled from time to time by a few individual investigators, to a flourishing discipline with worldwide application. As is well known, this change was brought about by the development of two techniques.

1. Certain changes in cytological techniques, of which the most important was the treatment of chromosomes with hypotonic solutions prior to fixation. This has the effect of swelling metaphase nuclei and dispersing the chromosomes, as was accidentally discovered by Hsu (1952), and almost simultaneously by Hughes (1952b). This discovery proved an essential step in counteracting the tendency of mammalian chromosomes to crowd together, which had previously proved such a hinderance to their analysis. The spreading of the chromosomes is further assisted by treatment with the drug colchicine, which shortens the chromosomes and thus helps to prevent overlap. In addition, colchicine increases the number of nuclei which are in metaphase, by preventing the cell from going into anaphase. Colchicine was introduced for mammalian chromosomes by C. E. Ford and Hamerton (1956a) and was used by Tjio and Levan (1956a) in their now classic work on the chromosome number of man. Subsequently C. E. Ford and Hamerton (1956b) not only confirmed the chromosome number of 46 but provided unequivocal evidence for the presence of an X- and a Y-chromosome, in terminal association, in human spermatocytes.

2. In addition to improvements in cytological technique, modern work on human chromosomes would have been impossible without the developments of techniques of cell culture, which provide the necessary numbers of dividing cells of human origin. The following tissues may be used to set up cultures for this purpose: peripheral blood leucocytes, bone marrow, and small pieces of skin taken by biopsy, as well as material from aborted embryos. The various culture techniques employed in connection with chromosome analysis have been described by Clarke (1962), by Yunis and collaborators (Yunis, 1965), and by Turpin and Lejeune (1965).

Human chromosomes derived from skin cultures are illustrated in Fig. 8.1. In somatic metaphase cells, the sex chromosomes are not distinguished either by differential staining or any other characteristic tendency for homologous partners to stay together in the nucleus. The sex chromosomes are recognized because they form an unequal pair in the male, while in the female two X-chromosomes are similar in appearance to the single X-chromosome of the male.

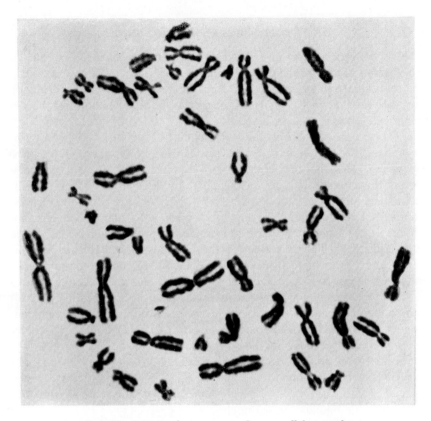

FIG. 8.1a. Mitotic chromosomes of man—cell from male.

It was agreed by the Denver Conference (1960) that for the classification of human chromosomes in mitotic metaphase the autosomes should be serially numbered in descending order of size from 1 to 22, and that the position of the centromere should be an additional distinguishing mark. A serial arrangement of the chromosomes of one cell is known as a "karyotype" (more rarely a "karyogram"). When the chromosomes are numbered in this way, the two X-chromosomes of the female as well as the single X-chromosome of the male resemble the autosomes in group 6–12, i.e., they are medium-sized chromosomes with the centromere near the middle (metacentric); the X-chromosome resembles the larger of these chromosomes. The Y-chromosome resembles the autosomes 21 and 22, which are small chromosomes with the centromere near one end (acrocentric). The difficulty of identifying the X-chromosome is also apparent from the report of the London Conference

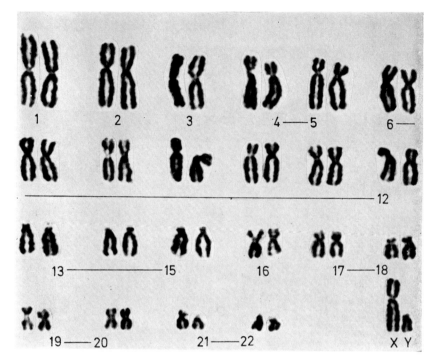

FIG. 8.1*b*. Mitotic chromosomes of man—karyotype from male.

(1964), which states: "of the autosomes in this group (i.e., 6–12 and X), four are comparatively metacentric. It is proposed that they should be numbered 6, 7, 8, and 11. The X-chromosome belongs to this subgroup. Three chromosomes are submetacentric. They should be numbered 9, 10 and 12." One of the two X-chromosomes of normal females can be identified unequivocally by the use of radioactive thymidine, which this chromosome takes up considerably later than other chromosomes (see Chapter 10, Section VI). "The identification of the Y-chromosome presents fewer difficulties. The most common Y is larger than either 21 or 22, its centric constriction is often indistinct, and a secondary constriction is frequently seen in the long arm; the terminal region of the long arm may be poorly defined. Typically, the two long arm chromatids of the Y appear to diverge less than those of other chromosomes" (London Conference, 1964). Thus the Y-chromosome can be identified in a large proportion of cells of male origin, though probably not in all. It is obvious, however, that whether or not the sex chromosomes can be individually identified, it does not affect one's conclusions as to the sex-chromosome

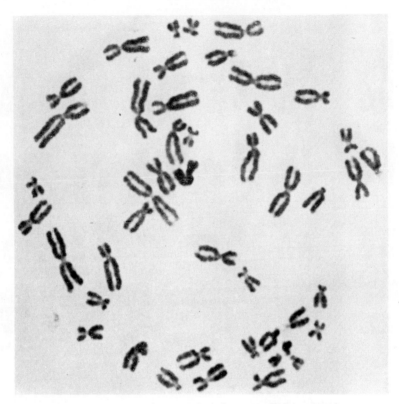

FIG. 8.1c. Mitotic chromosomes of man—cell from female.

status of a particular cell. Normal males have fifteen chromosomes in group 6–12 and five in group 21–22, while normal females have sixteen chromosomes in group 6–12 and four in group 21–22.

Penrose (1964) has calculated that if the length of a haploid set of autosomes is arbitrarily fixed at 100.00 units, the length of an X-chromosome is 5.80 units. The length of the Y-chromosome was calculated as 1.96 units. However, the Y-chromosome is remarkable in showing considerable variation in length. Court Brown et al. (1965) found that among 517 males whom they examined, 12 (2.3%) had a Y-chromosome which was either appreciably longer or shorter than the common form. The large Y-chromosomes were as long as or longer than chromosomes 19–20, while the small Y-chromosomes were one-half the length of chromosomes 21–22, or less. Y-chromosomes of abnormal length tend to be transmitted from father to son and are not necessarily ac-

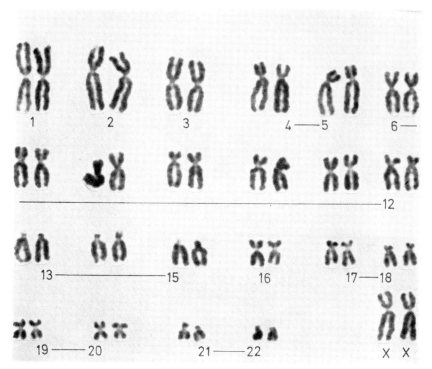

FIG. 8.1*d*. Mitotic chromosomes of man—karyotype from female. (Fig. 8.1 *a–d* contributed by Dr. Joy Delhanty. Acetic orcein × 2200.)

companied by any observable phenotypic abnormalities (de la Chapelle *et al.*, 1963).

Recent developments in cytological techniques have benefited not only the preparations of mitotic chromosomes but have also resulted in startling improvements in the appearance of human chromosomes in meiosis. By the use of hypotonic solution on testicular material C. E. Ford and Hamerton (1956b) were able to show that in the majority of cells in diakinesis and first meiotic metaphase the X- and Y-chromosomes are paired in an end-to-end association, as is typical for male mammalian sex chromosomes; but in a proportion of such cells the X- and Y-chromosomes had already separated, so that such cells contained 24 chromosomal bodies. More recently, the technique introduced by E. P. Evans *et al.* (1964), which involves the separation of testicular cells and their suspension in various solutions, has been a further step forward in the resolution of yet more cytological detail of the chromosomes during meiosis of the male (Fig. 8.2). When viewing the beauty of these prepa-

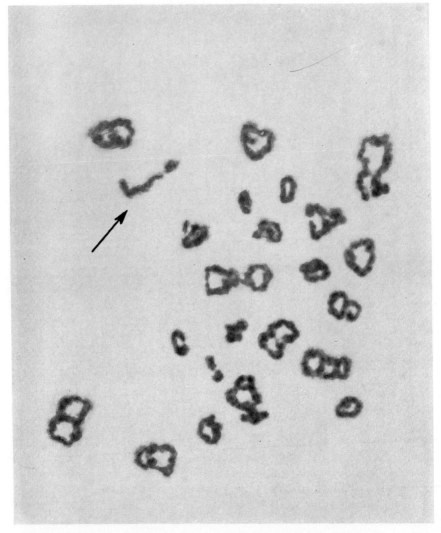

FIG. 8.2. Meiotic chromosomes of man. Diakinesis of first spermatocyte. × 2000 (Contributed by Dr. E. P. Evans.)

rations it must be a cause for regret that similar improvements of technique are not yet available for the earlier stages of meiotic prophase, when the sex chromosomes of the male are heavily condensed (Fig. 8.3.). Thus, the problem as to the mode of pairing of the X- and the Y-chromosomes during pachytene has not yet been resolved (Chapter 9, Section XIII).

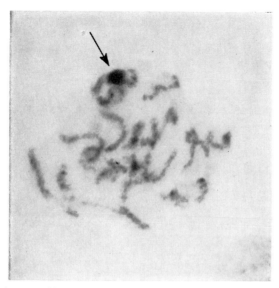

Fig. 8.3. Pachytene of human meiotic chromosomes with condensed XY-bivalent. (× 2200.)

IV. Klinefelter's Syndrome

Klinefelter *et al.* (9142) described a clinical condition in male patients, who suffered from increased development of the breasts, lack of spermatogenesis, and increased excretion of follicle stimulating hormone. Although "Klinefelter's syndrome" is now the most usual name for this clinical entity, other names, such as "gonadal dysgenesis," have sometimes been used (see Overzier, 1963c). The genitalia are undoubtedly male, though the testes are smaller than normal. Many patients are very tall, and mental development is often somewhat retarded. In 1954 it was shown by several groups of workers that the majority of such patients have sex chromatin in their interphase nuclei (see Chapter 10). Jacobs and Strong (1959) found that a patient with Klinefelter's syndrome had 47 chromosomes, which could best be interpreted as including two X-chromosomes as well as a Y-chromosome (Fig. 8.4). This report provided the first concrete evidence that abnormalities of sexual development may be caused by an abnormal sex-chromosome constitution.

The XXY-sex-chromosome constitution has proved to be the most common one in Klinefelter's syndrome (see Turpin and Lejeune, 1965), but other chromosome combinations can give rise to essentially the same clinical condition. Thus Barr *et al.* (1959) found three patients with an XXXY-sex-chromosome constitution (48 chromosomes in all) and Frac-

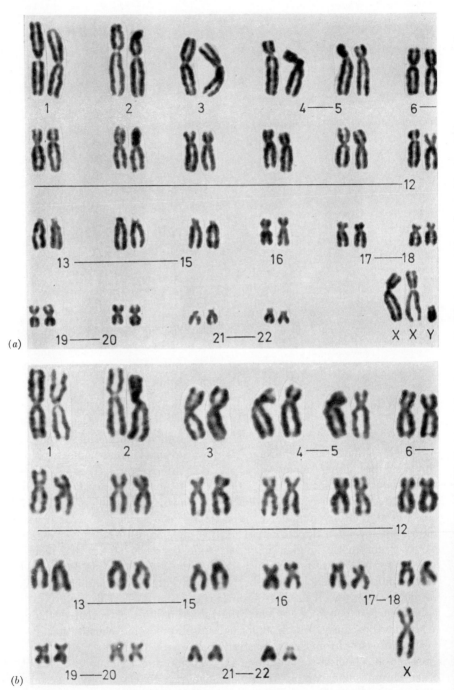

Fig. 8.4. Karyotypes of patients with numerically abnormal sex chromosomes. Top (a) XXY; bottom (b) XO.

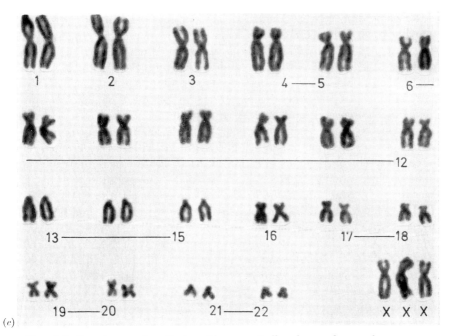

(c)

Fig. 8.4. Karyotypes of patients with numerically abnormal sex chromosomes. (c) XXX. (Contributed by Dr. Joy Delhanty.)

caro and Lindsten (1960) reported a boy with 49 chromosomes and XXXXY-sex chromosomes. The clinical picture of XXXY-patients does not seem to differ materially from that in XXY-subjects, but patients with four X-chromosomes and a Y-chromosome tend to have additional congenital abnormalities (Barr *et al*, 1962; Scherz and Roeckel, 1963). These include skeletal malformations, underdevelopment of the genitalia, and increased risk of severe mental deficiency.

Another variant met with in Klinefelter's syndrome is the XXYY-sex chromosome constitution (Muldal and Ockey, 1960; Ellis *et al*., 1961; Barr *et al*., 1964; G. C. Robinson *et al*., 1964). Barr *et al*. conclude that the presence of an additional Y-chromosome in Klinefelter's syndrome has a variable and as yet not clearly delineated harmful effect, which may possibly express itself in predisposition to vascular and cutaneous abnormalities in older patients. These findings are in accordance with the assumption that the genetic effect of a Y-chromosome is relatively nonspecific, apart from its function of sex determination (see Chapter 12, Section IV). A patient with XXXYY-sex chromosomes has also been described (Bray and Sr. Josephine, 1963).

Some patients with Klinefelter's syndrome have abnormalities of the sex-chromosome constitution which are not the same in all the cells of the body. Evidence for the existence of human chromosomal mosaics was first presented by C. E. Ford *et al.* (1959c), who found in the bone marrow of a patient with Klinefelter's syndrome cells with 46 and 47 chromosomes which were interpreted as containing XX- and XXY-sex chromosomes, respectively. The existence of this type of mosaicism was soon fully confirmed, and, in fact, it became clear that mixed chromosome constitutions account for a considerable proportion of patients with Klinefelter's syndrome and other abnormalities of the sex chromosomes (see Harnden and Jacobs, 1961; McKusick, 1964, Court Brown *et al.*, 1964). Thus, among eighteen newborn males in whom sex chromatin was found by Maclean *et al.* (1964; see Chapter 10, Section XIV), twelve had an XXY-sex-chromosome complement, one was XXYY, and five were mosaics with XY/XXXY sex chromosomes. Among 128 patients of varying ages, Court Brown *et al.* (1964) found 99 with XXY-sex chromosomes, four with XXXY, one with XXXXY, and three with XXYY-sex chromosomes, while 24 were sex-chromosome mosaics. Of these, two were XX/XXY, fifteen were XY/XXY, two were XXXY/XXXXY, while four were triple mosaics; these included one patient each with the following sex chromosome arrangements: XO/XY/XXY, XX/XY/XXY, XY/XXY/XXYY, and XX/XXY/XXXY.

It is now assumed that the sexual development of an embryo is determined by the sex chromosome constitution of the rudimentary gonad (see Chapter 12). Provided a normal Y-chromosome is present in the gonadal ridges of an otherwise normal embryo, the gonad will develop into a testis and the embryo into a male, but if the sex-chromosome constitution is abnormal, e.g., XXY, the testis develops abnormally. With mosaicism of the XY/XXY-type, a more normal development might be expected, provided the XY-cells were present in sufficient numbers in the right place at the right time. Court Brown *et al.* (1964) provided evidence that at least one such patient had children, whereas paternity has not so far been substantiated in patients with exclusively XXY-sex chromosomes. The fact that Court Brown *et al.* (1965) found no example of this type of mosaicism among a sample of 517 males chosen at random suggests that the condition is not very frequent in the general population.

The origin of one or more additional sex chromosomes in Klinefelter's syndrome is presumed to be due to a failure of the chromosomes to separate normally during cell division, an event which is known as "nondisjunction" (p. 28). Nondisjunction may occur during meiosis of the germ cells, either in the father or the mother of patients, or it may happen during mitosis in an early cell division of the embryo. If mosaicism is present, this must be due to mitotic nondisjunction, which may either be the cause of the chromosomal abnormality or may be a secondary disturbance occurring in cells which already have an abnormal chromosome constitution. Theoretically, another possibility which might give rise to offspring with abnormal chromosomes might be a mitotic error in one of the parents occurring before the meiotic divisions of the germ cells. Although it is difficult to obtain direct information on this point, it may perhaps be assumed that this possibility is the least likely, since cells with an abnormal chromosome constitution are at a disadvantage during meiosis. Last, some rare types of mosaicism may be due to fertilization of an ovum by two spermatozoa (see below).

The origin of the additional X-chromosome in patients with XXY-sex chromosomes can sometimes be determined by the distribution of sex-linked genes (see below Section XII) in the patient and his family. Genes which are particularly useful for this purpose are those for color blindness and for the sex-linked blood group, Xg. With the aid of these markers, Ferguson-Smith et al. (1964a; see also Race, 1965) were able to show that some patients with XXY-sex chromosomes had derived both X-chromosomes from their mother, while others had obtained an X- and a Y-chromosome from their father. The authors also presented preliminary evidence that in those patients who had received two X-chromosomes from their mother the mother's age at the birth of the patient was on an average higher than normal, whereas no increase in maternal age was observed in patients who had received an additional sex chromosome from their father. The significance of this finding will be discussed below.

It will be remembered that meiosis consists of two cell divisions which give rise, in the male, to four haploid spermatozoa and, in the female, to one haploid ovum and three haploid polar bodies or one haploid and one diploid one (Chapter 2, Section V). It must also be remembered that, although primary spermatocytes and primary oocytes are diploid as regards their chromosome number, at the onset of meiosis they are tetraploid as regards the number of chromatids and the amount of DNA present, because each chromosome has duplicated itself prior to this stage. Therefore, a secondary spermatocyte or oocyte has the haploid number of chromosomes but the diploid number of chromatids, and only spermatids, spermatozoa, and ova are truly haploid with regard to the number of chromatids and the amount of DNA present.

If nondisjunction occurred in the first meiotic division of spermatogenesis, two of the resulting spermatozoa would contain an X- and a Y-chromosome, while the other two spermatozoa would contain no sex chromosome (Fig. 8.5a). A sperm containing both an X- and a Y-chromosome will on fertilization give rise to an embryo with XXY-sex chromosomes. Similarly, nondisjunction during oogenesis, either in the first or the second meiotic division, may give rise to an egg with two X-chromosomes (Fig. 8.6a,b), and if such an egg is fertilized by a

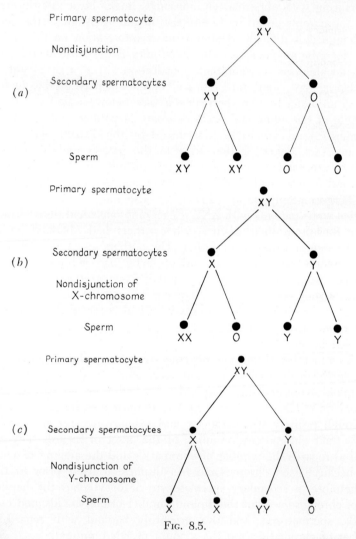

FIG. 8.5.

Y-bearing sperm, the resulting embryo will again have XXY-sex chromosomes.

Exceptionally, nondisjunction of the sex chromosomes may occur both in the first and in the second meiotic division. If this happens in the male, a sperm with two X- and two Y-chromosomes will be formed (Fig. 8.5d), and such a sperm will give rise to an individual with XXXYY-sex chromosomes. Alternatively, if nondisjunction has occurred in the first meiotic division, it may occur again in the second division

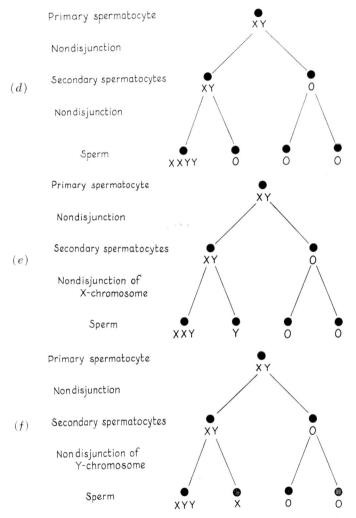

FIG. 8.5. Nondisjunction of sex chromosomes in spermatocyte. (a) During first meiotic division; (b) and (c) during second meiotic division; (d) during first and second meiotic divisions; (e) during first division and one chromosome during second division; (f) during first division and other chromosome during second division. Note: the chromosomes of primary and secondary spermatocytes contain the duplicated amounts of DNA.

in only one of the sex chromosomes. This process in the male will give rise either to a sperm with two X- and one Y-chromosomes, or to a sperm with one X- and two Y-chromosomes (Fig. 8.5e,f); such sperms will form individuals with XXXY- and XXYY-sex chromosomes, respectively. De la Chapelle *et al.* (1964b) have provided evidence that a patient

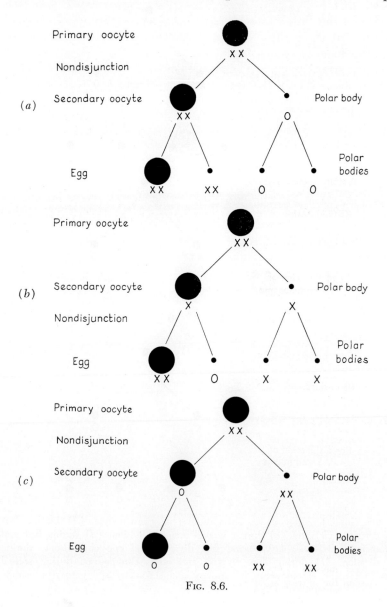

Fig. 8.6.

with XXYY-sex chromosomes has originated in this way. Nondisjunction in both meiotic divisions of the mother may give rise to an egg with four X-chromosomes (Fig. 8.6d) which on fertilization by a Y-bearing sperm will form an embryo with XXXXY-sex chromosomes. Blood group studies carried out by F. J. W. Lewis et al. (1964) indicate the possibility that two patients with XXXXY-sex chromosomes may have originated by this type of double meiotic nondisjunction in the mother. It is clear that the process of nondisjunction of the sex chromosomes during gametogenesis of one parent can give rise to almost any sex-chromosome arrangement met with in Klinefelter's syndrome, as well as to other abnormalities of the sex chromosomes, which will be discussed below.

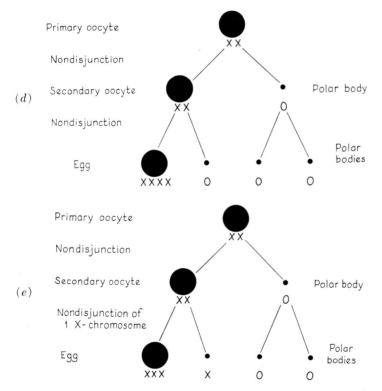

FIG. 8.6. Nondisjunction of sex chromosomes in oocytes. (a) During first meiotic division, giving rise to XX eggs; (b) during second meiotic division, giving rise to XX eggs; (c) during first meiotic division giving rise to eggs without X-chromosome; (d) during first and second meiotic division; (e) during first and one chromosome during second meiotic division. Note: Chromosomes of primary and secondary oocytes contain the duplicated amount of DNA.

The chromosomal findings in Klinefelter's syndrome provide an important clue about the function of the Y-chromosome in human sex determination. It will be remembered that in *Drosophila* an XXY-sex chromosome constitution results in female flies, which are fertile, whereas in man not only XXY-, but also XXXY- and XXXXY- sex chromosomes lead to the formation of an unmistakably male phenotype, even though such males are not fertile. As regards the sex-determining effect of the Y-chromosome, man is therefore more similar to the flowering plant *Silene* (Chapter 3, Section III) than to *Drosophila*.

The male-determining function of the Y-chromosome is also borne out by the chromosomal findings in Turner's syndrome.

V. Turner's Syndrome

Turner's syndrome is one of the numerous names given to a clinical entity in women, which comprises rudimentary gonads and absence of secondary sexual characteristics as well as a number of somatic abnormalities, including short stature and webbed neck. The condition has been reviewed by Polani (1962), Hauser (1963), Lenz (1964), de la Chapelle (1962), Lindsten (1963), Engel (1964), and Turpin and Lejeune (1965). The bewildering variety of names—there are about 30—reflects the complexity of the clinical findings, for the same abnormalities are not invariably found in every patient. Nevertheless, the three conditions just mentioned, i.e., rudimentary gonads, short stature, and short neck do in fact tend to go together and thus form a recognizable disease picture, or syndrome. In addition other abnormalities may be present, of which an abnormality of the blood vessels, known as coarctation of the aorta, is perhaps the most significant. Although "Turner's syndrome" (after Turner, 1938) appears to be the most commonly used name for this disease, many authors prefer others, particularly "gonadal dysgenesis" and "ovarian dysgenesis."

Apart from Turner's syndrome, a condition exists in which rudimentary gonads are associated with normal stature and no somatic abnormalities. This condition is known as "pure gonadal dysgenesis" (Polani, 1962). Whereas in the great majority of patients with Turner's syndrome the condition is due to an abnormal sex-chromosome constitution, pure gonadal dysgenesis does not represent a clear-cut picture in this respect. Some of the patients have XY-sex chromosomes (Harnden and Stewart, 1959; Polani, 1962; de la Chapelle, 1962; Court Brown *et al.*, 1964).

The abnormality of the gonads in Turner's syndrome was first described by Wilkins and Fleischmann (1944). Instead of normal ovaries, these authors found only ridges of whitish tissue, a condition which is generally referred to as "streak gonads."

In 1954 it was shown by Polani *et al.* and by Wilkins *et al.* that the majority of patients with Turner's syndrome lacked sex chromatin (see Chapter 11); and in 1959 C. E. Ford *et al.* (1959b) as well as Fraccaro *et al.* showed that the sex-chromosome constitution of three such patients consisted of a single X-chromosome, giving a total chromosome number of 45.

Although the XO-chromosome constitution is the one most commonly met with in Turner's syndrome, there are many other combinations of sex chromosomes which can give rise to essentially the same phenotype. The possible variations comprise (1) the presence of a structurally abnormal sex chromosome; (2) mosaicism; and (3) a combination of (1) and (2).

Jacobs *et al.* (1960) described a patient who had 46 chromosomes, only one of which looked like an X-chromosome, while an additional chromosome looked like number 16 (Fig. 8.7a). Because of the clinical condition of the patient, with features of Turner's syndrome, and the fact that she had sex-chromatin bodies, which appeared to be smaller than usual (Chapter 10, Section V) the additional chromosome was interpreted as an abnormal X-chromosome, from which part of the long arm had probably been deleted. The interpretation of this and other types of chromosomes as representing structurally abnormal X-chromosomes has subsequently received strong additional support, not only from studies of sex chromatin, but also from experiments involving the incorporation of radioactive thymidine into dividing cells (Chapter 10, Section VI).

Jacobs *et al.* (1961) described another patient with Turner's syndrome, who also had 46 chromosomes and apparently small sex-chromatin bodies. The karyotype included seven chromosomes in group 13–15, and one of these was interpreted as an abnormal X-chromosome, from which the short arm had probably been deleted (Fig. 8.7b).

Lindsten *et al.* (1963a) and Fraccaro *et al.* (1960a) described five patients with Turner's syndrome each of whom had 46 chromosomes and sex chromatin. There were 15 chromosomes in group 6–12–X and three chromosomes which looked like number 3 (Fig. 8.8a). One of these was interpreted as a structurally abnormal X-chromosome, containing the two long arms of X, and having lost its short arm. Chromosomes of this type, in which the centromere is exactly in the middle and which are assumed to consist of a single duplicated chromosome arm, have been described by Darlington (1940) in the flowering plant *Fritillaria*. Darlington called such chromosomes "iso-chromosomes" and concluded that they originated by an occasional crosswise division of the centromere at meiosis. Iso-

chromosomes in wheat were studied by Sears (1952), who concluded
that they were formed either at the first meiotic division, or that they
resulted at a later cell division from telocentric chromosomes, which
were themselves formed by an error during the first meiotic division.
Since isochromosomes are particularly likely to occur from misdivision of
univalent chromosomes, this might explain their preferential formation

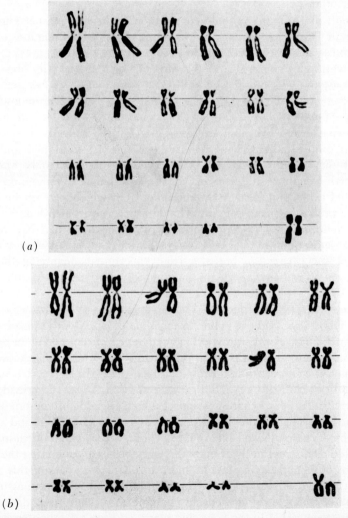

(a)

(b)

FIG. 8.7. Karyotypes from female patients showing one deleted X-chromosome.
(a) Deletion of long arm; (b) deletion of short arm. (Contributed by Dr. J.
Lindsten.)

during meiosis in the male (see below), when the X-chromosome is unpaired. Nevertheless, it should be stressed at the present stage that as regards the isochromosome in man described by Lindsten *et al.* (1963a) and others there is as yet no conclusive evidence of their mode of origin nor of their chromosomal contents. On the other hand, there can be no doubt that they represent structurally abnormal X-chromosomes, since they form sex chromatin and incorporate radioactive thymidine later than other chromosomes. Accordingly, such chromosomes are properly called "presumptive isochromosomes for the long arm of the X-chromosome" and "the word 'presumptive' is implied even when it is not stated" (Fraccaro and Lindsten, 1964).

A mechanism which gives rise to an isochromosome of the long arm might be expected to result also in isochromosomes of the short arm of the X. It is possible that some chromosomes which are regarded as deletions of the long arm are, in fact, isochromosomes of the short arm of the X-chromosome.

The presumptive isochromosome for the long arm of the X is a common chromosomal variant in Turner's syndrome. A more unusual type of chromosome was discovered by Lindsten and Tillinger (1962). Their patient differed from the ones which have been described so far in that different cells showed more than one karyotype. Cells grown from peripheral blood had 45, 46, and 47 chromosomes, respectively; those with 45 chromosomes contained a single apparently normal X-chromosome, those with 46 contained one normal X and one chromosome in the shape of a ring (Fig. 8.8b), while cells with 47 chromosomes contained one normal X- and two ring chromosomes. The ring chromosome was capable of forming sex chromatin and, in experiments using radioactive thymidine, incorporated the thymidine later than the other chromosomes (Lindsten, 1963), thus behaving like an X-chromosome. Other examples of a ring X-chromosome associated with symptoms of Turner's syndrome have been described by Lüers *et al.* (1963), by Hustinx and Stoelinga (1964), and by Bain *et al.* (1965). Ring chromosomes had previously been described in maize (McClintock, 1938).

Yet another type of structurally abnormal X-chromosome was discovered by Gouw *et al.* (1964) in a patient with Turner's syndrome in whom the total chromosome number was 46. One of the X-chromosomes was larger than any autosome; its short arm was roughly the length of the long arm of a normal X-chromosome and its long arm was considerably longer.

The presence of different cell lines with different sex-chromosome constitutions is frequently encountered in Turner's syndrome; structurally abnormal X-chromosomes may or may not be involved. Evidence for the existence of mosaicism in Turner's syndrome was first provided by C. E. Ford (1961) in 1959. The patient in question had two cell lines with 45 and 46 chromosomes, respectively. The cells with 45 chromosomes contained a single X, while the cells with 46 chromosomes had two apparently normal X-chromosomes. Blank *et al.* (1960) described a patient with XO- as well as XY- sex chromosomes. Some other, rarer, types of mosaicism have from time to time been encountered. Thus Hayward and Cameron (1961) described the first case of triple mosaicism with cells of 45, 46, and 47 chromosomes and containing XO-, XX- and XXX-sex chromosomes, respectively. In a few instances it may be impossible to

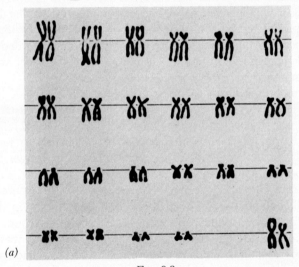

(a)

FIG. 8.8a

ascertain the exact karyotype. For instance, two patients described by Court Brown *et al.* (1964) had, in addition to cells with XO-sex chromosome constitution, other cells with one X-chromosome and a minute chromosome fragment. No sex chromatin was found. If a chromosome fragment is very small, it may be impossible to establish its relationship with other chromosomes. Moreover, in a few patients the clinical diagnosis remains doubtful. Another patient described by Court Brown *et al.* had 46 chromosomes, including one X, and another chromosome which was interpreted as an isochromosome for the long arm of the Y-chromosome. The patient had some, but not all, of the features of Turner's syndrome. Only connective tissue was found in the gonads, so that it is impossible to say whether they represent a failure of ovarian or testicular development.

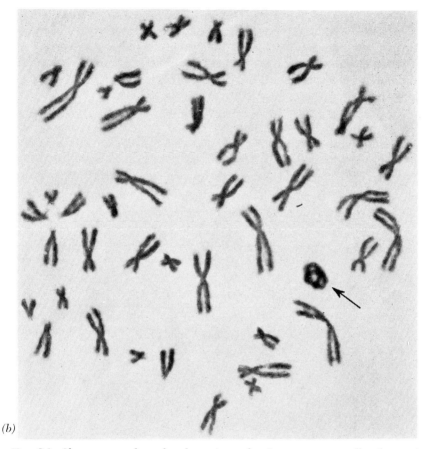

(b)

Fɪɢ. 8.8. Chromosomes from female patients showing one structurally abnormal X-chromosome. (a) Presumptive isochromosome of the long arm of the X; (b) cell containing ring X-chromosome. (Contributed by Dr. J. Lindsten.)

The sex chromosomes found in five surveys of Turner patients are shown in Table 8.I. It must be emphasized that the five series are not entirely comparable, since different criteria were used for selecting the patients. In addition, the survey by Court Brown et al. includes only those patients in whom the sex chromosomes were abnormal. In spite of these differences, the general picture which emerges regarding the sex chromosomes in Turner's picture is fairly uniform. Thus, the XO-condition represents the largest entity, accounting for roughly half the cases; about one-third of the cases are mosaics; and the presumptive isochromosome of the long arm of the X-chromosome represents the commonest structural abnormality.

The chromosomal abnormalities in Turner's syndrome, like those in Klinefelter's syndrome, may theoretically be expected to originate either during gametogenesis of one of the parents or during an early mitotic division of the embryo. If mosaicism is present, this must have originated during embryogenesis, but, if it occurs in conjunction with a structurally abnormal X-chromosome, it is likely that the original zygote was already abnormal. Nondisjunction of the sex chromosomes in spermatogenesis, as illustrated in Fig. 8.5a as resulting in Klinefelter's syndrome, would result in Turner's syndrome if fertilization were effected by a sperm lacking a sex chromosome. The different types of nondisjunction in the mother (Fig. 8.6) could give rise to an XO-condition if in each instance

TABLE 8.I

SEX CHROMOSOMES IN TURNER'S SYNDROME

Sex chromosomes	Authors and numbers of patients				
	Court Brown et al. (1964)	Lindsten (1963)	Engel (1964)	Ferguson-Smith et al. (1964b)	de la Chapelle (1962)
XO	38	35	17	7	10
XO/XX	4	7	1	8	6
XO/X $\times$, XO/X$\times$,[a] XO/X$\times\times$	5	9	8	4	2
X $\times$	3	2	5	1	0
XO,XY	5	0	2	1	0
XO,XYY	1	0	0	0	0
XO/X∧[b]	0	1	1	0	0
XO/X$\times$[c]	1	0	0	1	1
X∧	1	0	0	0	0
X$\times$	1	0	0	0	0
XO/XX$_R$/XX$_R$X$_R$, XO/XX$_R$[d]	0	1	0	1	0
XO/XXX, XO/XX/XXX	3	0	0	2	0
XO/X + large X	1	0	0	0	0
XO/X + minute fragment	2	0	0	1	1
XX	0	1	0	3	2
XO/?	0	1	1	0	0
XO/X $\times$ /?XXX	0	0	0	1	0
	65	57	35	30	22

[a] $\times$, Presumptive isochromosome for the long arm of the X-chromosome.
[b] ∧, Presumptive deletion of short arm of X-chromosomes.
[c] $\times$, Presumptive deletion of long arm of X-chromosome.
[d] X$_R$, Ring X-chromosome.

the additional X-chromosome would go into the polar body, thus leaving the oocyte or egg without an X-chromosome (e.g., Fig. 8.6c). Fertilization of such an egg by an X-bearing sperm would give rise to a zygote with a single X-chromosome, while fertilization by a Y-bearing sperm would give rise to an inviable zygote. In addition to nondisjunction, the XO-condition could also arise by the loss of a sex chromosome during cell division. That this possibility may actually occur in practice is suggested by the findings of Jacobs et al. (1964), who studied the chromosomes in cultured blood cells of apparently normal individuals over 65 years of age. They found that in 4% of cells in males, and in 8% of cells in females, one chromosome was missing; in half of these cells from males and a higher proportion in females, the missing chromosomes were of the size and shape of a Y- or X-chromosome, respectively.

Although the actual mechanism giving rise to an XO-sex-chromosome constitution remains in the realms of conjecture, it can often be determined whether it is the father's or the mother's sex chromosome which has been lost. The sex-linked blood group Xg has been particularly useful in this respect. Race (1965) has shown that in 102 families containing an XO-patient, the maternal X-chromosome had been lost in about 24% of cases, and the paternal one in 76% of cases. These results suggest that in the majority of cases the lost sex chromosome is the father's.

Since all the types of nondisjunction which may give rise to Klinefelter's syndrome (see Figs. 8.5 and 8.6) may also result in Turner's syndrome, and since in addition an XO-sex-chromosome constitution could arise by the loss of a chromosome, Turner's syndrome might be expected to be more frequent than Klinefelter's syndrome. However, as will be shown later (Chapter 10, Section IV) the opposite is true. The incidence of Klinefelter's syndrome at birth has been estimated at about 2 per 1000 and the incidence of Turner's syndrome as roughly 4 per 10,000. The most likely explanation for this apparent discrepancy may be found in the results of chromosome studies on aborted embryos. Carr (1965) reported that among 200 spontaneously aborted embryos, eleven had XO-sex-chromosome constitution while none were XXY. This suggests that the frequency of Turner's syndrome at birth may be only a few per cent of that at conception. It is possible that the abnormalities of the heart and blood vessels associated with this syndrome may result in a high mortality before birth. If this were true, Turner's syndrome must be regarded as a highly lethal condition, of which we see only a small proportion of survivors.

Ferguson-Smith (1965) has attempted to correlate the various types of abnormalities of the X-chromosomes met with in Turner's syndrome with differences in phenotypic expression. His main conclusion is that the loss of any part of an X-chromosome leads to the formation of streak gonads but that only the loss of some or the whole of the short arm causes short stature and other somatic abnormalities. These abnormalities occur less commonly in deletions of the long arm than in deletions of the short arm of the X-chromosome. Since deletions of the Y-chromosome may also give rise to stigmata of Turner's syndrome, Ferguson-Smith suggests that part of the short arm of the X-chromosome is homologous with part of the Y-chromosome. The idea of a pairing segment between the X- and the Y-chromosome in man had previously been put forward by C. E. Ford (1963).

VI. Female Patients with Multiple X-Chromosomes

Both Turner's syndrome and Klinefelter's syndrome were originally recognized as clinical entities. When chromosome studies became available, these provided a biological basis for the two diseases. By contrast, the patients to be described now do not comprise a well defined clinical group, and they were discovered only as a result of chromosome studies.

Jacobs et al. (1959a) reported on an adult female patient with some sexual abnormalities, who had a total of 47 chromosomes, including 3 X-chromosomes (Fig. 8.4c). A second patient described by Jacobs et al. (1960) was feeble-minded but appeared to have no abnormalities of sexual development nor any other physical abnormalities. The term "super-female," which had been taken over from the cytogenetics of Drosophila (Chapter 4, Section III) was at first used to describe the chromosomal condition in man, but has now been largely discontinued.

An outstanding feature of the triple X-condition is that patients have two sex-chromatin bodies in cells of their buccal mucosa and in other tissues (Chapter 10, Section IV) and this makes it possible to diagnose the abnormality from mass surveys. Such surveys have been made both on new-born infants and on patients in hospitals for the mentally retarded (see Chapter 10, Section XIV). The frequency of the triple X-condition was found to be higher among the mentally retarded than at birth, which suggests that the chromosomal constitution predisposes to mental retardation. Some abnormalities of sexual development also appear to be fairly frequent (Johnston et al., 1961). However, some women with three X-chromosomes may be quite normal, as regards both intelligence and sexual development. Close (1963) described two such women, one of whom had borne two normal sons. The majority of children born to triple-X women seem to be normal males or females, but Rosenkranz (1965) has reported two patients with Klinefelter's syndrome, whose mothers had XXX- and XXX/XX-sex chromosomes, respectively. The simplest explanation to account for the origin of these Klinefelter patients is that each arose from an egg with two X-chromosomes, which was itself the product of secondary nondisjunction (Chapter 4, Section III). Secondary nondisjunction in man was first described in the autosomal trisomic condition, mongolism (Hanhart et al., 1961). In the rare event of children being born to mongol mothers, about half the children carry the additional chromosome number 21 and are themselves affected. Apart from secondary nondisjunction, mitotic nondisjunction in the offspring of patients with chromosomal abnormalities may be a further cause of aneuploidy (Penrose and Smith, 1966).

Female patients with more than three X-chromosomes are also known. Carr et al. (1961) described two mentally retarded patients with four X-chromosomes, and a child with five X-chromosomes, making a total of 49 chromosomes has also been described (Kesaree and Woolley, 1963; Grumbach et al., 1963). This patient was an infant with physical abnormalities in addition to mental retardation.

Mosaicism involving trisomy of the X-chromosome has been described, but less often than for either the XXY- or the XO-sex-chromosome constitution. De Grouchy et al. (1961) described a woman with abnormal ovaries, who had cells with XX- and XXX-sex chromosomes, and Bergemann (1962) found three women with XXX/XXXX- and one with XX/XXX/XXXX-sex chromosomes in the same family (see later). Mosaics with XO- and XXX-cell lines may give rise to Turner's syndrome as well as to other phenotypes, the difference probably depending on the type of cell present in the gonads at particular stages of embryogenesis.

The triple X-condition could arise from nondisjunction of the X-chromosomes in either the first or second meiotic division of the mother, giving rise to an egg with two X-chromosomes (Fig. 8.6). Similarly, the origin of karyotypes with four and five X-chromosomes could be explained by the occurrence of nondisjunction in both the first and second meiotic divisions, which would give rise to eggs with three or four X-chromosomes (Fig. 8.6d,e). The triple X-condition could also arise by nondisjunction of the X-chromosome during the second meiotic division in the father (Fig. 8.5b).

VII. True Hermaphrodites

True hermaphrodites have gonads containing both ovarian and testicular tissue. The distribution of these tissues varies in different patients. Lateral hermaphrodites have an ovary on one side and a testis on the other. Bilateral hermaphrodites have both ovarian and testicular tissue on both sides: a gonad containing ovarian as well as testicular tissues is known as an "ovotestis." Finally, unilateral hermaphrodites have an ovary or testis on one side and an ovotestis on the other (Overzier, 1963a). However, since a decision of what constitutes ovarian or testicular tissue must be based on the histological appearance, and since the entire gonad may have to be examined in this way it is clear that a correct diagnosis cannot always be made. All human hermaphrodites are sterile. The usage of the term is therefore different from that in animals and plants, in which "hermaphrodite" designates an organism which is capable of producing viable male and female gametes.

The external genitalia may show all gradations from the typically male to the typically female conditions. Of 171 patients listed by Overzier (1963a), 94 had been brought up as males and 49 as females, in 4 cases there was some ambiguity, and in 14 there was no information. None of the patients appear to be fertile although both ova and spermatozoa may be formed.

A hermaphrodite was one of the first human subjects in whom sex chromatin was demonstrated in 1953 (see Chapter 10, Section II). Sex chromatin has since been found in the majority of such patients and chromosome studies have shown that most hermaphrodite patients have XX-sex chromosomes (Shearman et al., 1964). The first such patient whose chromosomes were described (Hungerford et al., 1959) was phenotypically male, with a testis on one side and an ovotestis on the other. The second patient, described by Harnden and Armstrong (1959), was phenotypically more like a female and had one ovary and an ovotestis. Both patients had XX-sex chromosomes. A minority of hermaphrodite patients have an XY-sex chromosome constitution (Grumbach et al., 1960; Sandberg et al., 1960; Blank et al., 1964; Shearman et al., 1964).

Hirschhorn et al. (1960) described mosaicism with XY/XO-sex chromosomes in an infant who may have been a hermaphrodite. Another mosaic, with XX/XY-sex chromosomes was described by Gartler et al. (1962) and Giblett et al. (1963) in a unilateral hermaphrodite, and the authors suggested that the most likely explanation to account for this chromosome constitution was by double fertilization of an egg (containing two haploid nuclei) by an X- as well as a Y-bearing sperm. Blood group studies showed that the patient carried more than two alleles at the MN and the rhesus loci. In addition she had one brown and one hazel eye. A similar origin was thought likely for another hermaphrodite found by Josso et al. (1965); this patient who also had XX/XY-sex chromosomes, had a mixture of haptoglobins in his serum, which were of phenotype Hp 1.2 and Hp 2.2. In another patient with

XX/XY-sex chromosomes, described by Bain and Scott (1965), double fertilization was thought likely but could not be proved. The patient was phenotypically a female, with a streak gonad on one side; on the other she had a tumor, which was diagnosed as a dysgerminoma, i.e., originating from testicular tissue. Fraccaro *et al.* (1962a) reported a hermaphrodite infant with triple mosaicism, the sex chromosomes being XX/XXY/XXYYY. This was interpreted as having arisen from a XXY-zygote, in which nondisjunction of the Y-chromosome resulted first in XX- and XXYY-cells, and secondarily in cells with XXYYY-sex chromosomes. It is of interest that Blank *et al.* (1964) subsequently described a hermaphrodite infant with XX/XXYY-sex chromosomes, in whom blood group findings did not suggest an origin by double fertilization.

It appears that in contrast to Klinefelter's and Turner's syndromes the majority of hermaphrodite patients have a sex chromosome constitution which is intrinsically normal, being either XX or less commonly XY. In addition, cases of mosaicism appear to be less common than in conditions with abnormal sex chromosome constitutions. The possibility of unde-tected mosaicism involving cells containing a Y-chromosome is of par-ticular relevance in patients in whom only XX-sex chromosomes have been found. Rosenberg *et al.* (1963) described three hermaphrodites with male phenotype within a single sibship, in all of whom the sex-chromosome constitution was XX, and the authors think it unlikely that cells containing a Y-chromosome would have been missed in all three patients. On the other hand, Brøgger and Aagenaes (1965) described a child with lateral hermaphroditism in whom chromosome analyses from bone marrow, skin, blood, and testis revealed only XX-sex chromosomes, while in a second testicular biopsy a proportion of cells with XY-sex chromosomes were detected. Similarly, Soloman *et al.* (1964) found cells containing a Y-chromosome, though probably an abnormal one, in cell cultures derived from the testis of a boy (not a hermaphrodite) who had previously been reported to lack a Y-chromosome. The possibility thus remains that all hermaphrodites with an apparent XX-sex chromo-some constitution originate as XX/XY mosaics, in which the XX-cells gain ascendency. On the other hand, the alternative hypothesis, that in exceptional circumstances testicular tissue may be formed in the absence of a Y-chromosome, cannot at present be excluded.

VIII. Pseudohermaphrodites

Pseudohermaphrodites are patients with various types of abnormal sexual development, who have either ovaries or testes (but not both). If testes are present, the patient is known as a male pseudohermaphrodite, and if ovaries are present the patient is a female pseudohermaphrodite.

"Pseudohermaphroditism" is a blanket term, which comprises a variety of conditions of unknown origin. As a result of advances made in recent years, particularly through the recognition of sex-chromosome abnormalities, a number of entities, such as Klinefelter's syndrome and Turner's syndrome, have been characterized and are now no longer included under the general topic of pseudohermaphroditism (Overzier, 1963b). A further condition, the syndrome of testicular feminization, which was previously regarded as a type of male pseudohermaphroditism, will now be briefly described.

IX. Testicular Feminization

The name "syndrome of testicular feminization" was applied by Morris (1953), who described two patients and reviewed 79 others from the literature. Patients with this condition have a typically female appearance, with well-developed breasts and other female secondary sexual characteristics, but sparse pubic and axillary hair. They never menstruate and are sterile. In place of ovaries, there is a pair of undescended testes. The testes secrete considerable amounts of estrogens as well as androgens (Chapter 12, Section I), and if they are removed before puberty the female secondary sexual characteristics fail to develop (Hauser, 1963).

Grumbach and Barr (1958) found that four patients with testicular feminization lacked sex chromatin. The somatic chromosomes were first investigated by Jacobs *et al.* (1959b), who also investigated four patients and found that all had XY-sex chromosomes. The XY-sex chromosome constitution has since been confirmed by other authors (see Court Brown *et al.*, 1964).

In testicular feminization, therefore, testes develop in the presence of a Y-chromosome, but these testes are unable to induce the development of a male phenotype. The condition tends to occur in families, and there is evidence that it is transmitted by a single gene (Patterson and Bonnier, 1937; McKusick, 1964). This is transmitted through the patient's mother. The gene may be borne on the X-chromosome; alternatively, we may be dealing with an autosomal gene with dominant effect, which is expressed only in genetic males. The genetic interpretation of pedigrees is, of course, made difficult owing to the fact that the affected genetic males suffer from testicular feminization and are unable to reproduce.

This syndrome would appear to be of particular interest, in that a single gene turns the testes into organs controlling the development of female secondary sexual characteristics. It is, of course, not a case of sex reversal in any true sense, since ovaries are absent. It illustrates the delicate balance involved in sexual differentiation and should eventually help to throw light on this problem.

X. Males with XX Sex Chromosomes

An XX-sex chromosome constitution in human males appears to be a rare finding. The first case was probably published by de la Chapelle *et al.* in 1964 (1964a), another by Therkelsen (1964), and Court Brown *et al.* (1964) found two such patients among 134 males with abnormalities of the sex chromosomes. Previously Shah *et al.* (1961) had reported XX-sex chromosomes in a child with ambiguous external genitalia and abdominal testes ("male pseudo hermaphrodite") and Oikawa and Blizzard (1961) in a boy with features of Turner's syndrome ("Turner syndrome in the male"), in whom mosaicism was, however, likely.

The patient described by de la Chapelle *et al.* (1964a) had many of the features of Klinefelter's syndrome. Blood group studies involving the X-borne Xg-group (Section XIII) proved particularly informative, since they indicated that the patient must have received both X-chromosomes from his mother. A further point of interest was that the patient's father and brother had Y-chromosomes which were unusually large. There is, therefore, strong indirect evidence that at the beginning of the patient's development a large Y-chromosome was present and was subsequently lost.

It is likely, though not yet proved, that a Y-chromosome was initially present in all males in whom a Y-chromosome has not been demonstrated.

XI. Males with XYY Sex Chromosomes

The result of an XYY-sex chromosome constitution in man appears to be variable. Some, including the first case reported by Hauschka *et al.* (1962), are fully developed, fertile males, and of normal intelligence. The patient described by Court Brown *et al.* (1964) was sexually underdeveloped, and Fraccaro *et al.* (1962b) described two patients with XYY-sex chromosomes who were mentally retarded. Jacobs *et al.* (1965) found an increased incidence of this karyotype among mentally subnormal patients with agressive tendencies. These patients were also unusually tall.

An XYY-constitution could arise either as a result of nondisjunction during the second meiotic division of the male, giving rise to a YY-sperm, or through mitotic nondisjunction in an XY-zygote.

A patient with 48 chromosomes, which were interpreted as including XYYY-sex chromosomes, was described by Townes *et al.* (1965). He was a 5-year-old boy with only minor abnormalities, including an undescended testis. The occurrence of three Y-chromosomes cannot be explained simply by meiotic nondisjunction in the father, who had a normal XY-sex chromosome constitution. Since two nondisjunctional events of the Y-chromosome are required, at least one must have been mitotic.

XII. Double Aneuploidy, Familial Aneuploidy, and Possible Causes of Sex Chromosome Abnormalities

Abnormalities of the sex chromosomes may occur in conjunction with other chromosomal abnormalities either in the same person or in the same family.

The most common chromosomal abnormality involving an autosome is that in which chromosome 21 occurs in triplicate, giving rise to mongolism or Downs' syndrome. Less common autosomal abnormalities include trisomy for one of the chromosomes 17–18, and trisomy for one of the chromosomes in group 13–15.

The first known patient with two chromosomal abnormalities suffered from both mongolism and Klinefelter's syndrome. He had a total of 48 chromosomes, including two X-chromosomes and a Y-chromosome, and three chromosomes number 21 (C. E. Ford *et al.*, 1959a). Subsequently a number of such patients were found (see Polani, 1963), including two pairs of monozygotic twins (Hustinx *et al.*, 1961; Turpin *et al.*, 1964), both of whom had a combination of mongolism with Klinefelter's syndrome. Klinefelter's syndrome has also been found in conjunction with trisomy of chromosome 17–18 (Pfeiffer, 1964).

Turner's syndrome, with XX/XO mosaicism, has also been described in conjunction with mongolism (van Wijck *et al.*, 1964; Root *et al.*, 1964), while the triple-X condition has been found both in association with mongolism (Day *et al.*, 1963) and with trisomy 17–18 (Uchida and Bowman, 1961; Ricci and Borgatti, 1963).

Two different chromosomal abnormalities may also occur in different members of the same family. Thus, Miller *et al.*, (1961) reported a family containing a male with XXXXY-sex chromosomes, whose father suffered from leukemia; one of the father's sisters as well as a niece were affected with mongolism. Therman *et al.* (1961) described two sisters, one of whom had Turner's syndrome with XO-sex chromosomes and the other had trisomy of chromosomes 13–15; and Rosenkranz *et al.* (1964) reported a pair of dizygotic twins, one of whom suffered from Kline-felter's syndrome and the other from mongolism, as well as another pair of sibs who had Klinefelter's syndrome and Turner's syndrome, respectively.

It seems likely that there may be an association between Turner's syndrome and twinning. Turner and Zanartu (1962) described a monozygotic twin pair, both of whom suffered from Turner's syndrome, and two other such pairs have since been found (Lemli and Smith, 1963; Nance and Uchida, 1964). Lindsten (1963) found twins in four out of 53 families of Turner patients, two of the patients being themselves members of twin pairs. He concluded that an increased frequency of twins in families of Turner patients is likely though not yet proved. Further evidence in favor of such an association was provided by Nance and Uchida (1964), who found twins in seven out of 34 families.

Turpin et al. (1961) described a pair of monozygotic twins, one member of whom was male with XY-sex chromosomes and the other a female with Turner's syndrome, with XO-sex chromosomes. The latter abnormality must clearly have originated by mitotic nondisjunction in the zygote. A similar pair of twins, also apparently monozygotic, was described by Dent and Edwards (1963); here only XO-sex chromosomes were found in the boy and XO- as well as XY-chromosomes in the Turner patient. These results, however, do not necessarily reflect the true proportion of sex chromosomes in the two subjects.

Uchida et al. (1964) described a pair of dizygotic twins of different sex, both of whom were mosaics for XX- and XY-sex chromosomes. The twins were apparently normal infants. In the boy, the proportion of sex chromosomes found was 70 XX : 30 XY, while in the girl the proportion was 78 XX : 22 XY. Both twins had a mixture of red cells, of which about 85% were group O and the rest group A. A similar mixture of red cells in man was described for the first time by Dunsford et al. (1953). A 25-year-old woman, who was the mother of one child, had erythrocytes of group O as well as of group A. A twin brother had died in infancy. The origin of these mosaics can be due to vascular anastomoses in the placentae, and the condition is thus similar to that which gives rise to freemartins in cattle (Chapter 12, Section II). The results, however, seem to be different in man, inasmuch as the female co-twins reported so far have been sexually normal.

The incidence of dizygotic twins arises with increasing age of the mother, but the frequency of monozygotic twins shows no such relationship with maternal age (Lenz, 1964). Maternal age is also an important factor in relation to chromosomal abnormalities. The fact that the average maternal age at the birth of a mongol child is higher than the average at the birth of other children is now well established (Penrose and G. F.

Smith, 1966), and evidence has recently accumulated that a similar relationship holds also for some abnormalities of the sex chromosomes. Thus it has been shown that the average maternal age is raised in Klinefelter's syndrome but not in Turner's syndrome (Lenz *et al.*, 1959; Stewart, 1960a; Penrose, 1961; Polani, 1962). There also appears to be an increase in maternal age for the triple-X condition (Polani, 1962). Nance and Uchida (1964) have suggested that a raised maternal age may be associated with meiotic nondisjunction, whereas in Turner's syndrome the loss of a sex chromosome may often occur during an early mitotic division of the zygote. Moreover, it was shown by Lindsten *et al.* (1963b) on the basis of blood group studies, that in the majority of patients with XO-sex chromosomes, it was the paternal sex chromosomes which had been lost. Similar studies performed on patients with Klinefelter's syndrome suggest that the maternal age may be increased only in those patients in whom the two X-chromosomes were derived from the mother, while the maternal age is normal for patients who have received an X- and a Y-chromosome from their father (Ferguson-Smith *et al.*, 1964a); the data, however, are not yet conclusive.

Finally, abnormal thyroid function has been reported in Klinefelter's syndrome, in Turner's syndrome, and in mongolism, as well as in unaffected relatives of such patients (see G. R. Fraser, 1964). It has been suggested (Fialkow, 1964; G. R. Fraser, 1964) that abnormal thyroid function in the parents, which may possibly be aggravated by advancing age, might predispose to the formation of an abnormal chromosome constitution in the offspring. While clearly conjectural at present, this suggestion at least gives a lead to the search for a physical basis for chromosomal abnormalities in man.

XIII. Sex-Linkage in Man

Two genes are said to show linkage if they are borne on the same chromosome and are sufficiently close to one another (Chapter 4, Section II); the chromosome may be either an autosome or a sex chromosome. In man, many genes are located on the X-chromosome and very few, if any, on the Y-chromosome.

From time to time a number of conditions in man have been claimed to be due to genes borne on the Y-chromosome, but the reality of such Y-borne loci has either been disproved, or not been established with certainty (Stern, 1957). The latter statement probably applies also to the condition of hairy pinnae (hypertrichosis), for which Y-linkage has been claimed in recent years (Dronamraju, 1960, 1965).

Any gene borne on the X-chromosome exhibits a characteristic mode of inheritance which reflects the transmission of the X-chromosome itself. A recessive allele will be expressed more frequently in males than in females, since it will show itself in the single, hemizygous, state, but a dominant allele is more likely to be present in females, as it has a greater chance of being included in one of the two chromosomes. The majority of mutations on the human X-chromosome are recessive and exhibit the typical criss-cross mode of inheritance which was described for sex-linked genes in *Drosophila* (Chapter 4, Section II). All these features make the inheritance of characters determined by sex-linked genes particularly outstanding, and consequently such characters were the first whose mode of inheritance became at least partly understood.

Two classical conditions which are controlled by genes borne on the X-chromosome are hemophilia and color blindness. As long ago as 1803, J. C. Otto, a physician in Philadelphia, gave an account of "an haemorrhogic condition disposition existing in certain families" (see Bulloch and Fildes, 1912). He stated that "males only are affected and all are not liable to it. Though females are free, they are capable of transmitting it to their children." When Nasse, in Germany, wrote in 1820, a considerable number of such families had been observed. Nasse once again emphasized the fact that the bleeders are always male; women whose fathers are affected may transmit the condition to their sons, but the women themselves do not manifest any tendency to bleed. This mode of inheritance became subsequently known as "Nasse's law."

Color blindness, too, has been recognized for a long time. In 1777, Joseph Priestly published a letter written by J. Huddart, which described a man who was unable to distinguish different colors, though he had otherwise good eye sight and was highly intelligent. Two of the man's brothers were similarly affected, but two other brothers and sisters, as well as his parents, had normal color vision. The mode of inheritance of color blindness was demonstrated by Horner (1876) in Switzerland, on the basis of carefully collected pedigrees. The discovery that sex-linked inheritance in *Drosophila* was due to genes borne on the X-chromosome was made by T. H. Morgan in 1910, and soon afterward Wilson suggested a similar chromosomal basis for the observed inheritance of color blindness in man: "it now seems certain that in sex limited heredity—such as appears in the heredity of the color pattern in *Abraxas* (Doncaster and Raynor), of color blindness in man, or of eye color in *Drosophila* (Morgan)—the somantic characters are linked with a sex determining factor in respect to which one sex is homozygous, the other heterozygous" (Wilson, 1911).

The first example of linkage in man was demonstrated by Bell and Haldane (1937) for the genes for color blindness and hemophilia. They found only one crossover in six pedigrees and concluded that linkage was very close, with a crossover value of about 5%. A more accurate estimate was given by Haldane and Smith (1947), who concluded that the maximum likelihood for the recombination value was 9.8%.

These estimates were based on the assumption that both hemophilia and color blindness are unitary genetic entities, each of which occupies a single locus on the X-chromosome. However, it is now known that sex-linked hemophilia comprises at least two entities, of which the commoner one is known as hemophilia A, and the other one as hemophilia B, or Christmas disease, after the name of a boy who suffered from this disease (Biggs et al., 1952; Aggeler et al., 1952). Whereas in hemophilia A there is a shortage of antihemophilic globulin, this is present in normal amounts in the plasma of patients with Christmas disease, who have a deficiency of plasma thromboplastin.

Sex-linked color blindness, or red-green blindness, can also be subdivided into two groups. Protanopes, or red blind people, cannot see the red and bluish-green part of the spectrum, whereas deuteranopes, or green blind people, cannot see the green part of the spectrum. The two conditions can usually be distinguished by the use of special charts, which show numbers in different colors on a grey background (Ishihara, 1944). In actual fact, only about 80–90% of color blind people can be correctly classified by means of the Ishihara charts (Kalmus, 1965). Some of the remainder may be classified by using an anomalo-scope, which is an instrument enabling one to match variable mixtures of red and green light with a standard yellow light (see Kalmus 1965).

Both the protan and the deutan defects may be expressed with several degrees of severity, and it seems to be agreed that both series of defects are due to a series of allelomorphs at the same locus. There is, however, no general agreement on whether the protan and deutan defects themselves are allelic or occupy separate chromosomal loci. The fact that women who are heterozygous for both defects generally have normal color vision favors the two-loci hypothesis. In addition, two families have now been described which could best be explained by the assumption of crossing-over between the two loci (Kalmus, 1962; Siniscalco et al., 1964). The bulk of the evidence therefore favors the assumption that the protan and deutan defects are due to two separate chromosomal loci; Kalmus (1965) has estimated that these loci may be separated by 10 to 20 crossover units.

There is evidence, too, that hemophilia A and B are caused by two separate genetic loci. Whittaker et al. (1962) studied two families, one of which segregated for hemophilia A and deuteranopia, and the other for hemophilia B and protanopia. They found 6% recombinants between hemophilia A and deuteranopia, but 50% recombinants between hemophilia B and protanopia. Most of the patients studied by Haldane and Smith (1947) are known to have been affected with hemophilia A and the deutan defect. The two sets of observations, therefore, show satisfactory agreement.

The human X-chromosome bears a large number of genes in addition to those for hemophilia and color blindness. McKusick (1964) lists 59 genes whose position on the X-chromosome he considers as either proved or very likely, and a further 21 genes for which the evidence is inconclusive.

The discovery of a blood group antigen, Xg^a, which is situated on the X-chromosome (Mann et al., 1962) has been of particular importance for linkage studies, since the presence or absence of the antigen can be determined in every person, so that linkage studies are no longer confined to individuals having at least two more or less rare marker genes on the X-chromosome. For the same reason the Xg^a blood group has proved invaluable in marking the X-chromosomes in patients with abnormal X-chromosome constitutions, so that the derivation of the chromosome, whether paternal or maternal, can be determined in many cases. The Xg^a antigen has been found in about 89% of females and 62% of males tested. Its detection is dependent on the presence of a special antibody, which is made by only very few people.

A further gene which has been important in linkage studies is that responsible for the condition known as "primaquine sensitivity" or glucose 6-phosphate dehydrogenase deficiency" (G-6-PD). Hockwald et al. showed in 1952 that the drug primaquine caused a hemolytic anemia in 5 out of 105 American male negroes. This incidence appeared to be much higher than in an American white population (Clayman et al., 1952) but a relatively high incidence was subsequently found in groups of people of Mediterranean origin (Szeinberg et al., 1958). The investigations of Carson et al. (1956) led to the conclusion that the people who were sensitive had a deficiency of the enzyme glucose 6-phosphate dehydrogenase. This discovery in turn led to the development of methods by which primaquine sensitivity could be measured from the enzymic activity of the erythrocytes (Beutler et al., 1957; Motulsky and Campbell-Kraut, 1961). Both the biochemical and some of the genetic findings in this condition have been summarized by Harris (1962).

Childs et al. (1958) found that the incidence of primaquine sensitivity among American negroes was about 14% among males and about 5% among females. In addition, about 5% of females showed partial sensitivity. From this as well as from family studies the authors concluded that the most likely mode of inheritance of the condition was by means of a sex-linked gene with incomplete dominance, a hypothesis which was soon confirmed by other workers (see McKusick, 1964).

Other genes which are located on the X-chromosome include those for total color blindness, a rare condition associated with poor vision generally (see Kalmus, 1965); the Duchenne type of muscular dystrophy, with early onset; the Becker type of muscular dystrophy, with later onset; agammaglobulinemia, in which plasma cells are lacking and patients are unusually prone to bacterial infections; the sex-linked type of gargoylism, or Hurler's syndrome, a disease of mucopolysaccharide metabolism, resulting in dwarfism, mental retardation, and other abnormalities; hypophosphatemia, in which low serum phosphorus is associated with vitamin D-resistant rickets; and genes causing other abnormalities (see McKusick, 1964).

The attempts which have been made to place the genes on the human X-chromosome into their correct position have been summarized by Race and Sanger (1964). The distances between loci will be given as frequency of crossovers, representing the percentage of recombinants among the offspring. This percentage can also be expressed as the recombination fraction. In order to convert the crossover frequency into map units (i.e. "centimorgans," see   p. 58), it would be necessary to take into account also double and quadruple exchanges, which do not result in crossovers (Haldane, 1919; Kosambi, 1944). At present, however, estimates of human linkage are not sufficiently accurate to make such corrections necessary.

The locus for glucose 6-phosphate dehydrogenase deficiency was found to be closely linked to the *deutan* locus, with a crossover value of about 5% (Porter *et al.*, 1962). Again, the *deutan* locus shows about 12% crossover with that for hemophilia A (Haldane and Smith, 1947; Whittaker *et al.*, 1962). High hopes were set on the Xg blood group to establish the correct order of these loci, but the task still presents considerable difficulties. A linkage between Xg and G-6-Pd was reported by Adam *et al.* (1963), who obtained 27% crossovers. This was on data gathered in Israel and the results are in good agreement with those obtained by G. R. Fraser *et al.* (1964), which were based on a Greek population.

The linkage relation between Xg and *deutan* was studied by C. E. Jackson *et al.* (1964); on the basis of their data, Renwick and Schulze (1964), with the aid of a computer, calculated the recombination frequency to be about 42%. The recombination frequencies between Xg and hemophilia A and hemophilia B were found to be high (S. H. Davies *et al.*, 1963). Thus, the most likely order of the loci appeared to be: Xg–G-6-Pd–*deutan*–hemophilia A. Soon, however, a difficulty arose. The data collected by Siniscalco and his colleagues in Sardinia (Siniscalco, 1965) gave a considerably higher recombination frequency between Xg and G-6-Pd and subsequent work suggested that the original linkage value obtained may have been too close (Sanger, 1965). Thus, a great deal more data will have to be collected to establish the true linkage relation.

A further area of doubt is represented by the position of the *protan* locus (assuming *deutan* and *protan* occupy different loci). Kalmus (1962) suggested that the locus for G-6-Pd may actually lie between those for *deutan* and *protan*, and this hypothesis has been supported by Siniscalco *et al.* (1964).

Two other loci appear to be within measurable distance of the Xg group. One of these is the gene for sex-linked ichthyosis, a condition which causes dry scaling skin (C. B. Kerr *et al.*, 1964). Of 36 families investigated, 20 were informative and showed a crossover value of 23%. The other locus is that for angiokeratoma corporis diffusum, a dermatological condition with fatal consequencies; Opitz *et al.* (1965) found the recombination frequency with Xg to be about 27%.

No linkage could be detected so far between Xg and other loci on the X-chromosome, for instance the Duchenne type of muscular dystrophy (J. I. Clark *et al.*, 1963; Race and Sanger, 1964). Nor do we know for certain on which arm of the X-chromosome any of the genes are situated. Lindsten *et al.* (1963c) presented some evidence that the gene for the Xg group may be situated on the short arm of the X-chromosome. This was based on the finding that some patients with Turner's syndrome who had the presumed isochromosome of the long arm of the X-chromosome, and who had received this chromosome from their father, lacked the Xg antigen although it was present in the father; the argument being that the antigen was lost with the loss of the short arm during the formation of the isochromosome. This type of evidence, however, is not very strong at present since it is by no means certain whether genes on an isochromosome would be expressed, even if they were present (see Chapter 10, Section XV); and thus the task of allocating the genes to either arm of the X-chromosome must remain for the future.

In conclusion, it may be said that as a result of the work in recent years, linkage relationships have been established between about half a dozen gene pairs on the human X-chromosome. This is a considerable achievement when compared with our knowledge of genes on the autosomes, where, so far, only three pairs of linked genes are known, and none of them can be allocated with certainty to any one chromosome

(Lawler, 1964). But even though the genes on the X-chromosomes manifest themselves on account of their typical mode of inheritance, the task of mapping them is proving a formidable one. There are a number of reasons for this. To begin with, in order to provide information regarding linkage, the mother must be heterozygous for at least two pairs of genes, so that they have a chance of segregating in the offspring. With human linkage data this generally means that large amounts of material must be collected, of which only a part is informative. Moreover, it is known from *Drosophila* that the frequency of recombination may be dependent on environmental as well as genetic factors (Chapter 4, Section II), none of which are controllable in man. Indeed, data obtained by Renwick and Schulze (1965) as well as by Cook (1965) suggest that for autosomal genes in man, the recombination frequencies are different in males and females. If chromosomal rearrangements, such as inversions, were to exist in man, these would be difficult, if not impossible, to demonstrate, though they might give rise to completely novel linkage relationships. Last, human chromosomes are rather long and have many chiasmata (C. E. Ford and Hamerton, 1956b; E. P. Evans *et al.*, 1964). It has been estimated that the genetic length of the X-chromosome in the human female may be 200 map units (centimorgans) (Renwick and Schulze, 1964). Thus, on a purely random basis, it might be expected that the chance of any two X-borne loci showing less than 50% recombination is only seven in sixteen.

The collection of data for linkage in man is a most laborious task which yields its fruits only sparingly. On the other hand, the prospects for studying human linkage have greatly improved through the availability of electronic computers, as a result of which a vast amount of material can now provide information which could not be utilized before. Only the future can show the amount of progress which linkage studies in man will make. There can be no doubt, however, that knowledge of genes located on the X-chromosome will be in the lead.

CHAPTER 9

SEX CHROMOSOMES
IN MAMMALS OTHER THAN MAN

I. Introduction

Before the modern era of cytogenetics, studies on the chromosomes of nonhuman mammals were leading those on the chromosomes of man. Today the opposite is true and, particularly in the field of sex-chromosome abnormalities, the human ones have been the pace setters. However, following the success of human cytogenetics, knowledge about other mammalian species is increasing rapidly. Today we know the sex-chromosome constitution of a great many species; moreover, a number of them have been found to have sex-chromosome mechanisms of unusual types.

The earlier literature on mammalian sex chromosomes was reviewed by Matthey in 1949 and in 1958 (1958a). In 1949, it was still debated whether or not a Y-chromosome was present in the males of a number of species. With the benefit of hindsight, one can now say that this argument was based on findings on the cytology of insects. It is now becoming clear that, just as in man, the presence of a Y-chromosome is necessary for the development of a male phenotype in mammals generally.

The different mammalian orders on which chromosome studies are available will now be considered in turn, and representative examples illustrated. The descriptions of these orders are based on Burton (1962).

II. Monotremata

These are egg-laying mammals, that have affinities with the reptiles. The chromosomes, also, appear to resemble those of reptiles and birds rather than mammalian chromosomes. White (1954) examined the chromosomes of the spiny anteater (*Tachyglossus aculeatus*) and found a

141

very high chromosome number with many minute elements. Similarly Matthey (1949) found both macro- and microchromosomes in the duck-billed platypus (*Ornithorhynchus anatinus*). In spermatogonial meta-phases of *Tachyglossus aculeatus,* van Brink (1959) found the largest chromosome to be unpaired and concluded that this is probably the X-chromosome. This finding appears to be the only evidence so far of male heterogamety in the monotremes.

III. Marsupialia

The marsupials are mammals in which the young are born at an early stage of development.

The marsupials have a low chromosome number. Individual chromo-somes are comparatively large and show considerable morphological variation. Of all mammalian chromosomes, those of the marsupials are the most favorable for cytological investigation, and for a long time they were the best known. G. B. Sharman (1961)reviewed the chromosome findings, including the sex-chromosome constitutions, of 54 species.

Painter (1922a) was the first to establish the correct chromosome count as well as the sex-chromosome constitution of a marsupial. In the American opossum (*Didelphis virginiana*) he found a total of 22 chro-mosomes, with 2 X-chromosomes in the female and an X- and a Y-chromosome in the male. The sex chromosomes are the smallest of the complement, and the Y-chromosome is smaller than the X-chromosome. These findings were confirmed by Shaver (1962) on cultured cells. The X-chromosome was found to be metacentric and the Y-chromosome, which is nearly half the length of the X, is acrocentric.

Of the species listed by Sharman, fifty-two had an XX/XY-sex-chro-mosome mechanism and two species had multiple sex chromosomes. Multiple sex chromosomes in a marsupial were first described by G. B. Sharman *et al.* (1950). They found that in the rat kangaroo (*Potorous tridactylis*) the female had 12 chromosomes and the male 13. The chromosomes of the female could be arranged in 6 pairs, but in the male 3 chromosomes were unpaired. Of these one was a metacentric X-chromosome, one an acrocentric Y-chromosome, and one a very small Y-chromosome (Fig. 9.1). During meiosis in the male the 3 sex chromo-somes formed a trivalent, which was orientated so that the 2 Y-chromosomes would go to the same pole and the X-chromosome to the other. Thus, the male-determining sperm would contain 7, and the fe-male-determining sperm, 6 chromosomes.

The chromosome constitution of the rat kangaroo was confirmed by Walen and Brown (1962), Shaw and Krooth (1964), and by R. C. Moore

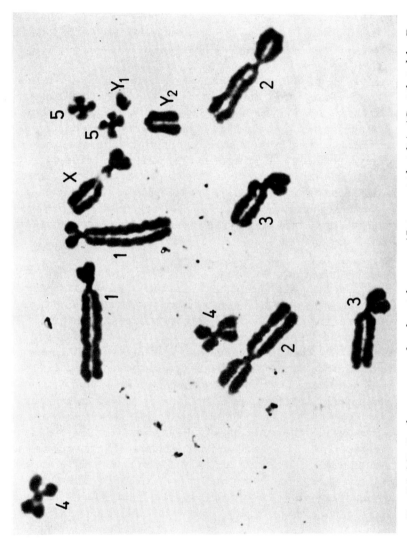

FIG. 9.1. Mitotic chromosomes of male rat kangaroo (*Potorous tridactylis*). (Contributed by Dr. Margery Shaw.)

(1965) in cells grown in tissue culture. Shaw and Krooth suggested that the large Y-chromosome be called Y_1 and the small one Y_2 in accordance with the Denver Conference (1960) classification for human chromosomes, according to which the larger chromosome is given the lower number. However, the older convention, which calls the small Y-chromosome Y_1, may be preferable, since there is evidence that this is the original Y-chromosome, while the large Y_2 has been derived from an autosome.

A similar type of multiple sex chromosomes with a large and a small Y-chromosome was found in the wallaby (*Protemnodon bicolor*) (G. B. Sharman, 1961; R. C. Moore and Gregory, 1963). This animal has only 4 pairs of autosomes, making the total number of chromosomes 10 in the female and 11 in the male. According to Sharman's interpretation the large, acrocentric Y-chromosomes as well as the greater part of the long arm of the metacentric X-chromosome originated as a pair of acrocentric autosomes, which have been incorporated into the sex-chromosome mechanism. White (1957) has called such sex chromosomes, which are of recent autosomal origin, "new" sex chromosomes.

IV. Insectivora

The insectivores are small or medium-sized mammals, with long snouts and characteristic teeth, which are adapted for catching and cutting up insects. The order includes the hedgehogs, shrews, and moles.

Bovey (1949) described the chromosomes in the males of five species. Four of these, including the common mole (*Talpa europaea*) and the hedgehog (*Erinaceus europaeus*) had XY-sex chromosomes, but two males of the common shrew (*Sorex araneus*) were found to have a total of 23 chromosomes, including 3 sex chromosomes which form a trivalent at meiosis. This was the first demonstration of multiple sex chromosomes in a vertebrate; previously they had been known only in insects (Chapter 6, Section II). G. B. Sharman (1956) examined females as well as males and found that the female had only 22 chromosomes. The female has 2 X-chromosomes, while the male has 1 X-chromosome and 2 Y-chromosomes, of which one is very small. These findings were confirmed by C. E. Ford *et al.* (1957) and by Matthey and Meylan (1961).

V. Chiroptera

The Chiroptera, or bats, are the only mammals capable of true flight. Their forearm and four fingers are greatly elongated and support a wing membrane.

Bovey (1949) made a systematic study of the chromosomes during spermatogenesis in this order. The males in all the species investigated had an X- and a Y-chromosome. The length of the Y-chromosome appeared to vary, being very small in *Rhinolophus ferrum-equinum*, the greater horseshoe bat, and apparently larger in the pipistrelle (*Pipistrellus pipistrellus*).

VI. Lagomorpha

The lagomorphs, which include the rabbits and hares, were formerly classified among the rodents. They are now placed in a separate order, which differs from the rodents by the presence of two pairs of incisors in the upper jaw.

The chromosomes of the European rabbit (*Oryctolagus cuniculus,* formerly known as *Lepus cuniculus*) were studied by Painter (1926), who found 44 chromosomes in amnion cells and spermatogonia and 22 pairs in spermatocytes. There was evidence for the existence of an XY-bivalent, though this was not striking. These findings have been confirmed on cultured cells (Clausen and Syverton, 1962; Teplitz and Ohno, 1963; Myers *et al.*, 1964; Nichols *et al.*, 1965). The X-chromosome appears to be a small, almost acrocentric chromosome and the Y-chromosome is also small and acrocentric. Neither can be individually identified.

VII. Rodentia

The outstanding feature of the rodents is a pair of chisellike incisors in the upper and lower jaw, allowing excellent gnawing ability. The rodents are a very large order containing 6400 species and subspecies, among which are some of the most intensively investigated laboratory mammals. Among the species whose chromosomes have been studied, some unusual types of sex chromosome mechanisms have been discovered.

In the chinchilla (*Chinchilla lanigera*), Galton *et al.* (1965) found a diploid chromosome number of 64. The X-chromosome is the largest in the set and the Y-chromosome is very small.

The chromosomes of American members of the squirrel family (Sciuridae) have been studied by Nadler and his colleagues (Nadler and Sutton, 1962; Nadler and Block, 1962; Nadler, 1964, 1965). The diploid chromosome of different species varied between 30 and 46. All had an XX/XY-sex-chromosome constitution, with a medium-sized, metacentric X-chromosome. However, the Y-chromosome showed some variation. It was found to be a medium-sized acrocentric chromosome in

Spermophilus tridecemlineatus and in *S. teridicandus neglectus*, whereas *S. beldingi* had a minute Y-chromosome.

One apparently normal female specimen of *S. beldingi oreganus* had an abnormal chromosome, which could have been a deleted X-chromosome. However, this interpretation could not be substantiated.

The two genera of chipmunks, *Tamias* and *Eutamias* also had a minute Y-chromosome. The diploid chromosome number was 38.

With the possible exception of man, the house mouse (*Mus musculus,* family Muridae) is the mammal whose genetics are best known. Testicular material from the mouse has proved quite favorable for chromosome studies. Cox (1926) reported a diploid chromosome number of 40 in spermatogonia and 20 pairs in spermatocytes and also described the XY-pair, with one rather large and one rather small element. The chromosome number of the mouse has been confirmed many times. However, it has proved virtually impossible to analyze the somatic chromosomes in any detail. All the chromosomes of the mouse are acrocentric and there is only a gradual diminution in size from the largest to the smallest. In the circumstances, neither the X- nor the Y-chromosomes can be identified. It is, however, possible to determine the sex of a mouse from its somatic chromosomes, as was shown by Stich and Hsu (1960) and subsequently by Levan *et al.* (1962), E. H. R. Ford and Woollam (1963), and Crippa (1964). The female has two chromosomes which can be recognized as the smallest, while the male has three such chromosomes, one of them being the Y. The X-chromosome appears to be one of the larger of the chromosomes.

Galton and Holt (1965) and H. J. Evans *et al.* (1965) added tritiated thymidine to mouse cells growing in tissue culture and *in vivo,* respectively, and found that in cells derived from females one of the larger chromosomes incorporated the radioactive matter late, while in cells from males one of the smallest chromosomes did so; these chromosomes may be presumed to be the X and the Y respectively. These findings will be further discussed later (Chapter 10, Section XI).

By contrast to mitotic cells, the XY-bivalent of the mouse is easily distinguishable during meiosis and has been extensively studied. The technique recently developed by E. P. Evans *et al.* (1964) gives particularly excellent results (Fig. 9.2).

During metaphase of the first meiotic division the X- and the Y-chromosome are associated in an end-to-end position, as described by Makino (1941) and Ohno *et al.* (1959a). This end-to-end configuration is the most common type of association between the X- and the Y-chromosomes during the first meiotic metaphase of the mammals. During the first meiotic prophase (pachytene), while the paired autosomes are still relatively extended and in appearance resemble a network of threads, the associated X- and the Y-chromosome are already much contracted and stain intensively (Fig. 8.3). The rather striking looking structure thus formed is often called a "sex vesicle." It had already been described by Minouchi (1928a) in the rat and was then called a "heterokaryosome." During metaphase of the second meiotic division, the sex chromosomes stand out by being more contracted and darkly staining than the autosomes.

The distinctive behavior of the sex chromosomes during meiosis in the male has given rise to much speculation as to the nature of the association between the X- and the Y-chromosome. This subject will be discussed later (Section XIII).

As a result of the intensive investigations which have been carried out on the genetics and the cytology of the mouse, a few abnormalities of the sex chromosomes have been identified. Mice with a total of 39 chromosomes and XO-sex chromosomes were first described by Welshons and Russell (1959) and subsequently by Kindred (1961) and by Cattanach (1961). Such mice are phenotypically apparently normal females and they are fertile. Cattanach (1962) made crosses between such females and normal males, which resulted in an equal proportion of XX- and XY-karyotypes, and a smaller number of XO-mice. Mice with only a Y-chromosome were not found, and this constitution must be regarded as lethal. The shortage of XO-mice could not easily be explained by preferential intrauterine mortality, and the possibility that chromosome sets lacking a sex chromosome are preferentially included in a polar body must be considered. It is of interest that Russell (1962) found that in the majority of mice with XO-sex chromosomes the X-chromosome was of maternal origin, i.e., the missing sex chromosome was the father's; the situation is, therefore, similar to that in man (Chapter 8, Section V).

Mice with 41 chromosomes and XXY-sex chromosomes have also been found (Russell and Chu, 1961; Cattanach, 1961; Kindred, 1961). Such mice are morphologically indistinguishable from normal males, but they are sterile. XXY-mice are less frequent than those with an XO-sex-chromosome constitution (Russell and Saylors, 1961), although, if they arose by nondisjunction in either parent, both abnormalities would be expected with equal frequency. Russell and Chu (1961) have suggested that, apart from nondisjunction, paternal sex chromosomes may be particularly liable to be lost in early embryogenesis.

It is possible that the apparent lack of phenotypic abnormalities in mice with abnormal sex-chromosome constitutions may be connected with the fact that the chromosomes of the mouse contain a large proportion of heterochromatin (Chapter 11), so that modifications of the karyotype may be less damaging than those in man. At the same time it must be emphasized that the environmental conditions for mice and men are so different that any direct comparison is hazardous. For instance, since mouse mothers have a tendency to eat any deformed young at birth, abnormal phenotypes may be missed for this reason.

In some African pygmy mice (*Mus minutoides*, formerly included in the subgenus *Leggada*), Matthey (1963a, 1964a) has found the sex chromosomes to be different. Specimens obtained from the Congo had a diploid chromosome number ranging from 34 to 30. This variation can be accounted for by the fusion in pairs of two acrocentric chromosomes to form one metacentric chromosome. In karyotypes with 34 chromosomes, all the autosomes are acrocentric, whereas in karyotypes with 32

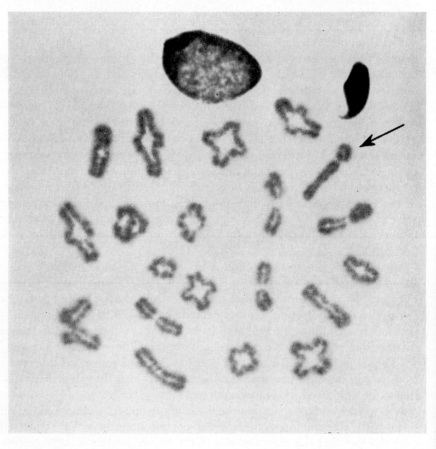

(a)

or 30 chromosomes, respectively, one or two pairs of the autosomes are metacentric. The X- and the Y-chromosome are always metacentric (Fig. 9.3). During meiosis, the X- and the Y-chromosome associate, not in the end-to-end position typical of sex chromosomes, but forming a definite interstitial chiasma between two of their respective arms.

To account for the formation of these sex chromosomes from the more primitive one in *Mus musculus*, Matthey assumes that both the X- and

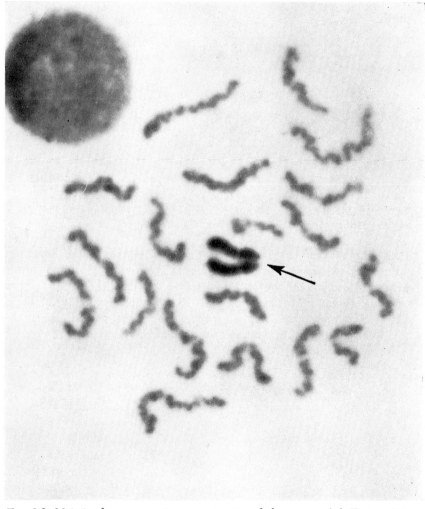

(b)

FIG. 9.2. Meiotic chromosomes in spermatocytes of the mouse. (a) First meiotic metaphase, × 2300; (b) second meiotic metaphase, × 3200. Note heteropycnotic X-chromosome in (b). Contributed by Dr. E. P. Evans.

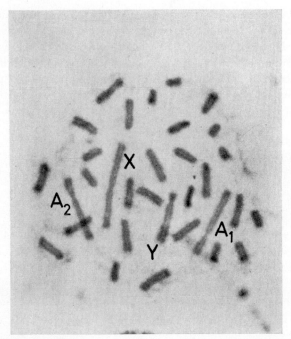

FIG. 9.3. Mitotic chromosomes of male pygmy mouse (*Mus minutoides*). 2n = 32. (From Matthey, 1965a.) Photograph contributed by Professor Matthey.

the Y-chromosome have become translocated onto a pair of homologous autosomes, giving rise to a new X-chromosome with two long arms and a new Y-chromosome with a long and a short arm, the latter representing the original Y-chromosome (see Fig. 9.4; also Fig. 6.1). Since the new sex chromosomes have one homologous arm, meiotic pairing can take place in a manner characteristic of autosomes.

In another species, *Mus (Leggada) triton*, from Central Africa, the

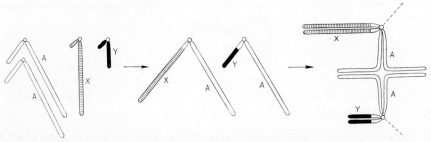

FIG. 9.4. Hypothesis to account for origin of metacentric sex chromosomes from acrocentric ones in *Cricetulus griseus*. (From Matthey, 1961).

X-chromosome is also metacentric. Matthey (1966) found that four out of seven females contained only a single normal X-chromosome. All other chromosomes were acrocentric and it was concluded that the second X-chromosome had suffered a deletion of the short arm. This type of abnormality had previously been known only in man (Chapter 8, Section V).

Matthey (1965a) found yet another sex-chromosome mechanism in some pygmy mice from Southern Rhodesia. These animals have 35 chromosomes in the male and 36 in the female. All the autosomes as well as the X-chromosomes are acrocentric, but the large Y-chromosome is metacentric. During meiosis the Y-chromosome associates with two other chromosomes, thus forming a trivalent. Matthey concluded that the shorter arm of the Y pairs with the original X-chromosome (X_1), while the longer arm is paired with the homolog of the original autosome, which now forms part of the Y-chromosome. Thus the homolog has also become part of the sex-chromosome mechanism and is called X_2. During the first meiotic division, X_1 and X_2 go to one pole, and the Y-chromosome goes to the other pole.

The origin postulated for this mechanism differs from the one previously described in that only the Y-chromosome has become translocated to an autosome. This is the first case described of a mammal having two X-chromosomes.

The chromosomes of the albino rat (*Rattus norvegicus*) were studied by Minouchi (1928a) during spermatogenesis. He found 42 chromosomes in mitosis and 21 pairs in meiosis; this number has been confirmed many times. Minouchi also described the sex chromosomes: the X-chromosome and a small Y-chromosome could be distinguished at the first metaphase of meiosis. During prophase of the first meiotic division the sex chromosomes formed a highly condensed, darkly staining body, which was situated at the periphery of the nucleus. Tjio and Levan (1956b) noted that, as prophase proceeds, the sex vesicle decreases in volume. At diakinesis, the vesicle disappears and the two chromosomes straighten out.

Ohno, Kaplan, and Kinosita (1960, 1961a) succeeded in studying the corresponding stages of oogenesis. They found that the two X-chromosomes of the female do not condense during the prophase of the first meiotic division and are, in fact, indistinguishable from autosomes during this stage. The fact that the unequal sex chromosomes of the male condense differentially during the prophase of the first meiotic division while the two X-chromosomes of the female do not, has been known in insects for a long time (see Schrader, 1928). The observations of Ohno *et al.* have shown that the same rule appears to apply to mammals.

In somatic metaphases, the X-chromosome is a large metacentric chromosome and the Y-chromosome is a small acrocentric (Tjio and Levan, 1956c).

In a South African species of rat, *Rattus natalensis*, Hamerton (1958) found the Y-chromosome to be rather large. During meiosis, the X-chromosome, which is even larger, pairs with the Y in a side-to-side position, forming a chiasma between them. The interpretation of this finding may be as for the pygmy mouse, *Mus minutoides*, mentioned above: both the original X- and the original Y-chromosome have become translocated onto a pair of autosomes.

Chromosomes of field mice of the genus *Apodemus* were first studied by Oguma (1934), who noted that the sex chromosomes of the male during meiosis were different from those normally found in mammals. Instead of the usual XY-configuration, a single, elongated element was present, which Oguma interpreted as a single X-chromosome, the Y-chromosome being apparently absent. This interpretation proved to be wrong; Matthey (1936, 1947), Koller (1941a), and Makino (1951) showed that a Y-chromosome is undoubtedly present. However, whereas in the large majority of male mammals the X- and Y-chromosomes separate at anaphase of the first meiotic division, it is commonly found in *Apodemus* that half an X- and a half a Y-chromosome go to each pole at first meiotic anaphase, so that the X- and Y-components are not separate until the second meiotic division. Thus, the sex chromosomes of *Apodemus* frequently exhibit postreduction, in contrast to most other mammals in which the X- and Y-chromosome show prereduction.

Matthey (1947), following Koller and Darlington 1934), accepted the hypothesis that there is a short pairing segment between the X- and the Y-chromosome, which includes the centromere. If a chiasma occurs in the arm away from the differential segment it will result in prereduction of the differential segment, whereas a chiasma in the arm containing the differential segment, or a chiasma each in both arms, will result in postreduction (Fig. 9.5). The problem of the pairing of the sex chromosomes will be further discussed later (Section XIII). It is, however, of particular interest in this connection that Wahrman and Ritte (1963) have found conclusive cytological evidence of chiasma formation between the X- and Y-chromosomes of *Apodemus mystacinus*, a species in which pre- and postreduction occur side by side.

The spiny mouse (*Acomys*), which occurs in Arabia and East Africa, shows polymorphism of the autosomes. Moreover, while some species, e.g., *A. cabirinus*, appear to have the usual type of XX/XY-sex chromosome mechanism (Matthey, 1963b), others have a more complicated sex-chromosome constitution, which has not yet been entirely elucidated.

Thus in *A. selousi* the diploid chromosome number is 60 (although somatic counts vary between 58 and 62) and both male and female mitoses contain one very large metacentric chromosome, which makes up 19% of the total haploid length of chromosomes (Matthey, 1965b). Studies during spermatogenesis show that this large chromosome is the X, which pairs with a Y-chromosome during meiosis. However, in the absence of data from oogenesis, the sex-chromosome constitution of the

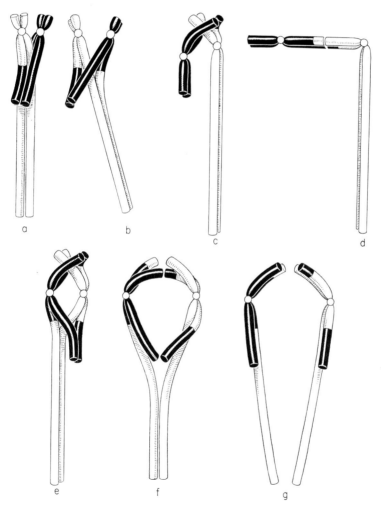

Fig. 9.5. Interpretation of XY-chromosome configuration in *Apodemus* during first meiotic metaphase. (*a*), (*b*), (*e*), (*f*), (*g*), postreduction; (*c*), (*d*) prereduction; (After Matthey, 1947).

female is not clear; nor is there as yet any explanation regarding the observed variation in the total number of chromosomes.

The Chinese hamster (*Cricetus griseus*) might be regarded as ideally suited for chromosomal study, having a diploid chromosome number of only 22 (Matthey, 1952a; Fredga and Santesson, 1964); nevertheless, the identification of the sex chromosomes has presented some difficulty. Yerganian (1959) concluded that the eighth pair in the male represents the heteromorphic sex chromosomes; Matthey thought it is the fifth, or possibly the fourth, pair; the difference in size between the X- and the Y-chromosome is not large and both are metacentric. The situation in the European hamsters (*Cricetus cricetus*) is similar—the diploid chromosome number is 22, and the X- and Y-chromosomes are of nearly equal size and difficult to identify. By contrast, the golden (or Syrian) hamster (*Mesocricetus auratus*) has a total number of 44 chromosomes, but its sex chromosomes are easily recognizable, since the X is the largest, and the Y the second largest chromosome in the complement. Experiments with tritiated thymidine, carried out by J. H. Taylor (1960) and by Galton and Holt (1964) have shown that in the female, one and a half X-chromosomes incorporate the labeled substance late during DNA synthesis (Chapter 10, Section XII), while in the male, one half of the X- as well as the Y-chromosome behave similarly. It appears therefore that in both sexes only one arm of the X-chromosome synthesizes its DNA at the same time as the majority of autosomes.

There is evidence that during meiosis in hamsters the X- and Y-chromosomes pair side-by-side along part of their length; and one or two chiasmata have been observed between the X- and the Y-chromosome of the Chinese hamster and the European hamster (Ohno and Weiler, 1962; Fredga and Santesson, 1964). Matthey (1961) interprets these sex chromosomes as having arisen from originally acrocentric X- and Y-chromosomes by translocation onto a pair of autosomes (Fig. 9.4).

The vole (*Ellobius lutescens*) as well as the creeping vole (*Microtus oregoni*) have sex chromosomes of a very unusual type. In *Microtus oregoni*, Matthey (1956, 1958b) found a diploid number of 17 in germ cells of the male and in somatic cells of the female. Ohno *et al.* (1963) confirmed these findings but found that somatic cells of males contained 18 chromosomes. Their explanation of the sex-determining mechanism in this species is as follows: there are 8 pairs of autosomes in both sexes, and the odd chromosome is an X- in the female and a Y-chromosome in the male. The males have originally an XY-sex chromosome constitution and retain this in their somatic cells as well as in spermatogonia. However, the X-chromosome is subsequently eliminated, so that equal numbers of spermatozoa are formed either lacking a sex chromosome or containing a Y-chromosome. The latter are male determining, while sperm without any sex chromosomes give rise to females. These are thought to have an XO-sex chromosome constitution in their somatic cells, but during oogenesis the X-chromosome undergoes nondisjunction resulting in oogonia and ova with two X-chromosomes. This theory of a sex-determining mechanism is obviously of great interest, even though critical evidence on some essential points, e.g., the elimination of the X-chromosome during spermatogenesis, as well as its restitution during oogenesis, are still outstanding.

The vole (*Ellobius lutescens*) also has 17 chromosomes in the somatic cells of the female and in the spermatogonia of the male, as was first established by Matthey (1953). In both sexes, the unpaired element is the smallest chromosome. During the first meiotic metaphase there are nine bivalents and one apparent univalent. At anaphase this element travels undivided to one pole (Matthey 1964b). During metaphase of the second meiotic division some cells contain eight and others nine chromosomes. White (1957) proposed the hypothesis that the unpaired element consists of a joined X- and Y-chromosome in the male and of two X-chromosomes in the female. Viable zygotes are formed only if a gamete containing nine chromosomes is fertilized by another with eight chromosomes. Thus, an egg with nine chromosomes fertilized by a sperm with eight would give rise to a female, and an egg with nine chromosomes would result in a male. Combinations of egg and sperm both containing either eight chromosomes or nine chromosomes would not give rise to viable offspring. Matthey (1964b) suggests that the elimination of half of the potential offspring would be compensated by better conditions for the survivors; it would thus act as a built-in birth control mechanism.

The short-tailed vole (*Microtus agrestis*) is of interest because, although its sex chromosomes are of the classic XX/XY-type, they are outstanding because of their size. The giant sex chromosomes of *Microtus agrestis* were first described by Matthey (1950) and subsequently by Sachs (1953), by Hansen-Melander (1965), and by Wolf *et al.* (1965). Matthey found that in mitotic metaphases the 48 autosomes measure up to three microns, whereas the length of the metacentric X-chromosome is 7.5 μ and that of the acrocentric Y-chromosome 5.3 μ. With newer techniques, Hansen-Melander found the length of the X-chromosome to be 14 μ, and thus one of the longest chromosomes known in mammals, while the Y-chromosome measured 8 μ. According to her measurements, the surface area of the X-chromosome constitutes about 30% of that of a haploid autosome set—a far higher proportion than has been found in any other species. During meiosis in the male, Matthey found that the Y-chromosome associates with the long arm of the X and that a chiasma is formed. During meiosis in the female a single chiasma is also formed between the two X-chromosomes of the female. The unusual picture of meiosis in the female is illustrated in Fig. 9.6 through the courtesy of Professor Matthey.

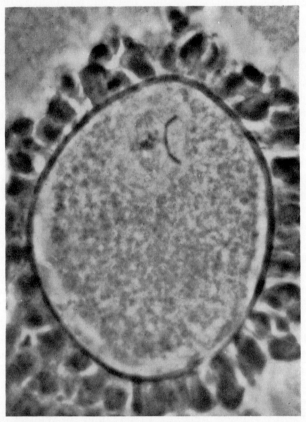

Fig. 9.6. Giant X-chromosomes in first meiotic metaphase of oocyte in *Microtus agrestis*. The X-chromosomes are united by a chiasma.

The last rodent genus to be considered, the gerbil or sand rat (*Gerbillus*), also shows variations of the sex-chromosome mechanism, at least in some species. Matthey (1952b, 1954) found that *G. campestris* and *G. garamantis* have a diploid number of 56 and 54 chromosomes, respectively, and a normal XX/XY-sex-chromosome mechanism, the X- and Y-chromosomes pairing in an end-to-end association during the meiosis of the male. Another species, G. *pyramidum*, had a diploid chromosome number of only 40, and here the sex chromosomes during male meiosis could behave in two different ways. In about half the cells the X- and Y-chromosomes associated in the usual way, whereas in other cells they associated with a pair of autosomes, forming a quadrivalent. These findings may be explained by postulating a small translocation between the X-chromosome and the short arm of the autosome. On the other hand Wahrman and Zahavi (1955) found only the standard type of XY-sex chromosomes in the specimens of G. *pyramidum* they examined, even though some individuals had different numbers of autosomes.

Yet another species, G. *gerbillus*, has multiple sex chromosomes. Matthey (1954) found 43 chromosomes in spermatogonial cells of the male and 42 chromosomes in oogonia of the female. During meiosis in the male, a trivalent was present, thus confirming the supposition of an XX_1Y_2-sex-chromosome constitution of the male. At first meiotic anaphase the X-chromosome moves to one pole and the two Y-chromosomes to the other. The existence of XY_1Y_2-sex chromosomes was confirmed by Wahrman and Zahavi (1955) for specimens of G. *gerbillus gerbillus*.

VIII. Carnivora

The carnivores differ widely in form, size, and habit, but agree closely in the arrangement of their teeth. Apart from a pair of large canines, most carnivores have in their upper and lower jaws a pair of greatly enlarged cheek teeth, known as carnassials.

The chromosomes of various types of domestic dog (*Canis familiaris*) were studied in detail by Minouchi (1928b). He found 78 chromosomes both in spermatogonial and oogonial cells. Of the 78 chromosomes, all but 2 were acrocentric in the female, and all but 1 in the male. Minouchi suggested that the metacentric chromosome was probably the X-chromosome. During meiosis in the male 38 autosomal bivalents were found as well as the X- and Y-chromosomes, which were associated end-to-end at the periphery of the metaphase plate.

A diploid chromosome number of 78 is one of the highest known in mammals and it is of interest to note that not only was this number correctly established for the dog in 1928, but even the more detailed description of the karyotype given by Minouchi was substantially correct. The chromosomes of various breeds of dogs have recently been studied by W. Moore and Lambert (1963) and by Gustavsson (1964a). The diploid number was always found to be 78, and all autosomes are acrocentric. The X-chromosome, which is one of the largest, is metacentric and so is the Y-chromosome, which is the smallest of the set. Both sex chromosomes of the dog are therefore clearly distinguishable.

The chromosomes of the fox (*Vulpes vulpes*) were investigated by Gustavsson (1964b). The diploid chromosome number is 38, of which 33 in the male, and 34 in the female, are metacentric; in addition, there are five minute chromosomes in the male and four in the female. Thus, the X-chromosome is a metacentric one, and the Y-chromosome a minute one, although neither can be distinguished individually.

The chromosomes of the black bear (*Euarctos americanus*), polar bear (*Thelarctos maritimus*), and a crossbred bear, offspring of a female kodiak bear (*Ursus middendorffi*), were studied by Low et al. (1964). The diploid chromosome number of all three animals was 74 and the karyotypes were similar, if not identical. The females had 5 pairs of metacentric chromosomes, of which the X-chromosome appeared to be the second largest; the Y-chromosome appeared to be a very small acrocentric chromosome.

A sex-chromosome mechanism, which so far appears to be unique, has been discovered by Fredga (1965) in the Indian mongoose (*Herpestes auropunctatus*). A female mongoose had 36 chromosomes, including 2 metacentric X-chromosomes, but two males had only 35 chromosomes; no Y-chromosome was visible (Fig. 9.7). However, cells during the first meiotic division of the male included one trivalent which appeared to consist of the X-chromosome joined end-to-end to an autosomal bivalent (Fig. 9.8). Fredga's interpretation is that a substantial part of the Y-chromosome has become translocated to an autosome (Fig. 9.9). If this composite autosome were to segregate at random with regard to the X-chromosome, half the offspring would be expected to have abnormal sex-chromosome constitutions, roughly corresponding to Turner's and Klinefelter's syndromes in man. So far, nothing is known about the existence of sex-chromosome abnormalities in the mongoose.

The chromosomes of the domestic cat (whose scientific name is variously given as *Felis domesticus*, *F. domestica*, or *F. catus*) have been studied on many occasions. The chromosome number was correctly established by Minouchi and Ohta (1934a) who found 38 chromosomes in spermatogonia and oogonia and 19 pairs in spermatocytes. The XY-bivalent was described as a "dot like and an elongated rod being connected linearly." The chromosome number was confirmed on cultured cells by Awa et al. (1959) and by others (see Hsu and Rearden, 1965). However, the identification of the X-chromosome presented some difficulty. In many of the published karyotypes, one of the small metacentric chromosomes was designated as the X, but at a conference held in Puerto Rico in 1964 to study the karyotype of the cat the conclusion was reached that the X-chromosome is in fact one of the medium-sized

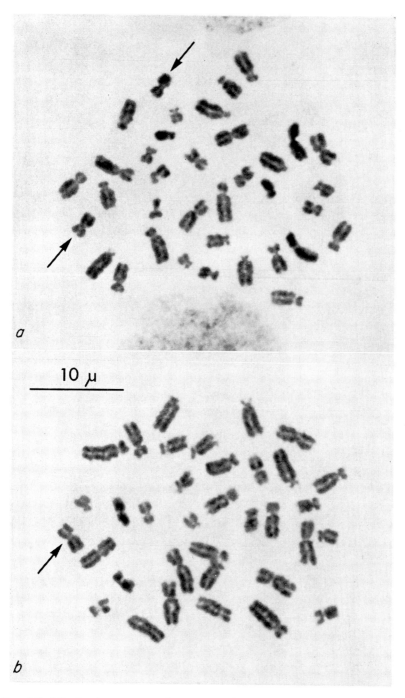

FIG. 9.7. Mitotic chromosomes of mongoose (*Herpestes auropunctatus*); (*a*) female (*b*) male. Arrows indicate X-chromosomes. (From Fredga, 1965.) Contributed by Dr. Fredga.

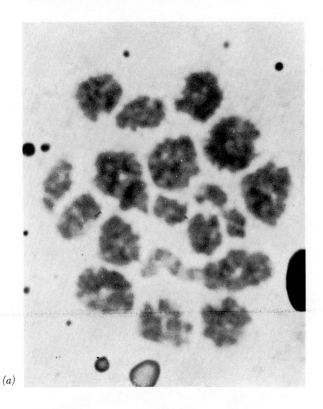

(a)

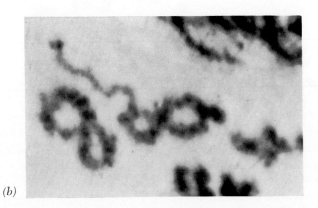

(b)

FIG. 9.8. Meiotic chromosomes of male mongoose (*Herpestes auropunctatus*): (a) whole cell; (b) showing sex trivalent. (From Fredga, 1965.) Contributed by Dr. Fredga.

chromosomes (Hsu and Rearden, 1965; Fig. 9.10). The Y-chromosome is a small acrocentric chromosome.

Although the domestic cat has not been used for large scale breeding in laboratories, a good deal is known about its genetics, particularly of its coat colors (see R. Robinson, 1959, for review); and this has led to the demonstration of sex-chromosome abnormalities. A problem which has puzzled geneticists for many years is the occasional occurrence of a tortoiseshell tomcat. The tortoiseshell phenotype is produced by combining the gene for yellow (y) with its nonyellow (y^+) allelomorph,

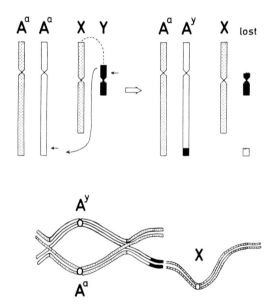

Fig. 9.9. Diagram illustrating hypothesis of Y/ autosome translocation in *Herpestes auropunctatus*. (From Fredga, 1965.)

and the normal breeding behavior shows that this gene is borne on the X-chromosome. Thus males are either yellow (y) or nonyellow $(y^+;$ generally black or tabby) while females may have three phenotypes, yellow (yy), nonyellow (y^+y^+), and tortoiseshell (yy^+). Most of the exceptional tortoiseshell males are sterile, and a large number of hypotheses have been formulated to explain their origin. In recent years Thuline and Norby (1961) have provided evidence that at least some such cats have an abnormal sex-chromosome constitution. Two tortoiseshell males with arrested or absent spermatogenesis had sex chromatin in their buccal mucosa and 39 chromosomes in cells cultured from peripheral blood. Although the sex-chromosome constitution could not be established with certainty, there is strong presumptive evidence of an XXY-sex chromosome constitution. Another tortoiseshell male cat was shown to be a mosaic with diploid and triploid cells (Chu *et al.*, 1964). The diploid cells had XX-sex chromosomes and the triploid cells were XXY. Further difficulties to be resolved relate to the exceptional oc-

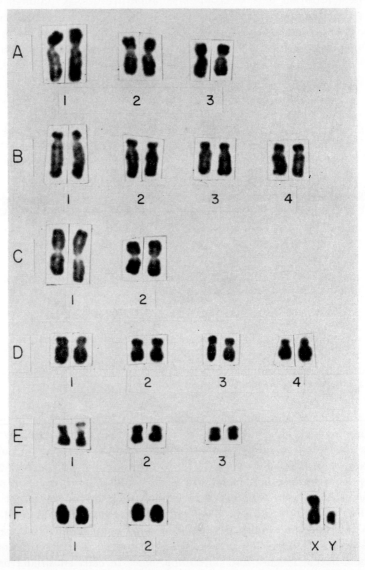

FIG. 9.10. Karyotype of cat (*Felis domesticus*). Contributed by Prof. T. C. Hsu.

currence of fertile tortoiseshell tomcats (Jude and Searle, 1957), as well as the occurrence of black females from matings in which they should not occur (e.g., yellow ♂ × tortoiseshell ♀). It has been suggested that such females may have an XO-sex chromosome constitution, but this has not yet been substantiated.

Material for studying the wild members of the cat family (Felidae) is clearly more difficult to obtain. Nevertheless, some data are now available. The tiger (*Felis tigris*) also has 38 chromosomes, although some of the autosomes differ in size and position of the centromere from those of the cat. The X- and Y-chromosomes are as in the cat (Hsu and Rearden, 1965).

Hsu *et al.* (1963) studied the chromosomes of nine other species of the cat family (Felidae). They were as follows: the lion (*F. leo*), the puma (*F. concolor*), the ocelot (*F. pardalis*), the marguay (*F. wiedii*) *F. yagouaroundi*, the jaguar (*Panthera onca*), the leopard (*P. pardus*), the cheetah (*Acinonyx jabatus*), and the bobcat (*Lynx rufus*). The ocelot and the marguay had only 36 chromosomes, whereas all the rest had 38. Although only one specimen, either male or female, was studied in each species, the evidence suggested that the X-chromosome in all is a medium-sized metacentric chromosome. However, the Y-chromosome was found to be somewhat variable. Its short arm appeared to vary in length, and in the ocelot the Y-chromosome was minute.

IX. Proboscidae

The somatic chromosome number of the Indian elephant, *Elephas indicus,* was found to be 56 by Sasaki and Veomett (1963). However, as no male specimen was available for study at the time, the sex-chromosome constitution could not be established.

X. Perissodactyla

The hoofed animals (Ungulates) comprise two orders (1) the Perissodactyla, or odd-toed ungulates, which include the horses, rhinoceroses and tapirs; and (2) the Artiodactyla, or even-toed ungulates, which include the pigs, camels, deer, antelopes, and cattle.

Although the chromosome number of the horse, *Equus caballus,* was not correctly established until the modern era of chromosome cytology, the sex bivalent was identified by Makino (1943) in meiotic cells. He described and illustrated it as a long and a shorter element associated end-to-end and found almost always at the periphery of the metaphase plate. However, Makino thought that the total chromosome number was

66, whereas modern techniques have shown it to be 64 (Rothfels *et al.*, 1959; Trujillo *et al.*, 1962; Benirschke *et al.*, 1962b; Mutton *et al.*, 1964; Mukherjee and Sinha, 1964). The X-chromosome is one of the larger metacentric chromosomes and the Y-chromosome is small, acrocentric, and indistinguishable from a group of other such chromosomes.

The same groups of authors also studied the chromosomes of the donkey (*Equus asinus*) and of the mule. The chromosome number of the donkey is 62; the X-chromosome is also one of the larger metacentric chromosomes and the Y- is the smallest acrocentric chromosome. Thus the Y-chromosomes of the horse and the donkey appear to be distinguishable; in the X-chromosome, the centromere of that of the donkey is nearer one end than in the X-chromosome of the horse.

A mule is a hybrid between a male donkey and a female horse, while the reciprocal hybrid (male horse by female donkey) is called a hinny. Both hybrids have a total of 63 chromosomes. Clearly, a male mule must contain the Y-chromosome of the donkey and a male hinny that of the horse. Male mules are invariably sterile, but there have been a number of reports on alleged fertile mare mules. Benirschke *et al.* (1964b) cast doubt on the authenticity of these reports. An alleged fertile mare mule studied by them had the karyotype of a donkey.

Horses and donkeys can also form hybrids with zebras; the chromosome number of the hybrid always appears to be the mean of the two parent species. Benirschke *et al.* (1964a) and Benirschke (1964) have examined the chromosomes of a female "zebronky," offspring of a male donkey and a female mountain zebra (*Equus zebra*). The zebronky had a chromosome number of 48, from which it was concluded that the diploid number of the mountain zebra should be 34. Moreover, studies with tritiated thymidine (Chapter 10, Section XII) showed that whereas in some cells the late-replicating X-chromosome resembled that of the donkey, in other cells the late-replicating chromosome had a more median centromere; this chromosome was accordingly presumed to be the X-chromosome of the mountain zebra.

Some other hybrids were studied by Mutton *et al.* (1964). The common (Grant's) zebra (*Equus burchelli böhmi*) has 44 chromosomes and Grevy's zebra (*E. grevyi*) has 46; the Y-chromosome in this species is metacentric. A hybrid between a male Grant's zebra and a female donkey had 53 chromosomes; although apparently a male, this animal appeared to be a mosaic with XX- and XY-sex chromosomes. All the X-chromosomes appeared to have been derived from the donkey mother. Another hybrid, offspring of a male Grevy's zebra and a horse, was a female with 55 chromosomes; the two X-chromosomes appeared not to be distinguishable.

Species hybrids with two morphologically distinguishable X-chromosomes are useful material for studying the differential behavior of the two X-chromosomes in females. This topic will be discussed in Chapter 11.

XI. Artiodactyla

The diploid chromosome number of domestic cattle (*Bos taurus*) is 60, as was first reported by Krallinger (1927) and confirmed on a number of occasions. Studies on cattle chromosomes using modern tech-

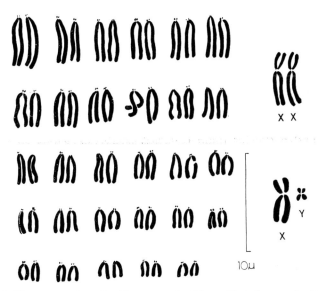

Fig. 9.11. Karyotype of cattle (*Bos taurus*). (From Nichols, *et al.*, 1962.) Contributed by the authors.

niques were carried out by Melander (1958), Nichols *et al.* (1962), and Ohno *et al.* (1962). An outstanding feature of the cattle karyotype which it shares with the karyotype of the dog (Section VIII) is that all autosomes are acrocentric, whereas the X- and Y-chromosomes are metacentric. The X is a large chromosome and the Y is the smallest of the complement. Thus both sex chromosomes are clearly distinguishable (Fig. 9.11).

The goat (*Capra hircus*) also has a chromosome number of 60 (Sokolov, 1930; Shiwago, 1931). The chromosomes of the goat were recently studied by Basrur and Coubrough (1964), who found all chromosomes to be acrocentric. The X-chromosome is large and the Y is minute and easily distinguished. One of the animals studied was an apparent female with abdominal testes in which spermatogenesis was observed. Cells from peripheral blood had two X-chromosomes and no Y.

The diploid chromosome number of the sheep (*Ovis aries*) is 54 (Shiwago, 1931). The chromosomes of cultured cells were studied by Melander (1958) and by Borland (1964). The X-chromosome appeared to be small but could not be individually identified; the Y-chromosome was found to be the smallest chromosome present.

XII. Primates

The primates have characteristically large brain cases and well-developed brains. They have long limbs, with thumbs and big toes opposable for grasping. The order includes the monkeys and apes, included in the suborder Anthropoidea, as well as lemurs, loris, bush babies, etc., which belong to the suborder Prosimii. The Anthropoidea are divided into new world monkeys and old world monkeys; the latter contain the anthropoid apes (Pongidae), which are distinguished by the absence of a tail and a greater brain capacity.

The primates provide an excellent illustration of the progress which has been made in our knowledge of mammalian chromosomes within recent years. In 1955 the chromosomes of only a few species were known (Darlington and Haque, 1955), whereas 10 years later several hundreds have been successfully examined. The new chromosome findings may prove to be of use in helping toward a proper classification of the primates. However, as regards sex chromosomes, the order shows only relatively minor variation. All the species investigated have an XX/XY sex-chromosome mechanism, but the sex chromosomes may differ in size and the position of the centromere.

The chromosomes of a member of the Prosimii, the bush baby (*Galago senegalensis*), were first described by Matthey (1955), who found a diploid chromosome number of 38. The X-chromosome was metacentric and the Y-chromosome short. Chu and Bender (1961) found that the Y-chromosome in this species was the smallest of the complement and acrocentric. Another species of bush baby (*G. crassicaudatus*) had similar sex chromosomes, but the total number of chromosomes was 62.

Members of the lemur family have been studied by Chu and Bender (1961), Chu and Swomley (1961), and Bender and Chu (1963). Even within the single genus *Lemur*, the chromosome number was found to vary between 44 and 60. The X-chromosome, too, can be either metacentric as in *L. variegatus*, or acrocentric as in the black lemur (*L. macaco*) and a number of other species.

The chromosomes of the tree shrew (*Tupaia glis*) were described by Klinger (1963). The total chromosome number is 62. The X-chromosome is the third longest chromosome and is easily distinguishable since no other chromosome has an arm ratio of 1.6–1.8 (ratio of length of long arm/short arm). The Y-chromosome, which is acrocentric, can also be clearly identified since it is the shortest chromosome of the complement.

The sex chromosomes of a monkey were first described by Painter (1922b, 1924c), who examined testicular material from a capuchin, (*Cebus* sp.) a member of the new world monkeys. A dipliod chromosome number of 54 was found; the X-chromosome was thought to have a subterminal centromere, while the Y-chromosome was found to be acrocentric and small. The chromosome number has been confirmed by a number of authors (see Bender and Chu, 1963), and mitotic cells grown in tissue culture have shown that both the X- and the Y-chromosome are acrocentric.

The chromosomes of other new world monkeys were studied by Bender and Mettler (1960), Bernirschke *et al.* (1962a), and Benirschke and Brownhill (1962, 1963). In the marmoset (*Callithrix jacchus*) as well as in the tamarin (*Tamarinus mystax*), 46 chromosomes were found, and the X-chromosome is one of the larger ones, with a nearly central centromere. However, the Y-chromosome in *Callithrix* is minute, whereas in *Tamarinus* it is about the same size as the smallest autosomes (Fig. 9.12). Benirschke and Brownhill found that the testes of three marmoset monkeys contained a proportion of XX-bivalents, which were thought to be derived from female co-twins.

The chromosomes of an old world monkey were also first described by Painter, who found 48 chromosomes in one male Rhesus monkey (*Macaca mulatta*; the name given by Painter was *Rhesus macacus*), including an X- and a Y-chromosome. However, Darlington and Haque (1955) found only 42 chromosomes and this number was confirmed by Chu and Giles (1957), and Rothfels and Siminovitch (1958). All the chromosomes are metacentric or submetacentric, with the possible exception of the Y-chromosome, which is minute, and in which the position of the centromere cannot be definitely determined. Rothfels and Siminovitch have also suggested that in the X-chromosome, as well as in one autosome, the position of the centromere may be variable.

A large number of species of old world monkeys including macaques, mandrills, and baboons have a karyotype similar to that of the Rhesus monkey (Bender and Chu, 1963; Baylet and Grattepanche, 1964). However, in the genus *Cercopithecus* chromosome numbers vary considerably. In the species investigated the X-chromosome is of moderate size and submetacentric, while the Y-chromosome is small and frequently metacentric, but acrocentric in some species. Ushijima *et al.* (1964) examined the chromosomes of two further species, *Cynopithecus niger* and *Presbytis entellus*. The former had 42 chromosomes including a minute Y, while the latter had 44 chromosomes, the Y being medium-sized.

The chimpanzee (*Pan*) was the first anthropoid ape whose chromosomes were examined (Yeager *et al.*, 1940). Using testicular material, the authors found that the most probable chromosome number was 24 pairs; one of the pairs resembled the XY-bivalent in man. The chromosome number of 48 in *Pan troglodytes* was confirmed by Young *et al.* (1960) using bone marrow cells, and by Chiarelli (1962), Bender and

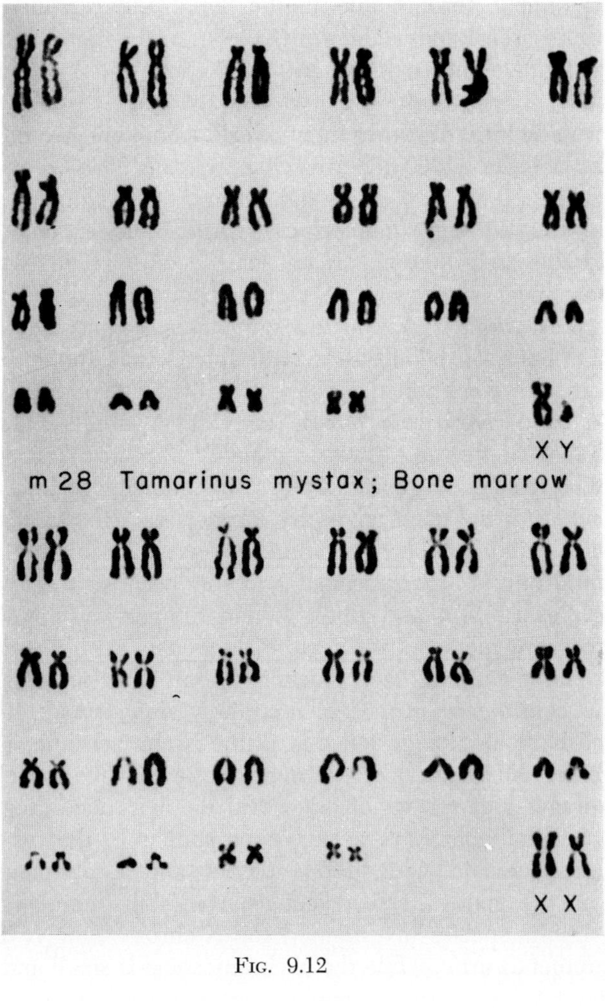

(a)

m 28 Tamarinus mystax; Bone marrow

X Y

(b)

X X

Fig. 9.12

Chu (1963), and Hamerton *et al.* (1963). The X-chromosome is metacentic and the Y-chromosome represents the smallest of the set and is acrocentric (Fig. 9.13a).

The gorilla (*Gorilla gorilla gorilla*) also has a chromosome number of 48 (Hamerton *et al.*, 1961). Both sex chromosomes are rather large. In their original publication the authors stated that the X-chromosome was the largest in the complement. Further examination showed, however, that the X-chromosome, which is metacentric, lies between fifth to eighth in length (Klinger *et al.*, 1963). The Y-chromosome is also metacentric and is the smallest in the complement (Fig. 9.13b). These observations are in agreement with those of Chiarelli (1962).

The orangutan (*Pongo pygmaeus*) also has 48 chromosomes (Chiarelli, 1961, 1962; Hamerton *et al.*, 1963). The X-chromosome is metacentric and lies fifth to seventh in size. The Y-chromosome is the smallest of the set and is also metacentric (Fig. 9.13c).

The chromosomes of the gibbon (*Hylobates lar* and *H. moloch*) differ considerably from those of the chimpanzee, the gorilla, and the orangutan. The gibbon has 44 chromosomes (Hamerton *et al.*, 1963; also see Bender and Chu, 1963). The X-chromosome is metacentric and lies in the larger size range of this group. The Y-chromosome is minute and the

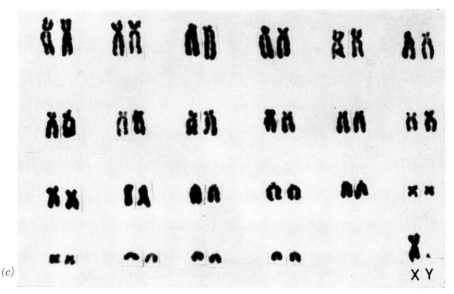

(c)

Fig. 9.12. Karyotypes of new world monkeys. (*a*) *Tamarinus mystax* ♂; (*b*) *T. mystax* ♀. (From Benirschke and Brownhill, 1963); (*c*) *Callithrix jacchus* ♂. (From Benirschke *et al.*, 1962. Contributed by Dr. Benirschke.)

(a)

(b)

(c)

(d)

position of the centromere cannot be definitely determined (Fig. 9.13d). The siamang (*Symphalangus syndactylus*), the largest of the gibbons, has 50 chromosomes (Klinger, 1963). The X-chromosome is metacentric but cannot yet be distinguished with certainty from autosomes 2–15. The Y-chromosome is the smallest of the set, but is not minute and metacentric.

XIII. Characteristics of Mammalian Sex Chromosomes

The spermatozoa of most mammals contain either an X- or a Y-chromosome, making them female-determining and male-determining, respectively. Many attempts have been made to separate these two classes. Among the criteria used are a possible difference in size or mass, in shape, as well as in electrical charges or immunological behavior. There have been repeated claims that certain procedures show at least partial success in separating X- and Y-bearing sperm; as yet, however, none of these claims has been substantiated (Rothschild, 1960).

It is clear from what has been said on the preceding pages that the classic theme of an XX/XY-sex determining mechanism can be played with variations. One variable illustrated by mammals lies in the size of the sex chromosomes, with the extreme example of the giant sex chromosomes in *Microtus agrestis*. Another possibility is the formation of multiple sex chromosomes, either two Y-chromosomes, as in the common shrew (*Sorex araneus*), or two X-chromosomes as found in some pygmy mice (*Mus minutoides*). Finally, there are the even more bizarre conditions as exemplified by the vole (*Ellobius lutescens*), and the creeping vole (*Microtus oregoni*), as well as the mongoose (*Herpestes auropunctatus*), in which an individual Y-chromosome has not been identified. Ultimately, a knowledge of the nature of the more unusual types of sex-chromosome mechanisms will clearly be essential for an understanding of the function of sex chromosomes in general.

From a purely cytological point of view, ordinary X- and Y-chromosomes present certain outstanding features. In a proportion of interphase cells of females, one of the two X-chromosomes becomes highly condensed and thus forms a sex-chromatin body (Chapter 10). In many mammalian species, therefore, the number of X-chromosomes present

---

FIG. 9.13. Karyotypes of male apes (sex chromosomes in second row at right): (*a*) chimpanzee (*Pan troglodytes*); (*b*) gorilla (*Gorilla gorilla*); (*c*) orang-utan (*Pongo pygmaeus*); (*d*) gibbon (*Hylobates lar*). Contributed by Dr. H. Klinger. (From Hamerton *et al.*, 1963.)

can be assessed from an inspection of interphase nuclei. The formation of sex chromatin is related to the timing of DNA synthesis, which occurs later in sex chromatin forming X-chromosomes than in the majority of other chromosomes. The Y-chromosome also tends to synthesize its DNA late, but in most mammalian species the Y-chromosome is too small to be recognized as a distinct body in interphase nuclei.

Although the single X-chromosome of males appears to be indistinguishable from autosomes both in interphase nuclei and during DNA synthesis of somatic cells, the X- as well as the Y-chromosome behave very strikingly during spermatogenesis, particularly during the first meiotic division of the spermatocyte. The appearance of the sex chromosomes during the first meiotic prophase in the male was described by Painter (1924b) for the opossum, by Minouchi (1928a) and by Tjio and Levan (1956b) for the rat, by Makino (1941), Sachs (1955), Ohno et al. (1959a), and Geyer-Duszyńska (1963) for the mouse, and by Sachs (1954) for man.

During pachytene of the spermatocyte, the paired autosomes are still fairly extended and in appearance resemble a network of beaded threads (Fig. 8.3). In addition, the nucleus contains an intensely staining body, which was noticed by workers in the late nineteenth century and has been given a variety of names, such as "Kernkörperchen," "corps intranucleáire," "curious secondary nucleolus," "chromatin nucleolus," etc. (see Makino, 1941). During the first quarter of the present century it became clear that this body represents the sex chromosomes. Makino (1941) thought that only the X-chromosome is associated with the body, which he called the "X-vesicle"; according to him, the X- and the Y-chromosome do not come together until diplotene, when the vesicle disappears. On the other hand, according to Sachs (1954) and Tjio and Levan (1956b) the vesicle contains both the X- and the Y-chromosome, and they call it a "sex vesicle." This appears to be the prevailing opinion today. During diplotene, when the sex vesicle disappears, the X- and Y-chromosome appear in end-to-end association and straighten out. Before its disappearance, the sex vesicle tends to be associated with the nucleolus.

A dense, darkly staining body is not an ideal object for detailed cytological investigation, and it is perhaps not surprising that the sex vesicle has become the subject of a good deal of controversy. On the one hand, Koller and Darlington (1934), in keeping with Darlington's (1931) idea that meiotic disjunction cannot proceed normally unless chiasmata have been formed, have paid scant attention to the sex vesicle beyond noting a tendency of the sex chromosomes to condense precociously, and have divided sex chromosomes into two regions: (1) a differential segment, which is different in the two sexes or present only in one sex, and (2) a pairing segment, which is homologous in the two sexes and in which chiasmata are formed. On this theory, if a chiasma is formed between the centromere and the differential segment, the ensuing bivalent will be symmetrical, and the X- and the Y-chromosomes will not be separated until the second meiotic division (postreduction—Fig. 9.5). In agreement with this hypothesis, Koller and Darlington (1934) described the formation of chiasmata between the X- and the Y-chromosome of the rat, followed by postreduction in some of the sex bivalents and prereduction in others. Subsequently, Koller (1936, 1937, 1938, 1939, 1941a,b) reported the simultaneous occurrence of pre- and postreduction, though in varying proportions, in such diverse species as marsupials, the golden hamster, the field mouse, the cat, and man.

The view of Makino (1941) is diametrically opposed to this. As mentioned above, he regards the X-chromosome at pachytene to be contained in its own vesicle, entirely isolated from the Y-chromosome. There is thus no possibility for the formation of chiasmata, and when the X- and Y-chromosomes at last come together at diplotene, they merely form a perfunctory end-to-end association. A similar view was expressed by Sachs (1954, 1955), even though he regards the vesicle as containing both the X- and the Y-chromosome.

The existence or absence of chiasmata between the X- and the Y-chromosome has implications for genetic theory. If there are no chiasmata, all genes on the X-chromosomes, and any that may be situated on the Y, will show total sex-linkage. On the other hand, if chiasmata were present, this would lead to crossing-over between the X- and the Y-chromosomes and thus give rise to partial sex-linkage. There is no evidence of partial sex-linkage in the mouse (Grüneberg, 1952a). In man, the possibility of partial sex-linkage has been raised by Haldane (1936) but conclusive evidence is still outstanding. Recently, a pairing segment common to the X- and the Y-chromosome has been postulated on different genetic grounds by C. E. Ford (1963), Ferrier (1964), and by Ferguson-Smith (1965), in order to explain the difference in phenotype between the XX- and the XO-sex chromosome constitution in man.

By the use of modern techniques, chiasmata have been unequivocably demonstrated between the X- and Y-chromosome of pygmy mice (*Mus minutoides*) as well as the Chinese and the European hamsters (*Cricetulus griseus* and *Cricetus cricetus*—Section VII), and it is also known that postreduction, as well as prereduction, occurs in *Apodemus* (Section VII). Even if, as in the majority of mammals, prereduction of the sex chromosomes appears to occur exclusively, this does not, of course, exclude the possible existence of a pairing segment with chiasmata in the distal segment of the sex chromosomes (i.e., beyond the centromere away from the differential segment). The conclusion at present must be, therefore, that homologous pairing with chiasma formation between the X- and the Y-chromosome has been observed in some mammalian species; while in those species in which evidence in its favor has not so far been forthcoming, the verdict must be considered "not proven" since, as was pointed out by Tjio and Levan (1956b), the possibility of a brief pairing segment in the short arm of the sex chromosomes cannot be excluded on cytological grounds. Moreover, if a single chiasma were formed in this situation, the resultant metaphase configuration following terminalization would be expected to be an end-to-end association, such as is found, for instance, in some of the short autosomes of mouse and man (Figs. 9.2, 8.2).

Last, it may not be out of place to mention that, as was recently shown by Westergaard (1964), crossing-over is one of the less well-understood phenomena of cytogenetics, which cannot as yet be fitted into a molecular theory. Since there is as yet no scientific definition of crossing-over, it is possible that some of the controversy over this phenomenon is not as meaningful as had been thought.

It is often assumed that the sex vesicle is a structure somehow distinct from the sex chromosomes, in which they are merely imbedded. Thus Geyer-Duszyńska (1963) illustrated an XY-bivalent released from its vesicle, and Ohno et al. (1959a) suggested that the vesicle is rich in ribonucleic acid. There is no doubt, however, that the structure can be stained with Feulgen and it is likely that essentially the sex vesicle represents the condensed sex chromosomes.

The behavior of the sex chromosomes in the female is quite different from that found in males. The pattern of condensation of the two X-chromosomes during oogenesis is the same as that of autosomes (Ohno et al., 1961a), but in interphase nuclei of somatic cells, one of the X-chromosomes condenses to form the sex-chromatin body. It is now known that this type of differential condensation is associated with later than average synthesis of DNA during cell division, and the possibility that both these phenomena may be connected with physiological inactivation of the genes borne on such chromosomes is being actively discussed. These topics will be dealt with in the following two chapters.

CHAPTER 10

SEX CHROMATIN

I. Introduction

The term "sex chromatin," in present day usage, denotes a body in the nuclei of cells, which shows a special relationship to the sex of the organism from which the cell originated. The sex-chromatin body is present in the nucleus only during interphase and disappears during mitosis. The term "sex-chromatin" had previously been used in a different sense by Wilson (1925) to describe the (hypothetical) part of the sex chromosomes which acted as a sex differentiator in development.

For a number of years the sex chromatin of man was the most intensely studied, but recently its behavior in other mammals has been given considerable attention. Although the study of sex chromatin is of comparatively recent origin, it has attracted great interest and today provides one of the most active growing points in cytogenetics. One reason for this is practical, for the sex-chromatin test provides a simple and often indispensable aid in the diagnosis of patients with abnormalities of the sex chromosomes (Section XIV et seq.). Moreover, the technique has made it possible to screen large populations and thus obtain estimates regarding the incidence of these abnormalities. On a more theoretical level, the origin of the sex chromatin and its relation to the sex chromosomes has given rise to speculations, which are further stimulating experimental work, as to the way in which the X-chromosome functions, both in sex determination and in general.

II. Some Landmarks in the Development of the Sex Chromatin Concept

The discovery of sex chromatin is generally placed in 1949, when Barr and Bertram, in London, Ontario described a morphological distinction between neurons of male and female cats. The sex difference consisted of a small body which was present in the nuclei of nerve

cells from female cats but was absent in those of males (Fig. 10.1). The
body, which stained with nuclear dyes, was intimately associated with
the nucleolus and was at first called a "nucleolar satellite." This term
became inappropriate when Barr (1951) found that in neuroglial cells
of the cat the sex-differentiating body lies against the inner side of the
nuclear membrane. Henceforth, the term "sex chromatin" was employed.
The finding of the sex chromatin in the cat was an unexpected result of
experimental neurocytology. Barr and Bertram (1949) wrote: "It appears not to be generally known that the sex of a somatic cell as highly
differentiated as a neuron may be detected with no more elaborate
equipment than a compound microscope following staining of the tissue
with the routine Nissl method." Sections of brain, spinal cord, or sympathetic ganglia could now be readily attributed to the correct sex of
the animal from which they originated.

A few years before the appearance of the paper by Barr and Ber-

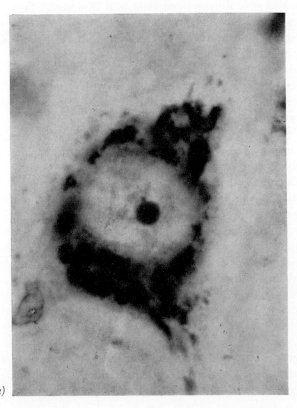

(a)

FIG. 10.1

tram, S. G. Smith (1944, 1945a,b), in Ottawa, Ontario found that in cells of the larvae of the spruce budworm [*Choristoneura (Archips) fumiferana*] a darkly staining body was present in the nuclei of females and was absent from males (Fig. 10.2). This body could be used for sexing larvae prior to the development of the gonads, and it was suggested that this method might be applied to other organisms, including mammals. These findings are of importance not only because they provided the first indication that a nuclear body present in interphase could be used as an indicator of sex, but also because the spruce budworm is a member of the Lepidoptera, in which the female is the heterogametic sex (Chapter 5). Since female spruce budworms have only one X-chromosome, Smith postulated that the single X remained condensed (heteropycnotic) in interphase nuclei, in contrast to the two X-chromo-

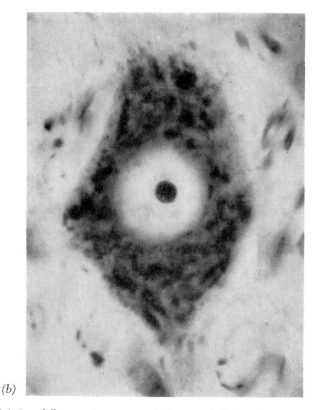

(b)

Fig. 10.1 Sex difference in neurons of the cat: (a) "nucleolar satellite" adjacent to nucleolus in female; (b) no nucleolar satellite in male. Photographs contributed by Professor M. L. Barr.

somes of the male, which became invisible. Thus, the situation appears to be precisely the opposite from that found in mammals. Sex chromatin in heterogametic females will be further discussed below (Section XIII).

Some still earlier works, which are relevant to the problem of sex chromosomes in interphase nuclei, are those of Geitler (1937, 1939). Geitler worked on insects belonging to the bugs (Hemiptera) and flies (Diptera), in both of which the female is homogametic and the male heterogametic. Geitler found that in somatic interphase nuclei the X-chromosome was heteropycnotic in both sexes, i.e., the female had two heteropycnotic bodies and the male one. This situation seems to differ from that both in spruce budworms and in cats. Therefore, at present any theories based on data from the sex chromatin of mammals will have to be confined to this group.

In 1952, Graham and Barr were able to show that in the cat, sex chromatin could be demonstrated in tissues other than neurons. The tissues examined included smooth, skeletal, and cardiac muscle, cartilage,

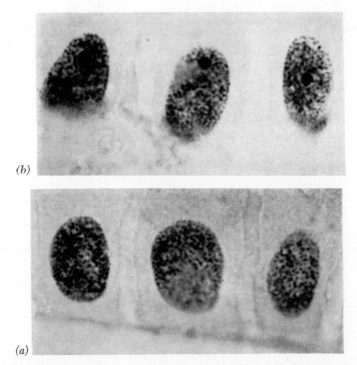

(b)

(a)

FIG. 10.2. Sex difference in the spruce budworm, *Choristoneura* (*Archips*) *fumiferana* (Clem.): (*a*) cells from female; (*b*) cells from male. Original photographs contributed by Dr. S. G. Smith.

epidermis, endothelium, gastric epithelium, liver, pancreas, adenohypophysis, thyroid, adrenal cortex and medulla, interstitial cells of ovary and testis, kidney, uterine epithelium, and prostate. Sex chromatin was found in all tissues except in liver and pancreatic acinar cells. The sex chromatin was present in one-half to two-thirds of the cells from female cats and only very rarely in those from males.

Just a year after the discovery of sex chromatin in the cat, a sex difference was shown to exist in human sympathetic ganglion cells (Barr et al., 1950; Bertram et al., 1950). Sex chromatin became part of human genetics in 1953 when K. L. Moore et al. showed that sex chromatin could be demonstrated in preparations of skin biopsies including that of a hermaphrodite. Cells in the stratum spinosum are particularly favorable in showing the sex chromatin. In an intensive survey of human tissues, K. L. Moore and Barr (1954) found sex chromatin in all the cell types examined, which included cartilage and adrenal cortex, smooth muscle, bladder, and thyroid cells. The material was mainly derived from autopsies.

As a result of using the technique of sexing skin biopsies, it was shown that most patients with Turner's syndrome lacked sex chromatin (Polani et al., 1954; Wilkins et al., 1954). In 1955 the sex-chromatin test became further simplified when it was found that the presence or absence of sex chromatin could be demonstrated in cells scraped off the buccal mucosa (Marberger et al., 1955; K. L. Moore and Barr, 1955). Yet another finding of great potential importance was the discovery that a sex difference could be demonstrated in the polymorphonuclear leucocytes of peripheral blood (W. M. Davidson and Smith, 1954).

The development of these new techniques provided an enormous impetus to sex-chromatin studies and in 1956 at least six groups of workers were able to show that sex chromatin was present in a majority of patients with Klinefelter's syndrome (Riis et al., 1956; W. P. V. Jackson et al., 1956; Plunkett and Barr, 1956; Bradbury et al., 1956; Nelson, 1956; Sohval et al., 1956).

When techniques for studying human chromosomes became available from 1959 onward, a striking correlation was revealed between the sex-chromatin status and the number of X-chromosomes in an individual. The presence of sex chromatin was found to be associated with the presence of two X-chromosomes (or, more accurately, 16 chromosomes in the 6–12 group, since these cannot be distinguished unequivocally from the X on morphological grounds); while the absence of sex chromatin was found to be associated with the presence of a single X-chromosome (15 chromosomes in the 6–12 group) (Barr and Carr, 1960; Stewart, 1960b). Thus, sex-chromatin studies have become indispensable in the elucidation of abnormalities in sexual development, for the following reasons: (1) The simplicity and speed of the techniques allows one to forecast the number of X-chromosomes present in patients suspected of an abnormality of the sex chromosomes; (2) since X-chromosomes in metaphase cannot be recognized unequivocally, the sex chromatin provides a check as to the number of X-chromosomes present; and (3) the method can be used in surveys of large groups of people.

The early assumption that the drumsticks of the polymorphonuclear leucocytes are equivalent to the sex-chromatin bodies of epithelial and other tissue cells has been substantiated by later work (see Section X). Therefore, the term "sex chromatin" now includes drumsticks as well as the sex-chromatin bodies in cells other than leucocytes. The latter are now often called "Barr bodies."

III. General Properties of Barr Bodies

A Barr body is a small, well-defined body which stains intensely with nuclear dyes (Figs. 10.3,4). It is present in a large proportion of nuclei of female origin and absent in male nuclei. The size of a Barr body is about 1 μ in diameter. The average size has been estimated as 0.7×1.2 μ, both in nuclei of buccal mucosa and in sections of several human tissues (K. L. Moore and Barr, 1954, 1955). Interphase nuclei are not always quite homogeneous, and they may contain a number of more or less darkly staining bodies, which are known as chromocenters. In cells of human origin, such nonspecific chromocenters are generally smaller than Barr bodies and have a less well-defined outline. In cases where a small percentage of Barr bodies have been reported in male nuclei, this

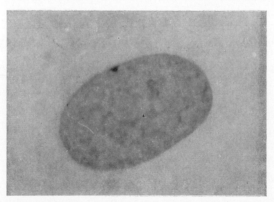

Fig. 10.3. Sex-chromatin body in fibroblast cultured from skin of female donor (Feulgen stain).

is almost certainly due to nonsex-specific chromocenters, which were sufficiently similar to Barr bodies to have been mistaken for them. In some mammals, particularly rodents, the chromocenters are much more prominent. Here the demonstration of Barr bodies presents considerable difficulties.

Barr bodies are most commonly situated at the periphery of the nucleus. However, a minority of Barr bodies are found in other parts of the nucleus, and many of these are situated in proximity to a nucleolus (Fig. 10.4). Klinger (1957) found that in amnion and connective tissue, 61.8% of the Barr bodies were at the nuclear periphery, 23.2% were lying

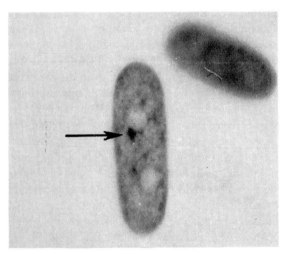

FIG. 10.4. Sex chromatin adjacent to nucleolus in fibroblast of female origin (thionin, × 2200). From Mittwoch (1964b).

against a nucleolus and 9.2% were apparently free in the cytoplasm (although it cannot be excluded that a Barr body which is seen in the center of a nuclear profile is not, in fact, lying against the nuclear membrane in the three-dimensional nucleus).

Barr bodies have one of several distinct shapes. Many appear to be plano-convex or wedge-shaped, with the plane side resting against the nuclear membrane and the convex part pointing toward the cytoplasm. Barr bodies in the center of the nucleus appear to be rectangular, and some rectangular Barr bodies may also be observed at the periphery of the nucleus. Some Barr bodies, particularly the rectangular ones, appear to be bipartite.

Some investigators, when scoring Barr bodies, include only those which are situated at the periphery of the nuclear membrane. This practice almost certainly underestimates the true incidence of the Barr bodies. On the other hand, since it is more difficult to distinguish central Barr bodies from nonspecific chromocenters, it may be wise to exclude all centrally placed bodies in preparations which are not of the highest technical standard, for instance, in preparations of buccal mucosa, which may contain a high proportion of moribund cells.

Barr bodies can be demonstrated particularly well in cells grown in culture. Thus Serr *et al.* (1958) found sex chromatin in 90% of the cells grown from human thyroid, while Fraccaro and Lindsten (1959), who cultured a large number of organs from human fetuses, reported incidences of sex chromatin varying between 34% and 88% in the cultures originating from female fetuses. Miles (1960) found a negative correlation between the incidence of Barr bodies and the frequency of mitoses in cultured amnion cells, and this relationship was confirmed (Therkelsen and Peterson, 1962, Schnedl, 1964) in fibroblast cultures of human origin. A technique for demonstrating sex chromatin in tissue culture has been described by Ross (1962). Sex chromatin may no longer be visible in tissue culture if large scale chromosomal changes have taken place, i.e., when the cells have been "transformed" (Orsi and Ritter, 1958; Miles, 1959). Apart from this, cultured cells are particularly favorable for the study of sex chromatin, since the cells are present in a single layer and the nuclei flatten themselves on the glass of the cover slip. For the same reasons, excellent preparations of sex chromatin may also be obtained from whole mounts of embryonic membranes, as demonstrated by Klinger and Schwarzacher (1960, 1962).

Barr bodies can be stained with a large number of nuclear dyes (see Culling, 1966). Staining techniques in common use employ cresyl violet (K. L. Moore and Barr, 1955), thionin (Klinger and Ludwig, 1957), and Feulgen. The fact that Barr bodies will stain by the Feulgen technique following acid hydrolysis, and have an affinity for methyl green rather than pyronin (Lindsay and Barr, 1955), indicates that they are composed of material similar to that of the chromosomes and contain DNA.

Barr bodies can also be seen in unstained and in living cells by means of phase contrast microscopy. This was described by James (1960), who observed sex chromatin in living cells cultured from a female cat and by Miles (1960), who cultured cells from human amnion. De Mars (1962), using fibroblast cultures obtained from human skin biopsies, observed the sex chromatin in the same cells both in the living condition and after fixation and Feulgen staining. The sex chromatin after staining was found to be in the same position where it had been in the living cell. Schwarzacher (1963) reported that in living human cells grown *in vitro*, sex chromatin was visible in 46% of the nuclei, whereas after fixation and staining it could be seen in about 90% of the cells. In the remaining 10% of the nuclei sex chromatin could not be seen by any method. De Mars (1964) found that in human cell cultures Barr bodies are not formed until at least 16 hours after mitosis.

It appears that in human cell cultures the presence or absence of Barr bodies is correlated with the size of the cells (Mittwoch et al., 1965). Measurements on cultured human cells have shown that fewer cells with very large nuclei had Barr bodies, while the smallest nuclei tended to have so many chromocenters that Barr bodies could not be distinguished. Barr bodies thus appear to be preferentially present in nuclei of inter-mediate size. This suggests that the formation of Barr bodies is related to the degree of condensation of the nucleus as a whole, but that the Barr bodies will condense in situations in which the rest of the chromatin does not.

The absence of sex chromatin in the largest nuclei is in agreement with findings on early embryos. Barr bodies can be seen in female embryos except the earliest ones. Glenister (1956) examined 22 male and 12 female human fetuses, of 18–150 mm crown–rump lengths. In all of them, the presence or absence of sex chromatin corresponded to the histological state of the gonads. In the female embryos, 30–50% of the nuclei had sex chromatin. Klinger (1957) found that in 21 embryos the sex chromatin state was in accordance with the external genitalia and the morphology of the gonads; of three further embryos, which were too young to be sexed in this way, one contained sex chromatin and two lacked it. Park (1957) studied serial sections from 33 human and 18 macaque embryos, belonging to the Carnegie Institute of Washington. The ages of the human embryos ranged between 36 hours and 24 days (the youngest was in the two-cell stage), and the macaque embryos were between 9 and 34 days. In the human embryos, sex chromatin was first seen in the trophoblast at about the 12th day of gestation and in the embryo itself after about 16 days. In the macaque embryos, sex chro-matin began to be seen on the 10th day in the trophoblast, while larger numbers of Barr bodies appeared in the embryo on the nineteenth day. Other embryos of equal age had no sex chromatin. These results are in accordance with observations on embryos of the cat, made by Graham (1954a,b) and by Austin and Amoroso (1957), who suggested that the absence of sex chromatin in early embryos is connected with the large size of their cell nuclei.

Sex-chromatin findings in tumor cells have been reviewed by Lennox (1963) and by Tavares (1966). Usually the sex chromatin status appears to be the same as that of the host. However, the teratomata seem to offer an interesting exception, as was first shown by Hunter and Lennox

(1954). All the teratomata in females contain sex chromatin, and sex chromatin is also found in the teratomata of half the males, while the other half lack it. Lennox explained this on the assumption that teratomata arise by the fusion of haploid cells; thus, two haploid male cells, each containing an X-chromosome, could give rise to a cell with two X-chromosomes, which would account for the Barr body. On the other hand, A. I. Taylor (1963a), who reported aberrant sex-chromatin findings in a proportion of embryonic teratomata and some other embryonic tumors, suggested that the most likely explanation is the presence of an abnormal sex-chromosome constitution, such as XO, XXY, etc.

Atkin (1960), working on uterine and other tumors in women found that when sex chromatin was present, those with a near diploid number of chromosomes had one sex-chromatin body in the majority of nuclei, while tumors with a near tetraploid number of chromosomes had two sex-chromatin bodies in most nuclei. The significance of this finding will be discussed in the following section.

IV. Numbers of Barr Bodies per Nucleus in Man

In general, the maximum number of Barr bodies per nucleus in man and most mammals is either none or one, corresponding to a karyotype containing one or two X-chromosomes, respectively. However, cells with multiple Barr bodies may be encountered, and this means that more than two X-chromosomes are present in the karyotype. The excess of X-chromosomes may be due either to aneuploidy (e.g., if three X-chromosomes are present in a diploid nucleus) or to polyploidy (e.g., as a result of doubling a female chromosome complement, resulting in a tetraploid nucleus with four X-chromosomes).

A female patient with three X-chromosomes was described by Jacobs et al. (1959a). On examining the buccal mucosa it was found that 14% of the nuclei contained two Barr bodies, the remainder having either one or none. Double Barr bodies are an invariable finding in these patients (Johnston et al., 1961). Such cells can be demonstrated in buccal mucosa or cultured fibroblasts employed for chromosome analysis (Fig. 10.5).

Carr et al. (1961) described two patients with four X-chromosomes, and these had a proportion of cells with three Barr bodies in their buccal mucosa. Last, Kesaree and Woolley (1963) described a female patient with five X-chromosomes, and she had four Barr bodies in many cells of the buccal mucosa.

The Y-chromosome appears to have no effect on the formation of Barr bodies, even though it results in a male phenotype. Patients with two or more X-chromosomes in addition to a Y bear the stigmata of Klinefelter's syndrome. Barr *et al.* (1959) described three such patients, in whom cells with two Barr bodies were found and all were found to have an XXXY-sex chromosome constitution. A patient with XXXXY-sex chromosomes was first described by Fraccaro *et al.* (1960b, 1962c) and Fraccaro and Lindsten (1960). Many such patients are now known (Atkins *et al.*, 1963) and all have cells with three Barr bodies in their buccal mucosa.

It is clear from the sex-chromatin findings in these patients, as well as in normal males and females, that in diploid cells the maximum number of Barr bodies is one less than the number of X-chromosomes. That polyploidy also effects the formation of Barr bodies became apparent

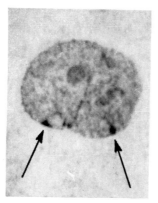

FIG. 10.5. Two Barr bodies in fibroblast nucleus of triple-X female (thionin, × 2200).

from the work of Reitalu (1957), who observed that in liver obtained from female embryos some of the larger cells, which were assumed to be tetraploid, contained two sex-chromatin masses; from Klinger and Schwarzacher (1960) who found two Barr bodies in cells from human amnion, in which DNA measurements indicated the presence of a large proportion of polyploid cells; and from the finding of Atkin (1960) that tumors of female origin with a near tetraploid number of chromosomes had two sex-chromatin bodies in many nuclei.

In order to explain the relationship between the number of Barr bodies, the number of X-chromosomes, and the degree of ploidy of the cell, Harnden (1961) proposed the formula $B = x - p/2$: where: B = number of Barr bodies; x = number of X-chromosomes; p = degree of ploidy. This formula fits in well with observation, providing (1) B is taken as the maximum number (which is not present in all cells) and (2) the ploidy number is even. Thus, in diploid cells the maximum number of Barr bodies is one less than the number of X-chromosomes, in tetraploid cells it is two less than the number of X-chromosomes, while in octoploid cells it is four less than the number of X-chromosomes (Figs. 10.5–7). However, the formula cannot be meaningfully applied to cells with uneven ploidy numbers, for in such cases the result would be in half Barr bodies.

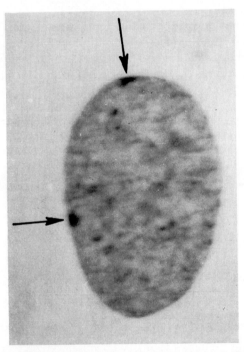

Fig. 10.6. Large fibroblast cell, presumed to be at least tetraploid, with two Barr bodies (thionin, × 2200).

The evidence regarding sex chromatin in triploid cells appeared at first conflicting. Böök and Santesson (1961), described the first patient who had, in addition to diploid cells with XY-sex chromosomes, triploid ones with XXY-chromosomes, and no sex chromatin was found; a similar result was reported by Ferrier et al. (1964). By contrast, Mittwoch and Delhanty (1961) found sex chromatin in cultured cells from a triploid XXY-fetus. Carr (1965) examined six such fetuses and found sex chromatin in five of them (although the incidence was sometimes very low) and no sex chromatin in one. Triploid cells with two X-chromosomes may contain a proportion of cells with two Barr bodies (Atkin and Klinger,

1962; Mittwoch *et al.*, 1963; Carr, 1965). These results may be explained as follows. Triploid cells can form the same maximum number of Barr bodies as diploid cells with the same number of X-chromosomes, but the tendency to do so is decreased. Therefore, in situations in which Barr body formation is normally low, e.g., if mitotic rates are high, none of the cells may show the maximum number of Barr bodies, whereas these will be present in circumstances favoring the formation of Barr bodies.

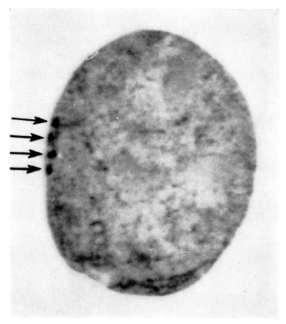

Fig. 10.7. Large fibroblast cell, presumed to be at least octoploid, with four Barr bodies. (thionin, × 2200).

V. Barr Bodies of Abnormal Size

Patients with Turner's syndrome and allied conditions who have, instead of a missing X-chromosome, one which is structurally abnormal, generally have Barr bodies of abnormal size. The so-called isochromosome of the long arm of the X is longer than a normal X-chromosome, and patients with this type of chromosome have Barr bodies which appear larger than normal (Lindsten, 1963). This impression was confirmed by measurements of the areas of the sex chromatin in patients with abnormal X-chromosomes and in normal women (Klinger *et al.*, 1965; Taft *et al.*, 1965). Measurements of the DNA content of the Barr bodies were also undertaken and indicated that the Barr bodies in the patients with iso-X-chromosomes contained on an average more DNA than those in normal women (Klinger *et al.*, 1965).

Evidence has also been presented that patients with deleted X-chromosomes have Barr bodies which are smaller than normal. The deletion may involve the long arm (Jacobs *et al.*, 1960) as well as the short arm (Jacobs *et al.*, 1961; Lindsten, 1963) of the X-chromosome.

VI. Late Replicating X-Chromosomes in Man

The findings on Barr bodies, in normal women and in patients with numerically or structurally abnormal X-chromosomes, have had striking confirmation as a result of experiments involving autoradiography. It was shown by J. H. Taylor *et al.* in 1957 that if growing cells are exposed to a solution of thymidine labeled with tritium for a brief period during DNA synthesis, the radioactive substance will be taken up by the chromosomes and can be revealed by applying a radiosensitive film. Using this technique, J. H. Taylor (1960) showed that in the Chinese hamster (*Cricetulus griseus*) not all chromosomes take up thymidine and duplicate their DNA at the same time. When tritiated thymidine is applied to cultures of human cells just before the end of the period during which DNA is synthesized, most of the chromosomes have almost completed their DNA synthesis; however, autoradiography reveals that in cells from normal females one chromosome in the 6–12 group is heavily labeled (Grumbach and Morishima, 1962; German, 1962, Gilbert *et al.*, 1962; Morishima *et al.*, 1962; Moorhead and Defendi, 1963; see Fig. 10.8). Since this chromosome does not occur in normal males, the chromosome which duplicates its DNA later is assumed to be the second X-chromosome. In patients with three X-chromosomes, two such late-replicating chromosomes are found in many cells (Grumbach *et al.*, 963; Gianelli, 1963) and in patients with XXXXY-sex chromosomes, three X-chromosomes are late-labeling (Rowley *et al.*, 1963; Gianelli, 1963) (Fig. 10.9); while in a female infant with five X-chromosomes, Grumbach *et al.* (1963) found four late-replacing X-chromosomes! It is apparent that the number of late-labeling X-chromosomes is like that of Barr bodies, one less than the total number of X-chromosomes, and there can be no doubt that these late-labeling chromosomes do, in fact, form the Barr bodies. This conclusion is further strengthened as a result of autoradiographic studies on structurally abnormal X-chromosomes. In patients with iso-X-chromosomes, this chromosome, and not the normal X-chromosome is found to be labeled with the isotope (Muldal *et al.*, 1963; Gianelli, 1963); in a patient who had one X-chromosome in the

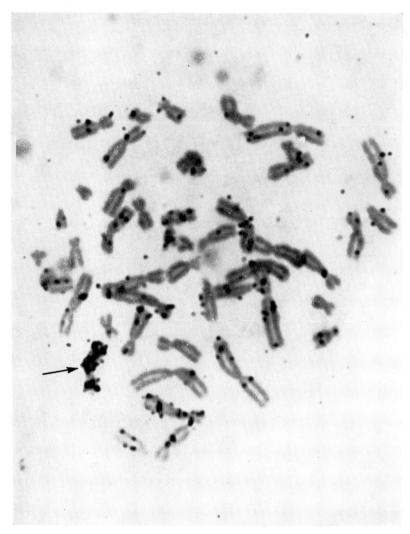

FIG. 10.8. Metaphase chromosomes of a human female, following application of radioactive thymidine and autoradiography. The late-replicating chromosome is assumed to be one of the X-chromosomes. Original photograph contributed by Dr. S. Muldal.

form of a ring, this ring chromosome was late-labeling (Lindsten, 1963); and in a patient with a deleted X-chromosome, the deleted chromosome as late-labeling (London *et al.*, 1964). These findings explain the fact that the Barr bodies associated with these abnormal chromosomes are of abnormal size.

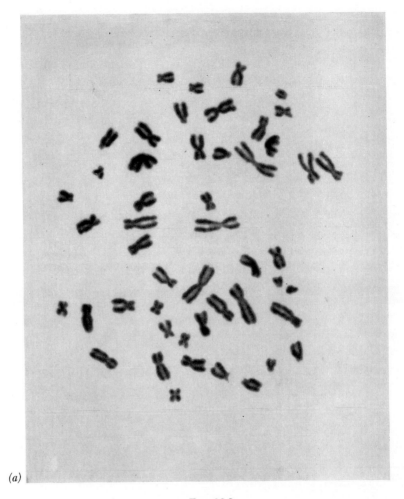

(a)

FIG. 10.9

Also using tritiated thymidine, Atkins *et al.* (1962) and Bishop and Bishop (1963) succeeded in labeling the Barr body in the interphase nucleus. After removing the grains, the most heavily labeled area of the cell was found to correspond to the Barr body in the same cell.

The Y-chromosome is also late replicating (Schmid, 1963; Atkins and Gustavson, 1964; Passarge and Thompson, 1964), but it is generally too small to form a recognizable body in interphase nuclei.

Late-replicating X-chromosomes in other mammals will be discussed later (Section XII).

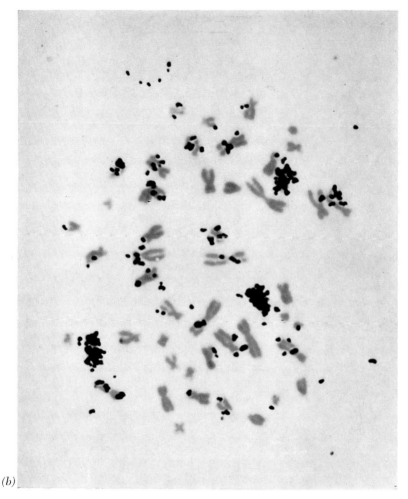

(b)

Fig. 10.9. Metaphase chromosomes of a patient with XXXXY-sex chromosomes: (a) before applying radiosensitive film; (b) after applying radiosensitive film. Original photographs contributed by Dr. O. J. Miller. (From Mittwoch, 1963b).

VII. The Origin of the Barr Body

The findings which have just been described have greatly clarified our ideas as to the origin of the Barr body. The older hypothesis, that a Barr body was formed from both members of a pair of X-chromosomes (K. L. Moore and Barr, 1953), became inadequate when the numerical relationship between Barr bodies and X-chromosomes was discovered, and was replaced by the idea, first formulated by Ohno *et al.* (1959b), that the Barr body is formed from a single X-chromosome. The observation underlying this idea was that during prophase of mitosis in liver cells of the rat, one chromosome in the female appeared to be more condensed than the rest and that such a condensed chromosome was not seen in the male. Tetraploid cells in the female appeared to have two such chromosomes. The numerical relationship between Barr bodies and X-chromosomes, as well as knowledge gained from autoradiographic studies, leaves no reasonable doubt that it originates from a single X-chromosome, which is highly condensed during interphase, while the rest of the chromosomes are extended. The other X-chromosome in females, as well as the single X-chromosome in males, is similarly extended. Thus, the behavior of the X-chromosome in somatic cells is exactly the opposite of that which it shows in germ cells for, as has been known for a long time, the single X-chromosome of insects becomes condensed (heteropycnotic) during the later spermatogonial divisions, and particularly during the prophase of meiosis in the spermatocyte, whereas the paired chromosomes of the female remain uncondensed (see Wilson, 1925; Schrader, 1928). Conspicuous heteropycnosis of the sex chromosomes in mammalian spermatocytes was also observed (Minouchi, 1928a). This contrary behavior of the X-chromosomes in germ and somatic cells of males and females applies also to man and other mammals (Ohno and Makino, 1961; Ohno *et al.*, 1961a). The single X-chromosome of the male condenses in the spermatocyte, whereas neither X-chromosome in the oocyte condenses; however in somatic cells, one of the X-chromosomes of the female becomes heteropycnotic and the X-chromosome of the male does not.

Chromosomes, or parts of chromosomes whose cycle of condensation differs from that of the majority, are said to exhibit "heteropycnosis" (Gutherz, 1907). Heteropycnosis is said to be positive if the chromosomes are more condensed, and negative, if they are less condensed than the rest (White, 1954). A Barr body, therefore, is the result of positive heteropycnosis of a single X-chromosome during interphase. This topic will be discussed more fully in the next chapter.

The remains of a Barr body can often be seen during the prophase of mitosis (Fig. 10.10). As prophase proceeds, heteropycnosis of the X-chromosome disappears and at metaphase the two X-chromosomes are indistinguishable from each other, nor, indeed, can they be distinguished with certainty from autosomes 6–12. It is possible that in the daughter nuclei one of the X-chromosomes may become heteropycnotic again during telophase, since a structure resembling a Barr body may sometimes be seen in such nuclei (Fig. 10.11); though the fact that telophase

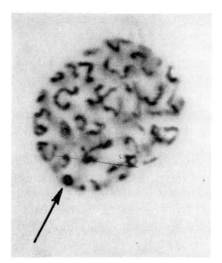

FIG. 10.10. Fibroblast nucleus in prophase showing remains of Barr body (thionin × 2200). From Mittwoch (1964c).

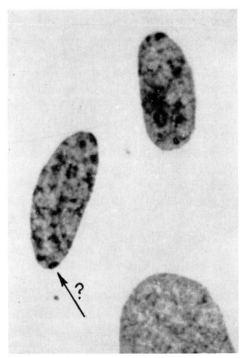

FIG. 10.11. Fibroblast nuclei in telophase, showing possible reformation of Barr bodies (thionin × 2200). From Mittwoch (1964c).

nuclei contain many chromocenters still leaves some doubt on this point. It is possible that the time which elapses until a Barr body is formed after mitosis may vary in different cells.

There is now considerable evidence that during mitotic metaphase the chromosomes do not distribute themselves at random within the cell, but that certain chromosomes tend to be found in characteristic positions (Schneiderman and Smith, 1962; Miller, 1964; Barton et al., 1963; Merrington and Penrose, 1964). In ordinary preparations, the X-chromosomes cannot be distinguished with certainty, but the Barr body-forming X-chromosome is clearly labeled in cells treated with radioactive thymidine. In such preparations it is found that this chromosome is situated at the periphery of the nucleus in the majority of cells. This observation doubtless throws some light on the fact, which had hitherto been puzzling (Miles, 1961), that the Barr body appears to be preferentially situated at this site.

The conclusion that the formation of a Barr body is a function which is intrinsic in the X-chromosome constitution rather than a general effect due to the sex of the organism, is entirely consistent with other observations. For instance, the sex chromatin of animals is not affected by castration (K. L. Moore and Barr, 1953); the membranes of male fetuses do not contain sex chromatin in spite of their maternal environment (Klinger, 1957); and in organisms which are mosaics with respect to their X-chromosome constitution, the sex chromatin occurs only in tissues containing at least two X-chromosomes. A particularly striking example of the last phenomenon was furnished by Klinger and Schwarzacher (1962) who described a fetus in which patches of cells containing sex chromatin and an XXY-sex chromosome constitution alternated with areas which lacked sex chromatin and had an XY-constitution.

The fact that sex chromatin is intrinsic in the X-chromosome constitution does not, of course, imply that its formation is entirely uninfluenced by external factors. The observation that the incidence of Barr bodies is low immediately after birth (D. W. Smith et al., 1962; A. I. Taylor, 1963b) may suggest such a possibility. Platt and Kailin (1964) reported a low frequency of Barr bodies in buccal and vaginal cells of psychotic women, as well as in some other clinical conditions. That there is an inverse correlation between the frequency of Barr bodies and the mitotic index has already been mentioned (Section III). Sohval and Casselman (1961) found that the effect of a number of antibiotics was to reduce the size of Barr bodies, without altering the incidence. Further work on the effect of external agents on Barr bodies would be of value in elucidating certain special problems concerning their formation.

VIII. Drumsticks: General Characteristics and Incidence

Following the discovery of the sex chromatin in a large variety of cells, W. M. Davidson and Smith (1954) searched for a similar sex difference among the leucocytes of the peripheral blood and found one among the granulocytes. The sex-specific body which is present in the blood films from females but not from males consists of a head, about 1.5 μ in diameter, which is attached to the body of the nucleus by means of a filament of varying length (Fig. 10.12). This appendage is commonly called a "drumstick," though some other names, such as "sex nodules," have sometimes been given to it. The occurrence and sex-

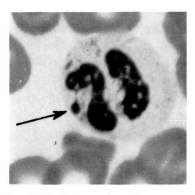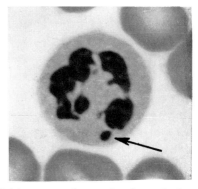

Fig. 10.12. Polymorphonuclear neutrophil leucocytes from a female, each showing a drumstick (May-Grunwald-Giemsa, $\times$ 2200).

specificity of drumsticks was soon confirmed by numerous investigators (e.g., Wiedemann et al., 1956; Lüers, 1956; also see W. M. Davidson and Smith, 1963).

Like the Barr bodies, drumsticks are stained by nuclear dyes, including basic fuchsin (Feulgen). Blood films stained with Romanowsky stains, such as the May-Grunwald-Giemsa technique, are suitable for the demonstration of drumsticks, but for a proper evaluation a high technical standard of preparation is necessary. For this reason blood films made by the cover-slip technique (Wintrobe, 1961) are preferable to those made on slides, since in addition to ensuring a more thorough distribution of the different cell types, the cover-slip method results in better cytological preservation.

Drumsticks may be demonstrated on all types of polymorphonuclear leucocytes, but for practical purposes only those present on neutrophils are usually considered.

The average incidence of drumsticks is about one per 38 neutrophils in the blood films from females, and they are absent in males. However, the nuclei of neutrophils may show a variety of appendages which are not sex-specific, and care must be taken to distinguish these from true drumsticks (Figs. 10.13, 14; see also W. M. Davidson and Smith, 1963). These nonsex-specific appendages are distinguished from drum-

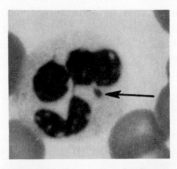

FIG. 10.13. Nonsex-specific appendage shaped like drumstick, but smaller and sometimes less intensely stained.

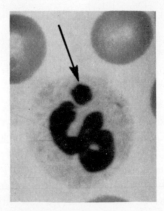

FIG. 10.14. Nonsex-specific appendage of nucleus of polymorphonuclear leucocyte —minor lobe, distinguished from drumstick by large size and irregular contours and outline.

sticks by (1) their size and shape, and/or (2) their less intense staining (drumsticks, like Barr bodies are highly condensed, deeply staining bodies). The majority of such nonspecific appendages (small clubs) are smaller than drumsticks (less than 1 μ in diameter); they may be intensely stained, and in such cases can be distinguished from true drumsticks only by size (but see Section IX). More rarely, an appendage of the size of a drumstick may have an unstained center ("tennis racket"; W. M. Davidson and Smith 1954), or an apparently larger appendage shows uneven staining, and generally also a more or less uneven outline (Fig. 10.14, "minor lobe"; W. M. Davidson and Smith, 1954). Minor lobes may be connected to the rest of the nucleus by one or two filaments.

In practice, no doubt, an occasional structure of this type may look sufficiently similar to a drumstick to be scored as such. Mittwoch (1961)

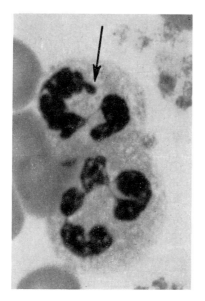

Fig. 10.15. Polymorphonuclear leucocytes from female, showing a "sessile nodule" (May-Grunwald-Giemsa, × 2200).

scored five drumsticks among 15,000 neutrophils from males and suggests that an error of this order of magnitude is unavoidable in the method of scoring drumsticks. This agrees with the opinion by Sohval (1963) that the finding of a single drumstick in less than a thousand cells has no certain diagnostic value.

In addition to drumsticks proper, in which the head is attached to the rest of the nucleus by a single thin filament, a proportion of neutrophils of female origin generally contain another type of appendage, consisting of a head which is attached more or less directly to the nucleus (Fig. 10.15). Such a structure is known as a sessile nodule [according to Kosenow and Scupin (1956), drumsticks are called "type A" and sessile nodules "type B" appendages]. A sessile nodule may be regarded as an incompletely developed drumstick and varying degrees of development may be observed. Although sex-specific, sessile nodules are more easily confused with nonspecific appendages than are drumsticks, and the error inherent in their determination is greater. From a practical point of view, sessiles are of value mainly in corroborating the evidence obtained from drumstick data. The two types of appendages should be scored separately.

The incidence of drumsticks in individual women varies very considerably. W. M. Davidson and Smith (1954) found that among 125 blood films from women the incidence of drumsticks varied between 1 per 98 neutrophils (1%) to 1 per 6 neutrophils (17%), with an average of 1/38 cells (2.9%). These frequencies were arrived at by enumerating the number of neutrophils containing six drumsticks, and it should be noted that this method results in a somewhat higher frequency of drumsticks (since the last cell always contains a drumstick) than if a constant number of cells is counted. This discrepancy is more marked if the incidence of drumsticks is low. Following Davidson and Smith, it has become an accepted rule among many investigators that a blood film from a normal female should contain at least six drumsticks per 500 neutrophils, and though this rule is obeyed in the majority of instances, there is a tail-end of the distribution which falls outside this range. Whether high or low, the drumstick counts of individual women show considerable constancy on repeated occasions (Briggs and Kupperman, 1956; Briggs, 1958; Mittwoch, 1961).

One factor which influences the incidence of drumsticks is the degree of lobing of the polymorphonuclear nucleus, the more highly lobed cells having a higher incidence of drumsticks (W. M. Davidson and Smith, 1954; Briggs, 1958). Drumsticks are rare in the Pelger anomaly (W. M. Davidson and Smith, 1954; Lüers and Petzel, 1958; Siebner et al., 1963). Thus, many but not all women with low drumstick counts also have low nuclear lobe counts. Mittwoch (1964a) found that in 12 apparently normal women, in whom a detailed analysis of drumsticks was undertaken, the incidence varied between 1.6% and 7.2%, and the correlation coefficient between the incidence of drumsticks and the mean lobe count was 0.56. When cells with constant lobe numbers were considered, it could be shown that in all women the drumstick count rose as the lobe number increased from one to four or five, but, for each given lobe number, the drumstick count of the woman with the highest number was about three to four times that of the woman with the lowest number.

There is, as yet, no explanation for observed variation in drumstick counts. However, there is evidence that the frequency of drumsticks is somewhat lower during the menstrual cycle and that this is due to hormonal influences (Caratzali *et al.*, 1957; Caratzali, 1963). Hormonal influences might also account for the increased incidence of drumsticks in newborn infants, and of their mothers immediately before and after parturition, which has been reported by von Harnack and Strietzel (1956), Peiper and Oehme (1956), and Romatowski *et al.* (1958). An increase in the incidence of drumsticks as a result of adrenocorticotrophin (ACTH) and insulin has also been noted (Caratzali and Phleps, 1958). A slight decrease in the incidence of drumsticks with increasing age of the individual has been described by Wiedemann (1958) and Tonomura *et al.* (1962). De Castro (1963) reported a low incidence of drumsticks in cachetic women, while fasting rabbits showed first a rise and then a drop, in the drumstick count.

Since the degree of lobulation of the neutrophil nucleus is an important factor in determining drumstick formation, lobe counts must be carried out whenever quantitative findings on drumsticks are of importance, or where the absence of drumsticks must be evaluated. Unfortunately, the criteria employed in enumerating lobes are very variable, so that different investigators counting lobes on the same blood film may arrive at widely differing counts. It is clearly essential that whenever the results of lobe counts are reported, these must be compared with the values obtained from a sample of apparently normal individuals counted by the same investigators.

IX. Drumsticks in Patients with Chromosomal Abnormalities

In mongolism (Down's syndrome) it was shown by Turpin and Bernyer in 1947 that the nuclei of the polymorphonuclear leucocytes have, on an average, fewer lobes than those of unaffected subjects, and Mittwoch (1957) reported that the average incidence of drumsticks in 18 girls with mongolism was only a fraction of that shown by 18 nonmongol mentally defective girls.

In Klinefelter's syndrome, an incidence of drumsticks considerably below that of normal females was noted by W. M. Davidson and Smith (1958). Mittwoch (1961) found the low incidence of drumsticks in these patients to be associated with decreased polymorphonuclear lobing. A low drumstick count coupled with a low lobe count has been noted in a few individual patients with XXXXY Klinefelter's syndrome (Miller *et al.*, 1961; Fraccaro *et al.*, 1962c; Barr *et al.*, 1962).

Table 10.I contains drumstick frequencies and mean lobe counts of patients with various chromosomal abnormalities and of mentally defec-

TABLE 10.I

DRUMSTICKS PER 100 NEUTROPHILS, AND MEAN LOBE COUNTS IN PATIENTS WITH CHROMOSOMAL ABNORMALITIES AND IN CONTROLS[a]

Patients	No. of patients	% Drumsticks for lobe numbers[b]					Drumsticks for all lobe numbers (%)	Mean lobe counts
		I	II	III	IV	V		
Non-mongol mentally retarded girls	28	0.48	1.59	3.19	5.68	6.83	2.74	2.61
Mongol girls	28	0.22	0.79	1.53	2.39	3.22	0.97	2.19
Klinefelters	12	0.77	0.83	1.87	2.36	(3.45)	1.27	2.26
Triple X females	3	0.77	2.26	2.20	3.92		2.07	2.26
Triple X Klinefelters	3	0.45	1.23	2.07	(1.56)		1.45	2.22

[a] From Mittwoch, 1964a.
[b] Numbers in brackets are based on less than 100 cells.

tive children, the majority of whom may be assumed to have normal chromosomes. The incidence of drumsticks in the mentally retarded controls is very close to that found in normal women (W. M. Davidson and Smith, 1954), but all groups of patients with chromosomal abnormalities have a lower incidence of drumstick, coupled with a lower mean lobe count, than the controls. Thus the mean frequency of drumsticks for mongol girls actually falls below the value of six drumsticks per 500 neutrophils, often regarded as the lower limit for normal female blood films.

The drumsticks in patients with three or more X-chromosomes present a special problem. As was mentioned before (Section IV) the Barr bodies in such patients present a very characteristic picture, since the maximum number of Barr bodies per cell is one less than the number of X-chromosomes. In addition, the proportion of cells containing Barr bodies is also higher than in normal females (e.g., Jacobs et al., 1959a; Barr et al., 1959; Ferguson-Smith et al., 1960). By contrast, the incidence of drumsticks in such patients appears to be below normal. This is particularly pronounced if a Y-chromosome is also present (e.g., Barr et al., 1959; Ferguson-Smith et al., 1960; Maclean, 1962), but it appears to apply also in females with XXX-sex chromosomes (Mittwoch, 1963b). The data so far suggest that, although there may be considerable variation in individual cases, the average incidence of drumsticks in patients with three X-chromosomes, both with and without a Y-chromosome, is below normal.

Jacobs et al. (1959a) reported the presence of a single cell with two drumsticks in a patient with XXX-sex chromosomes. Both the existence and the rarity of double drumsticks have been confirmed by Maclean (1962), who, surveying a large number of cells in twelve patients with XXX-sex chromosomes, found an incidence of such cells of less than one in two thousand (Fig. 10.16). Two sessile nodules (Fig. 10.17) or one drumstick and one sessile nodule occur somewhat more frequently than two fully filamented drumsticks in the same cell. In an infant with five X-chromosomes, described by Kesaree and Woolley (1963), there were a number of cells with two drumsticks and some with three, though no cells were found with four drumsticks. The conclusion seems justified that the theoretical maximum number of drumsticks, like that of Barr bodies, is one less than the number of X-chromosomes, but that owing to the low frequencies of drumsticks, the maximum number may be rarely, if ever, reached.

Patients with structurally abnormal X-chromosomes have drumsticks of abnormal size (Maclean, 1962; Bamford et al., 1963, 1964; Fraccaro et al., 1964). The drumsticks are larger than normal, as well as more frequent, in patients with isochromosomes of the long arm of the X, while deleted X-chromosomes appear to be associated with small drumsticks. Very large drumsticks were also found in a patient who had a X-chromosome which was longer than an isochromosome (Gouw *et al.*, 1964).

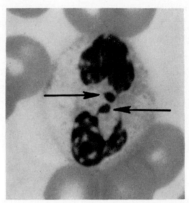

FIG. 10.16. Polymorphonuclear leucocyte with two drumsticks from a triple-X-female (May-Grunwald-Giemsa, × 2200). (From Mittwoch, 1963b).

Although large drumsticks are primarily associated with isochromosomes of the long arm of the X, they may also be found, though much more rarely, in patients with multiple X-chromosomes (Fig. 10.18). In general, the detection of large drumsticks will present little difficulty

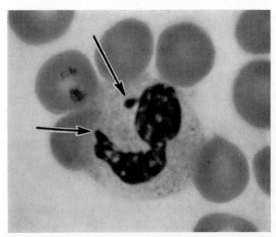

FIG. 10.17. Polymorphonuclear leucocyte with two sessile nodules from a triple-X-patient (May-Grunwald-Giemsa, × 2200).

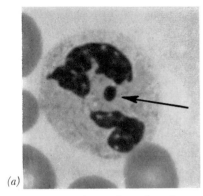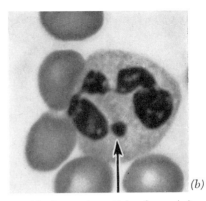

(a) (b)

FIG. 10.18. Polymorphonuclear leucocytes with large drumsticks from (a) an XXX-female, (b) an XXXY-male. Large drumsticks occur rarely in patients with multiple X-chromosomes, but are frequent in patients with isochromosomes of the large arm of the X.

to an experienced observer, since their intense staining and regular outline distinguishes them from other parts of the nucleus. On the other hand, it is sometimes not possible to distinguish small drumsticks from other nonspecific nuclear appendages.

X. The Relationship of Drumsticks to Barr Bodies

The significance of drumsticks and their relation to Barr bodies remained in doubt for some time for a number of reasons. To begin with, the morphological appearances of the two structures in stained preparations is different. The drumstick is larger, a head of normal size having a diameter of 1.5 μ while the diameter of the Barr body is about 1 μ. W. M. Davidson and Winn (1961), who measured the ratios of the areas of drumsticks and Barr bodies to their respective nuclei from enlarged prints, found that the drumstick occupies a larger relative area than the Barr body in relation to the rest of the nucleus. Although the authors concluded that this difference may be explained by differences in the shape and thickness of the nuclei in polymorphonuclear and epithelial cells, the alternative that drumsticks and Barr bodies are intrinsically different structures remained for some time a possibility (Klinger, 1957; Ashley, 1962).

In the majority of instances the results of tests on Barr bodies and drumsticks in the same individuals are in agreement, but a number of apparent discrepancies have been described. For instance, Kosenow (1957) found that among 15 patients with gonadal dysgenesis, 11 had neither Barr bodies nor drumsticks, three had both Barr bodies and drumsticks, while one had Barr bodies in the buccal mucosa but no drumsticks in the blood. The opposite situation, i.e., patients who lacked Barr bodies but in whom drumsticks were found, was reported by Ashley and Jones (1958). Other apparent discrepancies between findings in the buccal mucosa and in the blood have been described (Overzier, 1958; Izakovič, 1960; Greenblatt *et al.*, 1962; Turner and Zanartu, 1962).

While a few of these results may be due to faulty techniques, the results of chromosome analysis have shown that a considerable proportion of patients with abnormalities of the sex chromosomes are, in fact, mosaics with different sex-chromosome complements in different cells (see C. E. Ford, 1963). In the extensive data by Lindsten (1963), over one-third of the patients with Turner's syndrome were mosaics with XO-cells and others containing a second X-chromosome. In some cases the different karyotypes are intermingled while in others different tissues are characterized by different chromosome constitutions. Jacobs *et al.* (1960) described a patient with features of Turner's syndrome, whose bone marrow cells appeared to be XO, while the skin was predominantly XXX, but contained also XO-cells. The buccal mucosa contained cells with single and double Barr bodies, but no drumsticks were present in the leucocytes. The results of chromosome studies have shown that many of the so-called discrepancies between Barr body and drumstick findings provide, in fact, confirmation that both structures represent the sex chromatin in the cells in which they occur.

Other apparent differences between drumsticks and Barr bodies have also been largely explained. As pointed out by Sohval (1963), some of the so-called discrepancies between the two techniques are merely reflections of differences in the frequencies with which Barr bodies and drumsticks occur. While Barr bodies may be seen in more than 90% of suitable cells (Klinger, 1957) drumsticks occur only rarely in as much as 10% of neutrophils, and their average incidence in normal females is about 3%. Moreover, in patients with Klinefelter's syndrome the incidence of Barr bodies appears to be no different from that of normal females, but the frequency of drumsticks is abnormally low. If only a few drumsticks are to be expected within a given number of cells, none at all may be found in certain samples merely by chance. As was described above, evidence has now been adduced that both the incidence of drumsticks and the degree of lobing is likely to be below normal in a variety of chromosomal abnormalities.

It is becoming clear that the drumstick is an appendage of a morphologically highly specialized cell, and that the factors which cause the nucleus to divide up into lobes also affect the extrusion of drumsticks.

Many problems of drumstick formation remain to be solved, together with related problems of the physiology and pathology of the leucocytes. Similarly, problems remain regarding details of the formation of Barr bodies, and further studies on the effect of hormones and other external agents on the formation of drumsticks and Barr bodies are required.

Nevertheless, work of recent years has made it clear that the original suggestion by W. M. Davidson and Smith (1954) that the drumstick is equivalent to the Barr body, is valid. It may be concluded that both the Barr body and the drumstick of mammals are true sex chromatin, representing heteropycnotic X-chromosomes, which are present in addition to the first one.

XI. Sex Chromatin in Mammals other than Man

A sex difference is found in the interphase nuclei of many mammals, and the domestic cat was the first species in which this was described.

K. L. Moore and Barr (1953) undertook a systematic investigation of the nerve cell nuclei of eutherian mammals, with the following results. A sex difference was found in the dog (*Canis familiaris*), mink (*Mustela vison*), marten (*Martes americana*), ferret (*Mustela furo*), raccoon (*Procyon lotor*), and skunk (*Mephitus mephitus*), all of which belong to the order Carnivora; and in the goat (*Capra hircus* L.) and the deer (*Odocoileus virginianus*), both of which are members of the Artiodactyla. Cells from five regions of the nervous system were examined (pyramidal cells, Purkinje cells, spinal cord, dorsal root ganglion cells, and stellate ganglion cells. More than 80% of such cells from female animals contained a sex-chromatin mass, most of them adjacent to the nucleolus; similar masses were observed in up to 13% of male cells, but usually the frequency was less than 10%.

In the following animals a sex difference could not be observed: rat (*Rattus norvegicus*), mouse (*Mus musculus*), hamster (*Cricetus auratus*), and groundhog (*Marmota monax*), belonging to the order Rodentia; and the rabbit (*Oryctolagus cuniculus*), a member of the Lagomorpha. In these animals the cells of both sexes tended to contain coarse chromatin clumps, usually adjacent to the nucleolus, which obscured any sex chromatin that might have been present. The fact that sex chromatin is present in members of the carnivores and absent, or at least difficult to detect, in rodents and rabbits, has been largely confirmed by later workers (see Moore, 1966, for review). In the rat (rodent), Klinger (1957) was able to demonstrate sex chromatin only in spinal cord nerve cells, while Shantaveerappa and Bourne (1962) found it in pia-arachnoid membrane and perineural epithelium of sciatic nerves. Klinger (1957) was unable to show sex chromatin in the rabbit, but Hulliger et al. (1963) found sex chromatin to be clearly visible in rabbit cells cultured in vitro. Melander (1962) found sex chromatin in the rabbit from the fifth day of embryonic life onwards. Hay (1960) was unable to demonstrate sex chromatin in the armadillo (Edentata) and the prairie dog and the mouse, both of them rodents. However, in another rodent, the porcupine, sex chromatin was found. As regards the armadillo, it was found by Sullivan and Benirschke (1964) that although nervous tissue was not suitable, sex chromatin could be demonstrated in embryonic muscle and connective tissue cells, as well as in cultured cells.

One of the most difficult animals for demonstrating sex chromatin is undoubtedly the mouse. This is connected with the fact that interphase nuclei of mice tend to contain prominent chromocenters, and in such cells it is impossible to say whether sex chromatin is present or not. However, Berenbaum (1960) found a peripherally located sex-chromatin body in 30 to 52% of metamyelocytes of mice and rats; and Kenney and Mittwoch (1965) found that in primary fibroblast cultures grown from mouse tissues just over half of the nuclei contained prominent chromocenters; in the remaining nuclei of female origin, sex chromatin could be demonstrated, but only in about 10% of cells. A low incidence of sex chromatin may be correlated with results of autoradiographic studies in the mouse. By applying tritiated thymidine to tissue cultures of the mouse, Galton and Holt (1965) found that, in cultures originating from females, one of the larger chromosomes replicated late; but the difference in grain numbers between this and the other chromosomes appeared to be less than is generally found in cells of man and many other mammals. Similarly, H. J. Evans et al. (1965), who injected tritiated thymidine into mice in vivo, found that only a rather small proportion of labeled cells showed a recognizably late-labeling X-chromosome. It appears that in the mouse the Y-chromosome replicates later than the X-chromosome (Fraccaro et al., 1965a).

In the hoofed animals belonging to the order Artiodactyla sex chromatin can be distinguished in neurons, but in other cells the chromatin tends to be too coarse for a distinction to be made (see Barr, 1963). An interesting application of the nuclear sexing method was the demonstration of sex chromatin in the neurons of a freemartin (K. L. Moore et al., 1957). A freemartin is a sterile heifer born as a twin of a normal male. The external genitalia are predominantly female, while the gonads resemble testes. The finding of sex chromatin is in agreement with the interpretation that the freemartin is a genetic female which has become masculinized as a result of male hormone, following the fusion of chorions and vascular anastomosis in early embryonic life (Tandler and Keller, 1911; Lillie, 1917). Recent work having a possible bearing on the origin of freemartins will be discussed in Chapter 12 (Section XI).

Among hoofed animals belonging to the order Perissodactyla, sex chromatin has been found in cells of the vaginal mucosa of a female mule (Mukherjee and Sinha, 1964) and in cultured cells from a hybrid between a donkey and a zebra (Benirschke et al., 1964). Sex chromatin has also been found in the buccal mucosa of an Indian elephant (order Proboscidea) by Rao and Prasad (1963).

It appears that in apes and monkeys sex chromatin can be demonstrated as easily as in man. Thus Prince et al. (1955) found a well marked sex difference in the rhesus monkey (Macacus rhesus), and Hamerton et al. (1961, 1963) found sex chromatin in the buccal mucosa of the female gorilla and other apes belonging to the Hominoidea.

Drumsticks, too, are present in certain animals but not in others [see reviews by W. M. Davidson and Smith (1963) and by W. M. Davidson (1966)]. It is interesting that in the various groups of animals, there appears to be a close correlation between the presence or absence of drumsticks and that of Barr bodies. Thus, drumsticks have been demonstrated in primates (Chiarelli and Barberis, 1964), carnivores, and hoofed animals, but none have been identified in rodents, in which both sexes have nonspecific appendages which simulate drumsticks (Hinchrichsen and Gothe, 1958). Drumsticks are present in the rabbit.

XII. Late-Replicating X-Chromosomes in Different Mammals

Late-replicating X-chromosomes have been found in the females of all mammals which have been investigated for this purpose by means of autoradiography. The fact that the two X-chromosomes of female mammals incorporate tritiated thymidine and, by implication, synthesize their DNA at different times, was discovered by J. H. Taylor (1960) in cultured cells of the Chinese hamster (Cricetulus griseus). Ignoring minor variations in the time of DNA synthesis between different chromosomes and different regions of the same chromosome, one may generalize that, of the two X-chromosomes of female mammals, one duplicates its DNA at about the same time as the autosomes while the other one does it later (Hsu et al., 1964). This phenomenon has also been observed in the cow (Mukherjee and Sinha, 1963; Gartler and Burt, 1964; H. J. Evans, 1965), the horse, the donkey and the mule

(Mukherjee and Sinha, 1964), and a hybrid between a donkey and a zebra (Benirschke *et al.*, 1964a) the goat and the pig (H. J. Evans, 1965), as well as the dog (Fraccaro *et al.*, 1965b); and there can be no doubt that this list could be greatly extended. As mentioned before (Section XI), a late-replicating X-chromosome has been described in the mouse, although in this species the phenomenon appears to be less marked than in others.

In the mule, Mukherjee and Sinha (1964) found that in half the cells in which a late labeling chromosome could be seen this was the X-chromosome of the horse while in the other half of the cells the X-chromosome of the donkey was late-labeling. This finding is in accordance with the Lyon hypothesis of random inactivation (see Section XV).

There is, however, a modification to the rule that one X-chromosome in female mammals is early replicating, while the other is late replicating. In the golden hamster (*Mesocricetus auratus*), the X-chromosome is the largest of the karyotype (Chapter 9, Section VII), and it was found by Galton and Holt (1964) that in the female one entire X-chromosome as well as the long arm of the other X-chromosome was late replicating, and the long arm of the X-chromosome was also late replicating in the male. The longest known X-chromosome in any mammal occurs in the short-tailed vole (*Microtus agrestis*—Chapter 9, Section VII). According to Wolf *et al.* (1965) it is about four times as long as the X-chromosome in most mammals, and the authors found that in the female one entire X-chromosome as well as about three-quarters of the second X-chromosome replicate late, and three-quarters of the X-chromosome also replicate late in the male. In this species "sex chromatin" bodies are found in both sexes. In accordance with these findings, Ohno *et al.* (1964) have postulated that the length of the X-chromosome which replicates early in both males and females is about the same in all mammals; if the X-chromosome is longer, the parts in excess replicate late in both sexes.

XIII. Sex Chromatin in Animals with Female Heterogamety

Following the discovery of a heteropycnotic body in cells of female larvae of the spruce budworm [*Choristoneura* (*Archips*) *fumiferana*] by S. G. Smith (1944, 1945a,b)(see Section II), Frizzi (1948) found a similar sex difference in the silkworm (*Bombyx mori* L.). Cells from the silk glands of larvae, which were known to be female from the histology of the gonads, contained a heteropycnotic body, which was never found in the cells from males. The position of the heteropycnotic body was variable, occurring either in the center of the cells, or at the poles of elongated cells. Occasionally two bodies were seen in the same cell. This body provided a simple means for sexing larvae from the second instar onwards, when other means of sexing are very laborious.

The silkworm is an animal of economic importance and, though in common with other Lepidoptera its chromosomes are not favorable for cytological studies, a good deal is known about its genetics (see Chapter 5, Section III), and there can be no doubt that the female is the heterogametic sex. Frizzi (1948) postulated that the heteropycnotic body represents the condensed Y-chromosome.

The situation regarding sex chromatin in birds is not yet clear. Kosin and Ishizaki (1959) found sex chromatin in interphase cells of female chickens (*Gallus domesticus*). Cells of smooth muscle of the duodenum as well as dermal and epidermal cells at the base of growing feathers were particularly favorable for the demonstration of the sex-chromatin body. This occurred with an incidence varying between 15% and 56% in cells from female birds, while a similar body was seen in 0.4–5.4% of male cells. The sex-chromatin body was situated at the periphery of the nucleus and its appearance resembled that of the Barr body in mammals. The finding of sex chromatin in the fowl was confirmed by Ohno *et al.* (1959b) and by K. L. Moore and Hay (1961), while the presence of sex chromatin in female chick embryos was also confirmed by Ishizaki and Kosin (1960).

On the other hand, neither Ashley and Theiss (1959) nor Miles and Storey (1962) were able to demonstrate sex chromatin in the fowl. Ashley and Theiss examined sections of various tissues from the fowl, duck, parrot, and parakeet. They were unable to establish a sex difference, since cells from both males and females contained many chromatin masses. Miles and Storey, who examined cells from the fowl, both grown *in vitro* as well as sections from various tissues, also found chromocenters present in both sexes.

The problem of sex chromatin in the fowl was further tackled by Schmid (1962), who treated chicken cells grown in tissue culture with tritiated thymidine. He found that the labeling pattern of both X-chromosomes in the male, as well as the single X-chromosome in the female, was not different from that of the autosomes. However, in the female, one of the larger microchromosomes, which appeared to be identical with the Y-chromosome described by Fréderic (1961), exhibited a very heavy and comparatively late uptake of thymidine.

Although the data on sex chromatin in animals with female heterogamety available so far are scanty compared with those obtained in mammals, the problems which are raised are of the greatest importance for a general understanding of the subject. Schmid's (1962) finding that the Y-chromosome of the hen shows late DNA replication is in agreement with the observation that the Y-chromosome in man is similarly late-labeling (Section VI). On the other hand, the evidence available so far suggests that the situation with regard to the X-chromosome is very different from that found in mammals, as there appears to be no sex chromatin in the interphase nuclei of cocks, while the DNA labeling pattern of both X-chromosomes in the male and the single X-chromosome is like that of autosomes. Since any comprehensive theory on the significance of sex chromatin and heteropycnosis in mammals will have to take account of the findings in animals with female heterogamety, further studies of these phenomena in birds and Lepidoptera will clearly be of the greatest importance.

XIV. Some Practical Applications of Sex-Chromatin Determinations

The results of sex-chromatin studies provided the first indications of discrepancies between the genetic and phenotypic sex in some errors of human sexual development. Similarly, in present-day medical genetics, the presence or absence of Barr bodies and drumsticks will often give the first information regarding the numbers of X-chromosomes present in patients in whom abnormalities of the X-chromosome may be suspected.

In general, the sex-chromatin test will be most useful in detecting the classic XO-type of Turner's syndrome and the XXY-type of Klinefelter's syndrome, as well as karyotypes with multiple X-chromosomes, but the test will not usually detect chromosomal mosaics, unless the X-chromosome constitution is strikingly different in different tissues. For instance, the detection of a single Barr body in a proportion of buccal mucosa cells in a male patient will suggest the presence of an XXY-karyotype, but it will not give any information regarding further cell lines, which might have XO-, XY-, or XX-sex chromosome constitutions. Also, in some instances, the karyotype might be XXYY.

In patients with Turner's syndrome, who are XO/XX-mosaics, sex chromatin is usually present (de la Chapelle, 1962), and such patients will not generally be detected as a result of sex-chromatin testing. A low incidence of sex-chromatin bodies may raise the suspicion of a mosaicism of this type, but, particularly in buccal mucosa, a low incidence of Barr bodies may occur for other reasons.

Patients with isochromosomes of the long arm of the X-chromosome (X_I) tend to have a high proportion of large Barr bodies (Jacobs *et al.*,

1960; de la Chapelle, 1962; Lindsten, 1963). The drumsticks are also larger and much more frequent than normal (Section IX) since they occur with a frequency of about ten per hundred neutrophils; large drumsticks occurring with lesser frequencies may suggest the presence of mosaicism of the type XX_I/XO with a fair degree of accuracy. Smaller than normal Barr bodies are associated with deleted X-chromosomes. Although the drumsticks in such cases may also be smaller than normal, small drumsticks are difficult to distinguish from similar looking appendages of the neutrophiles which are not sex-specific.

From a genetic point of view, the most important application of sex-chromatin testing has been in establishing the incidence of abnormalities of the sex chromosomes as a result of screening large populations. Preparations made from the oral mucosa are the most suitable for this purpose and have been used almost exclusively. However, the survey by Shapiro and Ridler (1960) was based on leucocyte morphology, while Ridler et al. (1963) utilized both buccal mucosa and leucocytes.

Sex-chromatin surveys have been carried out on series of newborn infants (see Maclean, 1966) as well as on populations of the mentally retarded.

The largest survey on the sex chromatin of newborns was carried out by Maclean et al. (1964), who examined 10,725 live-born males, born consecutively, and 10,000 females. Among the male infants, twenty-one were found to contain single Barr bodies, and among the females, twelve had double Barr bodies and in four no Barr bodies could be found. On the basis of this and two earlier surveys by K. L. Moore (1959) and by Bergemann (1961), comprising 3800 males and 3600 females, the incidence of Klinefelter's syndrome at birth may be roughly estimated at about 2 per 1000 males, that of the triple-X condition at about 1 per 1000 females and that of Turner's syndrome without sex chromatin about 4 per 10,000 females. As was pointed out above, this approach is likely to miss those cases of Turner's syndrome who are mosaics or have isochromosomes. In the data by Lindsten (1963), sex chromatin was present in the buccal mucosa of 20 out of 57 patients with Turner's syndrome, and in the data by de la Chapelle (1962) there were 10 such patients out of 23. As a first approximation it may be assumed that the incidence of Turner's syndrome is about a third higher than would be estimated from sex-chromatin studies. While the results of these three surveys are in good mutual agreement, a sex-chromatin survey on newborn babies in India (2058 males and 832 females) failed to show any abnormalities (Naik and Shah, 1962).

Sex-chromatin surveys on male patients in mental deficiency hospitals have been carried out by Mosier et al. (1960), Barr et al. (1960),

Ferguson-Smith *et al.* (1960), Sanderson and Stewart (1961), Maclean *et al.* (1962), Hamerton *et al.* (1962), and T. S. Davies (1963). Out of a total of 7305 patients examined, 67 were found to have sex chromatin, giving an incidence of just under 1%. This incidence is several times as high as that found at birth. The incidence of Klinefelter's syndrome is also increased among boys attending schools for the educationally subnormal (see Israelsohn and Taylor, 1961).

Surveys on female patients were carried out by J. H. Fraser *et al.* (1960), Sanderson and Stewart (1961), Johnston *et al.* (1961), Maclean *et al.* (1962), Hamerton *et al.* (1962), T. S. Davies (1963), and Ridler *et al.* (1963). The total number of patients surveyed was 4575 and among these 18 patients with duplicated Barr bodies were found, giving an incidence of about 4 per 1000. In these patients an XXX-sex chromosome constitution was either verified or may be assumed, and it is clear that this condition also has a higher incidence among the mentally retarded than is found at birth. Among this group of patients only one had no Barr bodies (Maclean *et al.*, 1962) and another patient with an isochromosome of the long arm of the X was identified by Hamerton *et al.* (1962). Judging from these data, there is no evidence that the incidence of Turner's syndrome among the mentally retarded is appreciably higher than among the newborn.

Thus, in spite of certain limitations of the buccal smear technique for sex-chromatin investigations, it has provided results of the greatest interest to human cytogenetics. It is clear that without this technique estimates of the frequencies of the various abnormalities of the X-chromosome could not have approached the accuracy of those which are now available.

XV. Some Theoretical Considerations Concerning Sex Chromatin

The possibility that the sex-chromatin body might represent the second X-chromosome which, being genetically superfluous, is present in a condensed and inactivated form, was suggested by Stewart (1960b). Russell (1961) on the basis of data relating to the effect of rearrangements of the X-chromosome in the mouse, formulated the hypothesis that in mammals any X-chromosome in addition to the first assumes the properties of heterochromatin. However, the inactive X hypothesis in its wider form was advanced and developed by Lyon (1961, 1962, 1963, 1966).

The Lyon hypothesis consists of three parts. First, it postulates that the genes on the sex chromatin forming X-chromosomes are inactive;

second, that the decision as to which of a pair of X-chromosomes is to be inactivated is made early in embryonic life and that, once the decision is made, the descendants of each X-chromosome will be like the parent chromosome; and third, that the original inactivation in each embryonic cell occurs at random, so that in some cells a paternal and in others a maternal X-chromosome will be inactivated. Therefore, as the embryo grows, patches of cells with inactive X-chromosomes of paternal origin will alternate with inactive X-chromosomes of maternal origin. The theory was originally developed to explain the fact that female mice which are heterozygous for sex-linked genes are spotted (Lyon, 1961).

Since the effect of the theory would be that animals of both sexes have only a single dose of sex-linked genes, it is thought to provide the basis for dosage compensation in mammals (Lyon, 1963).

The term "dosage compensation" was introduced by Muller (1932) to describe the fact that in *Drosophila* the effect of genes borne on the X-chromosome is about the same in males, where they occur in single dose, and in females, where they are present in double dose. Muller's explanation was that the genes on the X-chromosome are balanced in such a way that the effects of dosage are cancelled.

There can be no doubt that dosage compensation occurs also in mammals. For instance in man, the gene controlling the production of glucose 6-phosphate dehydrogenase in erythrocytes is located on the X-chromosome, yet the enzyme is present in equal amounts in males and females (Marks, 1958) as well as in patients with abnormal numbers of X-chromosomes (Grumbach et al., 1962; Harris et al., 1963). In the mouse, animals with an XO-karyotype are viable and fertile females (Welshons and Russel, 1959).

In the mouse, Lyon (1963) has presented evidence that in females which are heterozygous for two pairs of genes, and in which one gene is borne on the X-chromosome and the other on a piece of autosome which is translocated to the other X-chromosome, only one of the genes is acting in any patch of cells. It is postulated that the X-chromosome bearing the translocation acts as an integral whole. Ohno and Cattanach (1962) have combined genetic studies of this type with cytological observations. They used female mice having one normal X-chromosome, X^n, and one bearing a translocation X^t, which made it about 18% longer than normal. The translocated chromosome contained the wild-type allele of the gene *albinism*, which, in this combination produces patches of wild-type color alternating with patches of white. The authors found that in the prophase of mitosis in skin cells, one chromosome was more condensed than the rest. Moreover, it appeared that the condensed chromosome in cells from the white patches was larger than the condensed chromosome in cells from the wild-type patches, which would fit in with the hypothesis that the genes on the condensed chromosome do not affect the phenotype. Further evidence relating to the random inactivation was provided by H. J. Evans *et al.* (1965), who injected tritiated thymidine into female mice which were heterozygous for this translocation and found that in about half of the cells in which a late labeling chromosome could be recognized, this was about the size of a normal X-chromosome, while in the other half this chromosome was very large and must have been the translocated chromosome.

However, in another translocation in the mouse, in which a piece of X-chromosome was translocated to an autosome, Lyon *et al.* (1964) found that the heterozygous females were not spotted. It appeared as if the genes on the translocated chromosome were active in all cells, while those on the normal X-chromosome were not expressed.

Further work along these lines would be most desirable. At present, it is one of the ironies of this subject that, although the theory of X-inactivation was originally formulated on the basis of genetic data on the mouse, this species has proved rather recalcitrant to the cytological demonstration of sex chromatin. This is at least partly due to the presence of multiple chromocenters, but the significance of these bodies requires elucidation.

In man, work on two genes borne on the X-chromosome is of particular relevance to the Lyon hypothesis. Women who are heterozygous for the gene causing glucose 6-phosphate dehydrogenase deficiency tend to have an enzyme level which is intermediate between that of normal and deficient subjects and Beutler *et al.* (1962) have presented evidence that the erythrocytes of such women are composed of two classes, with normal and very low enzyme levels, respectively. This finding was confirmed by R. G. Davidson *et al.* (1963) on cells grown in tissue culture. These authors succeeded in growing clones from single cells and found that such clones from heterozygous women either had a normal enzyme level or were deficient; even more strikingly, skin biopsies from women who were heterozygous for two different variants, A and B, produced clones of cells which showed either A or B, but not both.

By contrast, in women who are heterozygous for the sex-linked blood group antigen *Xg* (Chapter 8, Section XII), it appears that two separate classes of cells cannot be separated (Gorman *et al.*, 1963). To accommodate this and other facts which do not seem to fit in with the hypothesis that one of two X-chromosomes is inactivated, the idea is now gaining ground that the X-chromosome contains a portion which escapes inactivation even if present in two or more doses. The concept that sex chromosomes may be divisible into differential and pairing segments has already been discussed (Chapter 2, Section IV and Chapter 9, Section XIII). C. E. Ford, in 1961, extended this idea to human sex chromosomes and suggested that the somatic stigmata of Turner's syndrome may be due to the fact that only one pairing segment is present instead of two (C. E. Ford, 1963). Very similar ideas were developed by Ferrier (1964) and by Ferguson-Smith (1965), both of whom assume that the pairing segment is situated in the short arms of the X-chromosome and does not become inactivated. The likelihood that the X-chromosome does not become inactivated along its entire length was also put forward by Russell (1963, 1964) on the basis of data on the mouse. Russell found that the amount of spotting shown by different translocation heterozygotes depended on the position of the X-chromosome at which the break occurred; and she postulated that the inactivation may start from a certain point on the X-chromosome, from which it may spread along gradients.

By assuming that the second X-chromosomes of females (and of abnormal males) consists of two parts, a major one which becomes inactivated and a minor one which does not, all genetic effects of the X-chromosome could be formally explained. If the effect is independent of the number of X-chromosomes present, this must be due to the inactivated portion, but if different numbers of X-chromosomes produce different effects, the inactivated part may be implicated. However, many aspects regarding the Lyon hypothesis remain to be elucidated. For instance, we have to know why the maximum number of Barr bodies is not found in every cell, and cytological confirmation is required that the same X-chromosome always forms the Barr body following cell division. More needs to be known about the cytology of the mouse. But perhaps the greatest area of uncertainty is our lack of knowledge of the effect of genes, both autosomal and sex-linked, on individual cells.

The last ten years or so have seen a tremendous increase in our knowledge of what we might call formal human cytogenetics. Chromosomal abnormalities have been shown to be the cause of a variety of human malformations; and the discovery of the sex chromatin, and the development of suitable techniques to demonstrate it, have added a valuable test to routine pathology. At the same time, we are still far removed from any real understanding of the physical part played by the chromosomes in the development of the cells and the organism, which we know they control. We do not know the function of the chromosomes in normal development nor in the pathogenesis of abnormalities. The Lyon hypothesis has focused attention on some of the problems involving the X-chromosome. To solve these problems, we shall require much more knowledge of the relationship between cytogenetics and the emergence of the phenotype in man and other animals.

Stern (1960) wrote: "Dosage compensation forms one chapter in the history of genetic systems. Its analysis is not yet a closed chapter." Indeed, it has only just begun, and current work on sex chromatin will undoubtedly advance its development.

CHAPTER 11

HETEROCHROMATIN

I. Introduction

The concept of heterochromatin is intimately related to the subject of sex chromosomes in general, and to the phenomenon of sex chromatin in particular. The data relating to heterochromatin have been obtained from a variety of approaches, mainly cytological and genetic and to a lesser extent physicochemical, which together with a good deal of theoretical speculation, have resulted in a large and diffuse literature, from which it is by no means easy to crystallize any clear-cut concept.

This state of affairs has caused considerable dismay among workers in the field. J. R. Baker and Callan (1950) suggested that the use of the term "heterochromatin" is undesirable, since the name suggests the existence of a definite chemical substance, and it is unlikely that heterochromatin is such a substance. R. B. Goldschmidt (1955) wrote: "Heterochromatin is so elusive a structure that it would be better not to attempt a theoretical discussion, were it not that we know a number of interesting features which in the cells in which they are found are perfectly clear and straightforward." Similar reservations were made by Cooper (1959) "we very likely delude ourselves in the hypostasizations heterochromatin and euchromatin. . . . Nevertheless the fact of heteropycnosis is beyond dispute, and heteropycnotic regions and chromosomes are in themselves of exceptional interest." Finally, Pontecorvo (1958), while admitting the relevance of heterochromatin to the problem of chromosomal arrangement and function, wrote as follows: "The trouble here is that the study of heterochromatin is at a prescientific level. . . . We have no alternative but to ignore it." It is very fortunate that in the years that have elapsed the study of heterochromatin has made considerable progress toward acquiring a scientific basis. This will undoubtedly mean that the subject will evoke renewed interest and that more data will accumulate. There is now the distinct possibility that heterochromatin will prove of special relevance in sex determination.

II. Origin of the Concept of Heterochromatin

As was pointed out in Chapter 1, Section IX, the discovery of sex chromosomes in the early years of the twentieth century was inextricably bound up with their capacity of staining differently from the rest of the chromosomes, at least during certain periods of the mitotic or meiotic cycles. These differently staining chromosomes were called "heterochromosomes" by Montgomery (1904), who added the following description: "These are chromosomes which preserve to a great extent their compact form during the whole growth period of the spermatocytes, and during the rest stage of the spermatogonia, and retain throughout the whole period the deep staining characteristic which the other chromosomes exhibit only during the height of mitosis. Thanks to this peculiarity they can be followed with extreme certainty from generation to generation, even during the rest stage; and so are splendid evidence for the thesis of the individuality of the chromosomes." The difference in the state of condensation exhibited by these chromosomes when compared with the rest was called "heteropycnosis" by Gutherz (1907). The opposite term "isopycnosis," implying a state of condensation which is the same as that of the majority of chromosomes is due to Oestergren (1950).

Heitz (1928) found that in the liverwort *Pellia* some parts of the chromosomes did not become invisible at telophase but retained their compact form during interphase. By analogy with the term, "heterochromosomes," Heitz called the parts of chromosomes which showed different staining reactions "heterochromatin." Those chromosomes parts which became invisible at telophase Heitz called "euchromatin," by analogy with the term "euchromosomes," which had been introduced as an alternative to "autosomes."

Originally, therefore, the term "heterochromatin" described a purely cytological concept, the material basis of the previously known phenomenon of heteropycnosis. "Heterochromatin," however, soon became endowed with genetic characteristics. The idea most commonly associated with heterochromatin, that of its so-called genetic inertness, arose largely from work on *Drosophila*. It was shown by Muller and Painter (1932) that in *Drosophila* the whole of the Y-chromosome and a large part of the X-chromosome near the centromere are almost devoid of genes (Chapter 4, Section VI), and soon afterward Heitz (1933) identified these regions as heteropycnotic elements in mitotic chromosomes; while Painter (1934b), Bridges (1935), and Prokofyeva-Belgovskaya (1935) showed that these regions have a characteristic appearance in the salivary gland chromosomes, which is in striking contrast to that shown by the euchromatic regions.

Although the absence of major genetic effects of heterochromatin has on the whole been substantiated, the idea of its total lack of activity could not be maintained for long. The facts relating to the Y-chromosome of *Drosophila* again played an important part in this development, for it soon became clear that although the Y-chromosome had apparently no effect on viability or the development of a male phenotype, its presence was required to ensure motility of the sperm (Stern, 1929). In many other instances, too, it could be demonstrated by closer investigation that heterochromatin was associated with definite phenotypic effects. Indeed, an almost embarrassing array of genetic functions has been attributed to it. Thus, heterochromatin has been regarded as responsible for certain quantitative variations (polygenes; Mather, 1944), for regulating the rate of mitosis (R. B. Goldschmidt, 1955), affecting the nucleic acid cycle and the effect of adjacent genes situated in euchromatin (Schultz, 1936), bringing about neoplastic changes (Darlington and Thomas, 1941; Caspersson and Schultz, 1938; Koller, 1943; Caspersson and Santesson, 1942), and controlling nuclear size (Barigozzi, 1951; Commoner, 1964). Before discussing the genetic effects, some of the cytological features shown by heterochromatin will be described.

III. Cytological Characteristics of Heterochromatin

The concept of heterochromatin is based on the work of Heitz. In the liverwort, *Pellia epiphylla*, which is hermaphrodite, he found nine chromosomes in the haplophase (Chapter 2, Section V). In early prophase, the major part of one of these chromosomes appeared to be heteropycnotic, i.e., stained more intensely, and short heteropycnotic regions were also found on four of the other chromosomes, but were absent on the remaining four (Heitz, 1928). The heteropycnotic regions could not be distinguished in metaphase, but in telophase they retained their chromosomal characteristics while the other chromosomal regions became invisible. The densely staining chromosomal parts persisted throughout interphase. In another species, *Pellia neesiana*, the sexes are separate and the female contains a large X-chromosome, which is absent in the male. This X-chromosome appears to be largely heteropycnotic. Heitz believed that the capacity for differential staining was largely inherent in the chromosomal regions themselves, which he called "heterochromatin." By contrast, those chromosome parts which became unrecognizable at telophase were called "euchromatin."

Heitz (1933, 1934, 1935a) also studied the distribution of heterochromatin in *Drosophila*, both in mitotic and in salivary gland chromosomes.

He concluded that in *Drosophila melanogaster*, the whole of the Y-chromosome and about one half of the X-chromosome including the centromere, as well as smaller portions of autosomes, were stained more darkly than the rest of the chromosomes during mitotic prophase. These chromosome parts are clearly the same as those which are contained in the chromocenter of salivary gland chromosomes (Chapter 4, Section VII). Furthermore, the half of the X-chromosome including the centromere was regarded as genetically inert by Muller and Painter (1932) on the basis of combined cytological and genetic studies. The darker staining of heterochromatin in the chromosomes of mitotic prophase is specially pronounced in *Drosophila pallidipennis* (Dobzhansky, 1944). An attempt to subdivide heterochromatin further on the basis of its cytological appearance in salivary gland chromosomes was made by Heitz (1934). The greater part of the heterochromatin, and the only part which is visible in prophase chromosomes, was thought to be incapable of uncoiling and was called α-heterochromatin; this was thought to be associated with a smaller amount of β-heterochromatin, which is relatively uncoiled and in the form of a diffuse mesh.

There is considerable evidence that the region adjacent to the centromere is heterochromatic in many animals and plants (see Levan, 1946). Levan found that after special treatment, the heterochromatin of several *Allium* and other plant species showed differential staining also in metaphase chromosomes and that the heterochromatin of the centromeric region retains the stain longer than the rest of the heterochromatin. More recently Fredga (1964) showed that in pachytene preparations of Bennett's wallaby (*Protemnodon rufogrisea*—Marsupialia) each of the seven autosomal pairs contained a darkly staining spot, the position of which corresponded to that of the centromere in mitotic chromosomes. Lima-de-Faria (1956) carried out detailed investigations on the centromeric regions in a number of plant species and concluded that they were Feulgen positive but had a cycle of condensation which was distinct from that of the rest of the chromosomes.

In mitotic metaphase chromosomes of *Drosophila*, the presence of nonstaining gaps has been reported. In addition to the primary constrictions, which indicate the position of the centromere, secondary constrictions have been seen (Bridges, 1927; Kaufmann, 1934; Heitz, 1935a); the secondary constrictions of the X- and Y-chromosomes appear to be associated with the nucleolus.

Nonstaining gaps in the mitotic chromosomes of flowering plants were studied by Darlington and La Cour (1938, 1940). In a number of species of *Paris* and *Trillium*, two genera belonging to the lily family, certain chromosome segments were understained at low temperatures, but not at normal temperatures. In interphase nuclei, these segments appeared to be more darkly staining. The Feulgen reaction was used throughout. Darlington and La Cour postulated that heterochromatin fails to maintain its maximum nucleic acid charge during mitosis, at least under certain conditions, a view which is unlikely to be correct since the amount of nucleic acid is now regarded as constant throughout mitosis (Patau and Swift, 1953; J. H. Taylor, 1957). Using a microphotomeric method, Woodard and Swift (1964) did not find any measurable difference in the DNA contents of nuclei containing cold-induced constrictions of the chromosomes in *Trillium erectum*, and they conclude that such constrictions arise by a process of localized uncoiling. However, the hypothesis of allocycly, which was put forward by Darlington and La Cour, and which implies a lack of synchronization of heterochromatin with regard to its nucleic acid synthesis and other characteristics of chromosome behavior, has been strikingly confirmed by the results of autoradiography (see Section IV).

This out-of-phaseness is well illustrated by the behavior of sex chromosomes during spermatogenesis. In the grasshopper, *Locusta migratoria* L., the single X-chromosome in early mitotic divisions of the spermatogonia stands out from the other chromosomes by being thinner and less intensely stained; by contrast, during the prophase of the first meiotic division, it is much shorter and thicker and more heavily stained (White, 1935). White calls the former condition "negative heteropycnosis," and the latter "positive heteropycnosis." Negative heteropycnosis is observed less commonly than positive heteropycnosis. Darlington (1937) introduced the terms "undercondensation" and "overcondensation" to describe these phenomena. According to White (1940a) heteropycnosis of the sex chromosomes is due to a differential degree of coiling of the chromosomes.

The fact that the single X-chromosome of the male tends to become heteropycnotic during spermatogenesis has been known since the beginning of this century. It has also been known for a long time that both the X-chromosomes of the female remain isopycnotic during oogenesis (see Schrader, 1928). This contrasting behavior led Mohr (1915) to formulate the hypothesis that the heteropycnosis of the X-chromosome in the male might be due to the fact that, in contrast to the autosomes, it had to undergo meiosis without a partner. The discovery of the sex chromatin in somatic cells of the female, and the realization that it represents one heteropycnotic member of the two X-chromosomes, has added to the paradox of the situation.

Heterochromatic regions have a tendency to associate with similar ones in the nucleus. The attraction of heterochromatin of nonhomologous chromosomes may bring about their association in meiosis, as was demonstrated by Thomas and Revell 1964) in the flowering plants, *Cicer arietinum* and *C. gigas.* In maize plants, nonhomologous association in meiosis was described by McClintock (1933), both for the so-called supernumerary or B-chromosomes, as well as for some normal chromosomes of the complement. In maize, the normal complement consists of ten pairs of chromosomes, but many strains carry one or more extra chromosomes in addition (Randolph, 1928). During mitosis the B-chromosomes are thicker than the others, and during meiosis their distribution is irregular. They appear to have no obvious effect on the phenotype of the plants. By contrast, the presence of one of the standard chromosomes in triplicate causes the plant to be less vigorous. The B-chromosomes may thus be regarded as consisting of heterochromatin. Whether the nonhomologous pairing of other chromosomes in maize, as reported by McClintock, also affects heterochromatic regions is not certain.

A peculiar type of supernumerary chromosomes, designated as a "pseudo-multiple sex-chromosome mechanism," was described by S. G. Smith (1953) in an Indian species of the gryllid genus, *Euscyrtus.* This species normally has an XX/XO-sex-determining mechanism, with 20 chromosomes in the female and 19 in the male. In a proportion of individuals, one or two additional chromosomes were found in spermatogenesis. These chromosomes were transitorily heteropycnotic during meiosis, and in anaphase they disjoined from the X-chromosome. In some respects, they are therefore intermediate between supernumerary chromosomes and multiple sex chromosomes.

In species of the ladybird beetle (*Chilocorus*), S. G. Smith (1965) found that the chromosome numbers may vary considerably. This is due to the fusion of metacentric chromosomes; the loss of whole chromosome arms is tolerated, since in unfused chromosomes one arm is heterochromatic, while the other is euchromatic. Under the influence of colchicine, euchromatic and heterochromatic arms contract differentially.

According to Darlington and Upcott (1941), B-chromosomes are liable to irregularities at mitosis and, owing to lack of pairing, to loss at meiosis. The fact that they nevertheless persist in many strains must mean, therefore, that these chromosomes cannot be entirely inert but must confer some advantage to the plants which carry them. A similar conclusion was reached by Dobzhansky (1944) with regard to the heterochromatin adjacent to the centromeres in species of *Drosophila.*

Levan (1946) has reviewed the evidence for an association between the centromeric region and heterochromatin. Fredga (1964) compared the appearance of pachytene bivalents in the spermatocytes of Bennett's wallaby (*Protemnodon rufogrisea*), which has a diploid chromosome number of 16, with the homologous chromosomes in mitotic metaphase. He concluded that a heteropycnotic blob seen in each autosomic bivalent corresponded to the centromeric region. The XY bivalent was entirely heteropycnotic, forming a "sex vesicle" (Chapter 9, XIII).

Owing to its relative lack of staining, the centromeric region is often called the "primary constriction." Secondary constrictions, which may also be associated with heterochromatin, occur in many, but not all, chromosomes. If a secondary constriction occurs at the end of a chromosome, it divides off a pair of somewhat ill-defined, rather pufflike structures, which are known as trabants or satellites; they are attached to the main portion of the chromosome by two very thin threads. Such chromosomes are often called "SAT-chromosomes" (Heitz, 1931, 1932), a term which refers not only to the satellites, but also stands for an abbreviation of "Sine Aceto Thymonucleinico" (i.e., lacking DNA), because the threads bearing the satellites do not stain, or stain only very slightly, by means of the Feulgen reaction. In some plants, satellites persist during interphase.

There is considerable evidence that the satellite-bearing chromosomes are concerned with the formation of the nucleolus. According to Heitz (1931, 1932) there is a definite connection, both numerical and as regards their position in the nucleus, between nucleoli and satellite-bearing chromosomes in many species of plants. In maize, one of the ten pairs of chromosomes bears satellites, and this pair is associated with the nucleolus (McClintock, 1933). In man also it has been suggested that the nucleoli are formed by the five pairs of satellited chromosomes (Ohno *et al.*, 1961b; Ferguson-Smith, 1964).

In *Drosophila*, the heterochromatic parts of the X-chromosome as well as of the Y-chromosome act as nucleolar organizers (Kaufmann, 1934; Dobzhansky, 1944; Cooper, 1959); in both these chromosomes, secondary constrictions have been described, which appear to be associated with the development of the nucleolus.

Vanderlyn (1948, 1949) has made the important observation that heterochromatin tends to be preferentially associated with the nuclear membrane and the nucleolus. He arrived at this conclusion as the result of chromosome studies in the onion, *Allium cepa*, as well as from a review of a large body of literature encompassing many animal and plant species; and he put forward the hypothesis that the difference in nucleic acid cycle between heterochromatin, which is near the nuclear and nucleolar membranes, and euchromatin, which is further away from these membranes, may be a consequence of their different relationship with the cytoplasmic and nuclear environments. The subsequent discovery of the sex chromatin in mammals, and its special relationship with the nuclear membrane as well as the nucleolus, has added further to the significance of these observations.

IV. Physicochemical Characteristics of Heterochromatin

Casparsson and Schultz (1938) attempted to compare the relative amounts of nucleic acid produced by euchromatin and heterochromatin, using an ultraviolet absorption method. Their results seemed to show that the cytoplasm of eggs from XXY-females contained more nucleic acid than those from ordinary XX-females, and they concluded that heterochromatin is a particularly active synthesizer of nucleic acids. These results were not confirmed, however. Further experiments seemed to show that although the total amount of RNA in the cytoplasm of XX- and XXY-eggs was the same, the distribution of purine and pyrimidine bases appeared to be different. There was therefore a possibility that the effect of the Y-chromosome on RNA production might be a qualitative rather than a quantitative difference, and the same might be true of DNA (Schultz, 1956).

There can be no doubt that a real breakthrough in the clarification of the concept of heterochromatin came from the use of radioactive tracers in DNA synthesis. This method depends essentially on two facts: (1) elements such as carbon, hydrogen, nitrogen, and phosphorus, which are normally incorporated into cells, have radioactive isotopes with the same chemical properties as themselves, so that the cells do not discriminate between the nonradioactive and the radioactive isotopes; (2) once the radioactive element has been incorporated, it can be revealed by means of a radiosensitive film. This technique is known as autoradiography (Doniach and Pelc, 1950).

Howard and Pelc (1953) showed that cells of the root tips of the bean, *Vicia faba*, take up radioactive phosphorus, P^{32}, incorporated into sodium phosphate only during interphase and prior to a mitotic division. Most of the radioactive material seemed to be taken up by the chromosomes. Subsequently Plaut and Mazia (1956) used thymidine containing C^{14} in an attempt to label the chromosomes of the hawk's-beard, a flowering plant with only three pairs of chromosomes. Since thymidine occurs only in DNA and not in RNA, it is taken up exclusively by the chromosomes. The method therefore provides an accurate determination of the time at which the chromosomes incorporate thymidine in the process of DNA replication, and J. H. Taylor *et al.* (1957) introduced the use of thymidine labeled with tritium (hydrogen-3), which gives better microscopic resolution and thus enables one to detect whether individual chromosomes are labeled. Tritium-labeled thymidine has since been the substance of choice for this study.

Lima-de-Faria (1959) was the first to show that heterochromatin and euchromatin take up tritiated thymidine at different times. This was found in two widely different organisms, a grasshopper, *Melanoplus differentialis*, and a flowering plant, rye (*Secale*). In the grasshopper, the single X-chromosome of the male forms a heterochromatic body during prophase of the first meiotic division, and this chromosome took up the radioactive thymidine later than the autosomes. The rye chromosomes have heterochromatic regions near the centromere, and these regions took up the labeled thymidine at a different time from the rest of the chromosomes. Although the actual sequence of events could not be followed, Lima-de-Faria concluded, by analogy with the X-chromosome in the grasshopper, that the heterochromatin in rye also duplicates its DNA later than the euchromatin.

The first mammalian cells to be studied in this way were those of the Chinese hamster (*Cricetulus griseus*). J. H. Taylor (1960) used two strains of cells grown in tissue culture, one of which originated from a male and the other from a female individual. In the female strain, one of the X-chromosomes duplicated its DNA at the same time as the autosome, while the other X duplicated its DNA later.

The fact that one of the two X-chromosomes of human females duplicates its DNA late is now a well-known phenomenon; and it is known that this X-chromosome forms the Barr body in interphase nuclei. If more than two X-chromosomes are present in the nucleus, all except one replicate late and this number corresponds to the maximum number of Barr bodies.

The single X-chromosome of males replicates at the same time as the autosomes (Schmid, 1963), but the Y-chromosome replicates late (Chapter 10, Section VI). This suggests that the Y-chromosome is heterochromatic, and this is borne out by the apparent lack of genes on this chromosome (Chapter 4, Section VI and Chapter 8, Section XIII). There is no clear evidence whether the Y-chromosome forms a heteropycnotic body in interphase nuclei, but it is likely that such a body would be too small to be distinguished from small heterochromatic pieces present on the autosomes. Schmid (1963) found that many human autosomes have specific late-replicating regions. It is tempting to identify such regions with heterochromatin, which is liable to form small heteropycnotic bodies in interphase nuclei. Such heteropycnotic bodies are often referred to as chromocenters (Baccarini, 1908). Lima-de-Faria *et al.* (1965) subdivide these bodies found in human cells into (1) nucleolus-associated heterochromatin, consisting of autosomal segments surrounding the nucleolus or nucleoli and (2) scattered heterochromatin, consisting of a large number of positively heteropycnotic bodies scattered throughout the nucleus. It appears that both types of heteropycnotic regions are late replicating.

The fact that DNA synthesis occurs later in heterochromatin than in euchromatin was confirmed by H. J. Evans (1964) for the chromosomes of the bean, *Vicia faba*. This species has six pairs of large chromosomes, all of which contain heterochromatic regions. They can be recognized by their positive heteropycnosis in early prophase and in telophase, and they form chromocenters in interphase nuclei. Evans found that in the roots of seedlings, which had been exposed to a solution of tritiated thymidine, the heterochromatic regions took up the thymidine later than the euchromatic ones.

There can be no doubt that the successful application of autoradiography to the problem of chromosome duplication has provided a most important milestone in the history of heterochromatin. The realization that heterochromatin synthesizes DNA at a different time from euchromatin has at last put a solid foundation of fact on what had hitherto been a rather speculative subject; and the hypothesis of allocycly, put forward by Darlington and La Cour (1940), has been incontrovertibly vindicated.

One question that must now be answered is whether the difference in the time of DNA synthesis is qualitative, or whether intermediate states may be recognized. It had been suggested by White (1954) on morphological grounds that the distinction between heterochromatin and euchromatin may not be an absolute one, but that the terms might have been applied to the extremes of a continuous series, between which intermediates may exist.

Recent evidence on mammalian X-chromosomes has made it clear that the same chromosome may become either euchromatic or heterochromatic according to circumstances. The idea that euchromatin may under certain conditions turn into heterochromatin had previously been expressed by some authors (Schultz, 1941; Prokofyeva-Belgovskaya, 1947; Serra, 1949), who used the term "heterochromatinization" or "heterochromatization" to describe this phenomenon.

The amount of condensed chromosomal material (chromocenters) which is present in interphase nuclei is very variable. It is high in the nuclei of lymphocytes. Frenster *et al.* (1963) estimated that up to 80% of the nuclear material of lymphocytes from calf thymus is in the condensed state, which the authors called heterochromatin, the rest being in an extended "euchromatin" state. Studies with the electron microscope showed that the heterochromatin was composed of a dense reticulum of fibrils 100 Å thick, while the euchromatin consisted of fibrils of half this thickness. The metabolism of DNA, RNA, and protein in the two regions was studied by means of precursors labeled with C^{14}. It appeared that the heterochromatin was only about $\frac{1}{3}$ to $\frac{1}{8}$ as active in synthesizing RNA compared with DNA. A possible mechanism for the inactivation of DNA was suggested by Huang and Bonner (1962). These authors found that in nuclear material obtained from pea embryos, histones which were present in intimate association with DNA suppressed genetic activity by inhibiting RNA synthesis. That some of the properties of heterochromatin may be due to an association of its DNA with histones is at present an interesting conjecture.

V. Genetic Effects of Heterochromatin

Much of the evidence regarding the genetic effects of heterochromatin is derived from experiments in which the number of Y-chromosomes in *Drosophila* was varied.

The most striking effect of the Y-chromosome in *Drosophila* is its effect on fertility. Males which lack a Y-chromosome, or which have a deficient Y-chromosome, are sterile (Bridges, 1916; Stern, 1927; Panshin, 1935). As a result of a detailed analysis of the Y-chromosome in *Drosophila*, Stern (1927) showed that to ensure fertility both an intact long arm and an intact short arm of the Y-chromosomes were required but that the two need not necessarily be combined in the same chromosome. Stern left open the question whether the sterility of males with deficient Y-chromosomes is due to the absence of specific regions or the more general lack of sufficient Y-chromosomal substance. So-called fertility genes, or fertility factors, have often been postulated as present on the Y-chromosomes (Neuhaus, 1939; Hannah, 1951; Cooper, 1959), but no evidence has yet been provided to show that these are specific Mendelian genes.

Another striking genetic consequence of heterochromatin is the part it plays with regard to the phenomenon of position effect. Position effect was discovered by Sturtevant (1925), who found that in *Drosophila* two doses of the *Bar* gene situated on the same chromosome produce a more extreme effect than if one dose is present on each of the two homologous chromosomes; [the *Bar* "gene" is, in fact, a small duplication on the X-chromosome (Bridges, 1936)].

A special type of position effect is represented by the so-called eversporting type in *Drosophila*, which Muller (1930) found to be associated with chromosomal rearrangements. For instance, in the progeny of irradiated males carrying the normal allelomorph of the *white* locus, flies with different types of mottled eyes were found, and all were found to have chromosome breaks involving the *white* locus. Although this type of apparent phenotypic instability can be best demonstrated for genes affecting eye color (Fig. 11.1) it occurs also in other characters, for instance the development of bristles. Schultz (1936) examined thirteen types of mottled or variegated eye colors and found that in all of them the chromosomal rearrangement had brought an "active" gene into the proximity of the "inert" region of the chromocenter.

On the basis of these findings, E. B. Lewis (1950) divides position effects into two classes (1) the stable or S-type effect, which appears to involve wholly euchromatic regions of chromosomes; and (2) the more widely studied variegated, or V-type, position effect, which involves a

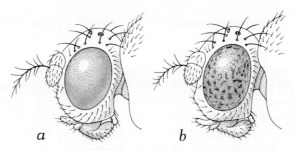

FIG. 11.1. Eye color in *Drosophila melanogaster*. (a) normal; (b) mottled, brought about in certain genotypes by presence of supernumerary Y-chromosome. (After Dubinin and Heptner, 1935). Redrawn by A. J. Lee.

juxtaposition of euchromatin with heterochromatin. In order to express the notion of a rearrangement resulting in a variegated phenotype, the term R is used; thus R (w^+) denotes a rearrangement with variegation of the normal allele of the white gene. A female fly with one chromosome of this type and carrying the *white* allele on the other, R (w^+)/w has mottled red and white eyes, but if the second X-chromosome carries the normal allele of *white*, the eyes are normal (red). It appears as if the rearrangement inhibits the expression of the normal allele in some of the cells. Panshin (1938) showed that the expression of the *white* gene is not affected by its distance from the chromocenter, but solely by the amount of heterochromatin which is inserted into the chromosome. He regards this as conclusive evidence that the chromosome is a "continuum of higher order" (see Chapter 12, Section IV).

The amount of variegation produced is influenced by a number of factors. For instance, the presence of additional Y-chromosomes inhibits variegation. Thus, XXY-females and XYY-males carrying R/w^+ do not show variegation in their color (Gowen and Gay, 1933, 1934; Demerec, 1940; W. K. Baker and Spofford, 1959). By contrast, Dubinin and Heptner (1935) reported that in the case of the gene for brown eyes, which is situated on the second chromosomes, the presence of an additional Y-chromosome in males or females also affects the expression of the gene *sparkling* which, although not due to position effect, is probably related to this phenomenon. The gene alters the texture of the eye and it has been shown (L. V. Morgan, 1947) that as more heterochromatin is added, the expression of the phenotype gradually diminishes. A long inversion of the X-chromosome, involving the insertion of heterochromatin into a euchromatic region, was described by Grüneberg (1935, 1937). This inversion may be associated with very rough eye texture. This case is of particular interest, since reinversion, giving rise to the normal arrangement of the X-chromosome, was observed and flies carrying this chromosome had normal eyes. Soon afterwards, Panshin (1938) showed that the position effect involving the gene for white eyes is also reversible. As a result of X-irradiation, the gene could be removed again from the proximity of heterochromatin, and the flies then had normal, instead of mottled, eyes.

Inevitably, the causes underlying the phenomenon of position effect have given rise to much speculation. Two main types of causes have been postulated (see E. B. Lewis, 1950): (1) that the new position of the genes affects the gene products; and (2) that the structure of the gene itself is altered, though in a reversible way. More recently, Hsu (1962) has advanced an explanation involving the hypothesis that heterochromatin, which is tightly coiled, may be relatively inactive as regards the production of RNA and proteins. According to Hsu, the variegated effect may be produced because genes moved into the vicinity of heterochromatin may become passively involved in the condensed segments, with the result that their activity may be inhibited or reduced; while in other cells the genes may be just outside the cells, so that their activity is unhindered.

The idea that heterochromatin controls the development of quantitative characters owes much to the work of Mather (1943a, 1944; Mather and Wigan, 1942). Mather found that in *Drosophila*, Y-chromosomes of different origin had different effects on the number of certain bristles. Bristle number could also be altered as a result of selection experiments. Mather postulated that the number of bristles to be produced is controlled by a large number of genes, each having a very small effect, which he called "polygenes." Polygenes are situated in heterochromatin and are joined together in blocks. Occasionally, crossing-over may occur within a block, and this gives rise to larger amounts of variation on which selection, either natural or artificial, can act.

On this view, it is a characteristic of heterochromatin to carry polygenes, whereas euchromatin carries the usual type of major genes, or oligogenes. Although there can be no doubt that major genes, in addition to their most striking qualitative effects, also have minor effects, which may be merely of a quantitative nature (Waddington, 1943; Fabergé, 1943), the possibility at least exists that polygenes are genes which have minor, but no major, effects (Mather, 1943b).

While the concept of polygenes still presents certain difficulties (see R. B. Goldschmidt, 1955), which may not become resolved until the different types of genetic control mechanisms can be analyzed at the molecular level, there remains the general impression that heterochromatin somehow controls the expression of quantitative variables. Barigozzi (1951) concluded, on the basis of work in *Drosophila,* that heterochromatin affects cell size, since the males were found to have smaller cells, and this was regarded as due to the presence of a Y-chromosome.

Darlington and Thomas (1941) found that in *Sorghum* plants the presence of B-chromosomes resulted in additional mitotic divisions. In this plant the B-chromosomes are confined to the line of cells which will form the germ cells, being eliminated from all others at an early stage of development. If there are too many mitoses in the pollen grain, it will be killed; hence the additional mitoses may be regarded as malignant, and the authors postulate that heterochromatin may in general be implicated in malignant change.

The view that heterochromatin may be necessary for inducing mitosis was also put forward by R. B. Goldschmidt and Lin (1947) to explain the phenomenon of chromatin diminution in the nematode (threadworm), *Parascaris equorum.* It was first shown by Boveri (1892) that in *Parascaris* the germ cells have a chromosome complement which is different from that of the somatic cells. In the germ cells there is either a single pair (var. *univalens*) or two pairs (var. *bivalens*) of chromosomes, according to the subspecies. Early in embryonic development the stem cells which are destined to produce somatic cells lose only the end portions of their chromosomes, while the center parts fragment into a large number of small chromosomes. There is general agreement that the chromosome ends which are retained only in the germ line are composed of heterochromatin, the presence of which appears to be unnecessary in the somatic cells (White, 1936; Swanson, 1958). R. B. Goldschmidt and Lin (1947) suggested that the reason might be found in the fact that in nematodes, the number of cells remains constant, so that the somatic cells undergo only few cell divisions, after which the cells grow merely in size. Only the germ cells remain capable of undergoing cell division, and they may require the heterochromatic chromosome ends for this purpose.

More recently, Commoner (1964) has put forward the view that DNA participates in two systems of genetic control. One of these systems accounts for the characters showing typical Mendelian inheritance, which may be assumed to be due to specific biochemical differences. This system is localized in the euchromatic regions of the chromosomes. In the second system, DNA gives rise to the genetic regulation of certain metabolic processes, thus determining quantitative characters such as cell size and rate of oxidative metabolism. This second system is assumed to be localized in the heterochromatin. It would appear that the sex-chromosome mechanism of mammals provides the most striking example of this type of dual control. The first X-chromosome of females, as well as the only X-chromosome of the male, are euchromatic and presumably exert their control via the sex-linked genes which they carry. By contrast, the second X-chromosome of females is heterochromatic and this chromosome ensures normal female development. If, by chance, such an additional X-chromosome is present in conjunction with a Y-chromosome, it substitutes the development of Klinefelter's syndrome for that of a normal male. As will be elaborated more fully in Chapter 12, Section IV there appears to be strong evidence that the difference between the sexes is of a quantitative rather than a qualitative nature and is not correlated with any biochemical specificity. It appears therefore that one X-chromosome is always euchromatic and controls biochemical specificity; the second X-chromosome (and any additional ones that may be present) is heterochromatic and control quantitative changes.

As will also be shown in more detail later (Chapter 12, Section II), it is assumed at present that the sex of a mammal rests on a decision made in the embryo according to which in the previously undifferentiated gonad the cortex develops at the expense of the medulla, or vice versa. If such a decision can be assumed to be a quantitative effect due to heterochromatic chromosomes, it is likely that some other relatively large differences may be controlled by a similar mechanism. The so-called podoptera effect in *Drosophila,* discovered by R. B. Goldschmidt *et al.* (1951), consists of a change from a wing into a leglike structure. The tendency for such a change was found to occur in many strains of *Drosophila,* but there was great variation as regards the frequency and the strength of expression. It appeared that the podoptera effect was not due to the action of definite mutant loci, but could be produced by various heterochromatic sections of different chromosomes. The Y-chromosome was particularly effective in all strains, and in some strains the females would show the effect only if they contained a Y-chromosome.

The podoptera effect has been called a "homoeotic change," which is defined as "substitution of serial (segmental) homologues for each other or for part thereof" (R. B. Goldschmidt *et al.*, 1951). Changes of this type are obviously of fundamental importance in embryogenesis as well as in evolution (R. B. Goldschmidt, 1953), and if their genetic control by heterochromatin could be substantiated, this material would have to be assigned a key position among genetic control mechanisms.

It is clear that much work remains to be done concerning the genetic effect of heterochromatin. In the meantime, the sum total of the data which has so far been accumulated provides strong evidence for the contention that heterochromatin exerts a quantitative effect in the development and differentiation of cells. In this capacity it may play a key part in sex differentiation through the agency of the sex chromosomes. In the next chapter we shall deal with possible mechanisms by which the sex chromosomes carry out their task of sex determination.

CHAPTER 12

THE FUNCTION
OF THE SEX CHROMOSOMES

I. Introduction

Since their discovery in insects at the turn of the century, sex chromosomes have been found in a vast number of organisms. Today, the statement that the sex chromosomes act as differentiators of sex in the majority of animals is merely a commonplace. Although the question of what determines the sex of an organism has thus been answered in a formal way, very little is known about the mechanism which underlies the action of the sex chromosomes. Therefore, any hypothesis attempting to explain such action must at present be in the nature of speculation.

Sex chromosomes are a feature of higher organisms, and to fulfil their function they must somehow modify the development of such organisms. Since different animals vary widely in their embryonic development, it is inevitable that the action of the sex chromosomes will vary accordingly. In insects, there is evidence that the sex chromosomes act directly on the cells which contain them. This is strikingly illustrated by the existence of gynandromorphs in *Drosophila,* in which aggregates of cells with an XX- and with an XO-chromosome constitution can be recognized by the expression of female and male characteristics, respectively. A direct effect of the sex chromosomes on sexual development exists also in the silkworm, *Bombyx mori* (Tazima, 1964). It is clear that such a straightforward relationship between sex chromosomes and phenotype cannot exist in vertebrates, in which sexual characteristics result from the action of hormones and the capacity of tissues to react to them (see Burns, 1961; Wolff, 1962; Corner, 1947). The sex hormones fall into two classes, namely estrogens, which bring about the development of female sexual characteristics, and androgens, which cause the development of male sexual characteristics. Both estrogens and androgens comprise a large number of individual hormones. All of them are lipids and belong to the chemical group known as sterols. Owing to the intermediary of the sex hormones, the sex chromosomes of vertebrates must act by a much more remote control than in insects. However, in spite of the great differences by which the development of mammals is distinguished from that of insects, the sex chromosomes in both groups exhibit the phenomenon of heteropycnosis in a particularly striking way; and the question therefore arises, whether at the chromosomal level some features involved in the process of sex determination may be similar even in widely different groups of animals.

In the following page, some data on the development of sex differences in mammals will be briefly reviewed, and this will be followed by a discussion on the possible mode of action of the sex chromosomes.

II. The Development of Sex Differences in Mammals

In human embryos, the gonads first appear at the stage of about 4–5 mm crown–rump length (about 30 to 35 days after conception) in the form of gonadal (genital or germinal) ridges, which develop on the mesonephros, one of the embryonic forerunners of the kidney (Hamilton et al., 1962). There is now considerable evidence that the germ cells do not originate in situ, but migrate to the primitive gonad from an extraembryonic site (Witschi, 1948; Zuckerman, 1960).

The development of the gonad may be divided into four stages (Franchi et al., 1962): During the first stage, the primordial germ cells migrate and settle in the genital ridges. During the second stage, both germinal and nongerminal cells proliferate, thus forming distinct gonadal primordia, which appear identical in both sexes. During the third stage, the gonads become differentiated into an outer cortex and an inner medulla, which are separated by a primary tunica albuginea. During the fourth stage, sex differentiation occurs. The majority of primitive germ cells settle in the cortex, and if the gonad is to develop into a testis, the germ cells are carried into the medulla by the ingrowth of so-called sex cords (Zuckerman, 1960). Henceforth the medulla develops further, while the cortex regresses. On the other hand, if the gonad is to develop into an ovary, the sex cells remain in the cortex, which henceforth develops at the expense of the medulla.

The gonads become sexually differentiated, i.e., histologically distinguishable into male or female, when the embryo is about 47 days old (or 17 mm long). Until this time the developing gonad is indistinguishable in male and females and is sometimes said to be "bipotential," even though its future development is of course predetermined by the sex-chromosome constitution.

In vertebrates, the gametes are conveyed from the gonads to the exterior by a different system of ducts in males and females. In the male, the mesonephric or Wolffian duct develops into the vas deferens, while in the female the paramesonephric or Müllerian duct conveys the ova to the exterior. Originally, however, both Wolffian and Müllerian ducts are laid down in male as well as female embryos, and it is only at a later stage that one system develops at the expense of the other.

There is now considerable evidence that following the differentiation of the gonads the production of hormones from the embryonic testis induces development of the male type. The idea was originally put forward by Lillie (1917) and by Tandler and Keller (1911) on the basis of observations on the freemartin, which is a sterile twin occurring in cattle. The authors showed that a freemartin results only if the twins are of unlike sex and postulated that it is a genetic female which develops as an intersex as a result of hormones secreted by the male. Vascular anastomoses were present between male and freemartin twins, but these could not be found in six pairs of a normal male and a normal female. The external genitalia of the freemartin are similar to those of a female. The internal reproductive organs contain both male and female elements and the gonads are ovotestes with varying amounts of testicular material (Wells, 1962).

The theory of a hormonal causation of the freemartin has possibly been thrown back into the melting pot by the discovery by Ohno et al. (1962; see also Fechheimer et al., 1965; Goodfellow et al., 1965) that twin calves often undergo a mutual exchange of cells, including those of the gonads. Thus the virilization of the freemartin might be due to the presence of XY-cells rather than the effect of male sex hormone carried over from the male twin. It is of interest to note, however, that in five freemartins in which gonadal cells were examined, only cells with XX-sex chromosomes were found, whereas in four of the male twins, cells with XX- as well as XY-sex chromosomes were present. But although the origin of the freemartin may at present be regarded as undecided, the conclusion that hormones affect the sexual development of embryos is undoubtedly correct.

The idea that the fetal testis produces hormones which result in male development of embryonic structures has received strong support as a result of castration experiments on rabbits performed by Jost (1947, 1960). When the testes were removed from two young rabbit embryos, the male ducts and organs were suppressed and the rabbits developed into females. The administration of testosterone to castrated embryos partially restored male development with Wolffian duct, prostate gland, and male external genitalia. Female embryos whose ovaries were removed developed essentially female characteristics, though the organs derived from the Müllerian duct were smaller than normal. Jost (1947, 1960) postulated that this type of underdeveloped female is the neutral sex which develops in the absence of sex hormones. Both in mammals and in birds the neutral sex resembles the homogametic sex. The development of the characteristics of the heterogametic sex requires the activity of the respective sex hormones.

The role of the gonads in mammalian sex differentiation has been discussed by Wells (1962). He suggests that new approaches should become available if the genetic sex of embryos could be established before the gonads become morphologically differentiated into developing ovaries or testes. The new techniques of chromosome analysis have made this approach entirely feasible.

III. Experimentally Administered Sex Hormones And Sex Reversals

Experiments in which embryos or larvae were treated with sex hormones have shown that development of the genetic sex can be suppressed so that the animal develops the characteristics of the other sex. Complete sex reversal has been achieved in amphibians, in which treated genetic males not only resembled females morphologically, but were able to produce viable eggs. In birds and mammals the reversed sexes were not fertile.

Chang and Witschi (1956) bred the African water frog, *Xenopus laevis,* in the laboratory and found that by adding the estrogen estradiol to the water in the aquarium, all the frogs developed as females. The genetic sex of these frogs could be established only by breeding tests (Fig. 12.1). About half the frogs among the all-female progeny that were tested produced males and females in about equal numbers, while the other half produced males only. These results are in accordance with the fact that in *Xenopus laevis* the female is the heterogametic sex (see Chapter 7, Section III), and the treated females with all-male progeny are to be explained as genetic males with XX-sex chromosomes.

By contrast to the complete sex reversal of genetic males achieved by estradiol, the treatment of genetic females with androgens, although resulting in precocious development and the formation of male secondary sexual characters, does not affect the gonads, which develop as ovaries. On the other hand, when male and female frogs were joined organically in parabiosis, the testes remained normal and the ovaries were suppressed. As a result of these experiments Chang and Witschi put forward the view that the sex hormones cannot act as the primary inductors of sex. This problem will be discussed further below.

In the fowl, Dantschakoff (1941) was able to show that by treating genetically male embryos (the genetic sex was determined by means of sex-linked characters after hatching) with the estrogen folliculin some, but not all, birds developed as females. Apart from their size and female arrangement of feathers, such birds had ovaries and oviducts; they did not lay eggs, however. Treatment with testosterone did not result in the sex reversal of genetic females, but resulted in a number of abnormalities which often proved lethal. Dantschakoff concluded from these results

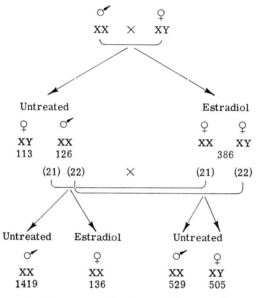

Fig. 12.1. Reversal of chromosomally determined sex in *Xenopus laevis* by treatment with estradiol. (After Chang and Witschi, 1956.)

that androgens are normally not present in chick embryos, and that, in general, the sex hormone of the homogametic sex is absent during embryonic development.

Experiments in which sex hormones were administered to mammalian embryos have on the whole not been successful in inducing sex reversal (see Burns, 1961; Wolff, 1962). It is difficult to interpret such negative results, for a number of reasons. The effect of sex hormones on early embryos is often lethal, and if they are administered later, the time at which sex reversal is possible may have been passed. Again, if the hormone is administered to the mother, it is not known how much of it passes through the placenta. Provided the theory of its hormonal causation is correct, the natural experiment of the freemartin suggests that at least under certain conditions, a hormone secreted by the fetal testis may induce partial sex reversal in a genetic female.

The only clear-cut results on the effects of sex hormones on mammalian embryos have been obtained by Burns, Moore, and others (see Burns, 1961) on marsupials. The opossum, *Didelphis virginiana*, is born 13 days after ovulation, and the young continues its development in the mother's pouch. At the time of birth, the secondary sex organs including the external genitalia are still in the undifferentiated stage, and the sex of the young opossum cannot be determined by inspection until 10 days after birth. Treatment with androgens results in the development of certain male secondary sexual characters in the female, while treatment with estrogen produces partial sex reversal in the male. If treatment with estrogen is begun sufficiently early, it may even affect the testis itself by converting it into an ovotestis. The last fact appears to be an exception to the rule that the hormone of the homogametic sex does not cause embryonic sexual differentiation.

While there are obviously many aspects of this subject which are not yet understood, the sum total of data relating to experiments on sex reversal point to the conclusion that in vertebrates embryonic hormones control the development of the organs of one sex at the expense of those of the other sex.

IV. Some Speculations on the Possible Mode of Action of the Sex Chromosomes

Returning now to the sex chromosomes, it is clear that the decision whether an animal develops as a male or as a female is ultimately theirs, and the question arises, what is the genetic mechanism by which the sex chromosomes fulfil this task? There is so far no answer to this question, and any discussion on this subject must at present be entirely speculative.

The orthodox mode of action of chromosomes is via the genes which they carry. There is of course not the slightest doubt that sex chromosomes carry genes, since a large number of sex-linked genes are known in man and other mammals, in the fowl, and in *Drosophila*, to name only a few organisms. There is every indication that the X-chromosome bears its full complement of genes, although there is usually a striking scarcity of genes on the Y-chromosomes. It has been generally assumed that the determination of sex, also, is determined by a gene or a number of genes. Indeed, the very term "sex-linkage," which was introduced by T. H. Morgan and Bridges in 1916, presupposes the existence of one or more such sex genes situated on the X-chromosome, to which the other genes would be linked. It must be admitted, however, that half a century later there is still no confirmation for the existence of sex genes.

The absence of sex-determining genes is most striking in *Drosophila*, for two reasons. First, more genes are known in *Drosophila* than in other organisms, and the position of these genes on their respective chromosomes has been accurately determined. Second, since in *Drosophila* the sex chromosomes appear to have a direct effect on the cells in which they are present, the somatic tissues can be scored as male or female with considerable accuracy. An estimate of the degree of maleness can be obtained merely by counting the bristles in the sex combs (Stern and Hannah, 1950). By contrast, since the sexual characteristics of mammals are determined in a much more indirect way, a definition of what should be regarded as a male or a female characteristic is less obvious (see Stern, 1963). A striking example of this is provided by the syndrome of testicular feminization in man, in which female development is dependent on the presence of testes (Chapter 8, Section IX).

It will be remembered that in *Drosophila* the sex of a fly depends on the ratio of the number of X-chromosomes to the number of hanologous autosomes. If this is one, the flies are female and if it is one-half, the flies are male, while intermediate ratios result in intersexes (Chapter 4, Table I). The general interpretation is that the X-chromosome in *Drosophila* is female determining, while the autosomes are male determining. Pipkin (1940, 1947, 1960) carried out an intensive search in an attempt to localize any sex genes which might be present either on the X-chromosomes or on the second and third chromosomes. In the case of the X-chromosome, short sections of this were added to triploid intersexes with two X-chromosomes, so that the additional segment was present in triplicate. Although the triplicated portions covered between them the entire X-chromosome, none of the intersexes were turned into females. This result makes the existence of a single female-determining gene on the X-chromosome of *Drosophila* unlikely. The different portions did, however, have a feminizing effect, which was roughly proportional to the length of the segment. No male-determining genes were found on any parts of the second or the third chromosome separately. Pipkin (1960) postulated that the joint action of second and third chromosomes may be necessary for the determination of maleness.

Sturtevant (1945) reported a gene in *Drosophila melanogaster*, which when present in homozygous dose converts females into males. However, in spite of the fact that this gene results in altering primary and secondary sexual characters of a female into those of a male, it does not truly determine the sex of these flies (Chapter 4, Section IV).

In man, too, a number of genes are known which interfere with sexual development. Perhaps the most striking is the syndrome of testicular feminization, in which female external genitalia and female breast development are associated with the presence of testes in the abdomen or the inguinal canal. The view has been put forward that this condition is due to a gene borne on the X-chromosome (McKusick, 1964). The same applies to a condition of male pseudohermaphroditism, in which testes are also present, but the external genitalia are ambiguous. The adreno-genital syndrome, in which the physique is masculinized owing to excessive production of androgens from the adrenal glands, may be an example of a condition transmitted by an autosomal recessive gene (Bierich, 1963). There is therefore clear evidence that in man individual genes can interfere with sexual development, even though there is no evidence that such genes determine normal development.

A gene may be defined either as a unit of recombination in heredity or in terms of the protein which it produces. Our views on the one-to-one relationship between genes and proteins, the foundations of which were to a large extent laid by Beadle and Tatum (1941), have recently become more sophisticated, as with the introduction of smaller and smaller organisms into genetic research the units of recombination could be determined with ever increasing precision. Thus, as a result of work on viruses, the classic gene, the concept of which was based on organisms at least as large as *Drosophila,* has become considerably refined (Benzer, 1957). However, at whatever level the gene may be considered, it would seem that one of its central attributes is that a given unit of DNA controls the production of a given unit of protein. Is there any evidence, then, that the production of a specific protein is involved in sex differentiation?

The existence of specific primary inductors of sex in amphibians has been postulated by Witschi (1931, 1957). According to this scheme, a gene F stimulates the cortex of the gonad to produce cortexin, which inhibits the medulla and controls oogenesis and the formation of female characters. In the male, a gene M stimulates the medulla to produce medullarin, which inhibits the cortex, stimulates spermatogenesis, and controls the formation of male secondary sexual characters.

By and large, however, the evidence for the existence of a specific chemical difference between males and females must so far be regarded as meager, and the genetics of sex determination has not yet become a part of the rapidly advancing subject of biochemical genetics. In the circumstances, it would seem to be legitimate to consider the possibility that sex differentiation may be initiated by a process other than a specific difference in the production of proteins.

If one were to look for positive characteristics of sex chromosomes, the most striking one is surely their tendency toward heteropycnosis. It is convenient to designate the chromosomal material which has this tendency by the term "heterochromatin," which implies a difference from the rest of the chromosomal material. Heterochromatin occurs also in autosomes, but in these it usually makes up only a small part of the chromosomes. The sex chromosomes are the only normally occurring chromosomes which are mainly composed of heterochromatin.

As was mentioned before (Chapter 11, Section V) the conviction has grown among biologists that the chromosomes may act in two different ways (Commoner, 1964): (1) via Mendelian genes, which are situated in euchromatin, and which result in specific biochemical effects; and (2) via heterochromatin, which acts as an agent of nucleotide sequestration, thus giving rise to genetic regulation of metabolic processes, which result in quantitative differences.

The fact that quantitative differences can give rise to two qualitatively different classes has been shown by Grüneberg (1952b), who called the phenomenon "quasi-continuous variation." Grüneberg found that in the mouse a number of skeletal characteristics, which fall into two different classes, have their genetic basis in so-called multifactorial inheritance, in which physiological thresholds result in two types of animals. Grüneberg believes that such multifactorial inheritance can be accounted for as the indirect effect of Mendelian genes and that basically all gene effects are of the same kind. On the other hand, Mather (1943a) used the name "polygenes" for entities with exclusively small quantitative effects and, presented evidence that such polygenes are situated in heterochromatin (Chapter 11, Section V). At the present time, however, it may perhaps be questioned whether it is useful to apply the term "gene" to entities which can neither be localized on chromosomes nor be recognized by specific chemical products. As an alternative, one should perhaps consider the possibility that such quantitative differences are brought about by the agency of relatively large chromosomal regions, or even by whole chromosomes. One might further postulate that such chromosomes, or parts of chromosomes are particularly likely to exhibit the properties of heterochromatin.

As applied to the problem of sex determination, this hypothesis is by no means new. R. B. Goldschmidt (1955) wrote as follows regarding sex determination in *Drosophila:* " 'Multiple sex factors,' in this case, does not mean much more than a statement that no single 'F gene' was found." Emphasizing the fact that sex chromosomes tend to be the richest in heterochromatin, Goldschmidt postulated that female development in *Drosophila* is brought about by the intercalary heterochromatin of the X-chromosome. The possible existence of continua of higher order super-genes and higher fields in genetics has also been discussed by Panshin (1938; see Chapter 11, Section V), Darlington (1958), Pontecorvo (1958), and Vogel (1964); while Swanson (1958) specifically mentioned the possibility that there may be no genes in the classic sense responsible for sex determination, but that this may be achieved by a different sort of balance in which whole chromosomes rather than individual, Mendelizing genes set the developmental pattern.

Recent discoveries in the field of mammalian sex chromosomes, particularly those of man, have added further evidence for the hypothesis that sex is determined by entire heterochromatic chromosomes, or relatively large portions of such chromosomes. The Y-chromosome, which is responsible for initiating male development, either has very few genes or none at all. It also synthesizes its DNA later than most autosomes and may thus be regarded as heterochromatic. The X-chromosome is ambivalent, behaving sometimes like euchromatin and sometimes like heterochromatin. The human X-chromosome carries a large number of genes. In somatic cells, the single X-chromosome of males, and one of the two X-chromosomes of females, are euchromatic as regards their appearance in interphase nuclei and their timing of DNA synthesis. These X-chromosomes appear to behave exactly like autosomes. By contrast, the second X-chromosome of females is typically heteropycnotic in interphase nuclei and synthesizes its DNA late. This X-chromosome must be regarded as heterochromatic, and, according to the Lyon hypothesis, the activity of the genes on this chromosome are suppressed. As was mentioned before (Chapter 10, Section XV), it is likely that a small portion of the X-chromosome in man remains permanently euchromatic. This part of the X-chromosome is probably homologous with a similar region in the Y-chromosome, and it may be assumed that the corresponding part of the Y-chromosome is also euchromatic. Thus it would probably be more accurate to say that the major, but not the entire, part of the second X-chromosome becomes heterochromatic, and the same applies to the Y-chromosome. It is of interest to note that during gametogenesis the X-chromosomes of males and females change over their roles of being either euchromatic or heterochromatic. The single X-chromosome of the male becomes heteropycnotic during gametogenesis, while both X-chromosomes of the female become isopycnotic.

A second X-chromosome with a tendency to become heterochromatic cannot be responsible for female development in man, since this will take place in an XO-sex-chromosome constitution, giving rise to Turner's syndrome. However, such a chromosome appears to be essential for oogenesis to occur. Furthermore, it appears that the entire X-chromosome is necessary for this purpose, since various abnormal X-chromosomes, although heterochromatic, nevertheless give rise to Turner's syndrome and allied conditions (Chapter 8, Section V). Apart from the absence of normal ovaries with oogenesis, such patients also have a number of somatic abnormalities, as was described before.

In human embryos, sex chromatin can be seen in the trophoblast on about the twelfth day and in the embryo itself on about the sixteenth day of gestation (Park, 1957). Although the time of sex-chromatin formation is likely to differ in different tissues it is clear that one of the X-chromosomes in genetic females shows heterochromatic properties at the time when the gonads differentiate.

It will be remembered that the gonads have a double origin, being formed from the gonadal ridges and the migrating germ cells. The results of experiments involving the selective destruction of germ cells indicate that in the absence of germ cells the gonadal ridges develop into sterile ovaries or testes according to their own sex-chromosome constitution (Zuckerman, 1960; Hemsworth and Jackson, 1963a,b). This situation is to some extent comparable to that found in Turner's syndrome and in Klinefelter's syndrome. In the latter condition, the presence of a Y-chromosome causes the gonads to develop into testes, and these in turn bring about the development of the Wolffian ducts and the suppression of the Müllerian ducts, thus causing the phenotype to be male. In the absence of a Y-chromosome, the gonads develop into ovaries, and the Müllerian ducts develop at the expense of the Wolffian ducts, so that the phenotype will be female. However, for the successful proliferation of germ cells, two X-chromosomes are required in the female, and an X-and a Y-chromosome in the male.

Thus, chromosomes with heterochromatic properties are clearly implicated both in the process of sexual differentiation of the phenotype, as well as in the production of germ cells. As was mentioned before, the idea has been gaining ground that heterochromatin is associated with quantitative effects in development. The question therefore arises whether the divergence between male and female development might ultimately be based on quantitative differences. Such a view would obviously become untenable, if a difference in, say, an enzyme were to be discovered, which distinguishes males from females and which might reasonably be assumed to be responsible for sexual differentiation. On the other hand, if sex differentiation were to be due to the activity of steroid hormones the possibility of a quantitative difference determining whether development is to be male or female becomes much more likely. Not long after the discovery of estrogen, it was found by Aschheim (quoted by Corner, 1947) that this enzyme was present in the urine of stallions. Not only are estrogen as well as androgens present in both sexes, but both types of hormones are in fact synthesized by the testis as well as the ovary (Zander and Henning, 1963). Moreover, although as a general rule male tissues react positively to androgens and either do not react to estrogens or are inhibited by them, so-called "paradoxical effects" have sometimes been obtained when abnormally large amounts of enzymes have been used (Burns, 1942); in such cases the hormone appeared to induce changes appropriate to the other sex. The lack of precise specificity of the steroid hormones, as well as the occurrence of androgens and estrogens in both sexes point at least to the possibility that the dimorphism between the sexes may have its origin in quantitative differences. If this assumption were correct, it would suggest that the sex chromosomes, in their function as sex differentiators, act without the intermediary of individual genes and do not produce gene-specific proteins.

A genetic hypothesis based on units other than genes may appear unsatisfactory, particularly at the present time when the relationship between genes and proteins is being consolidated in precise chemical terms. On the other hand, it has also become clear that conventional genes and gene products cannot account for all developmental processes (Waddington, 1961), and the participation of less conventional units in biological processes has already been postulated by a number of investigators (see above). Szent-Györgyi (1961) wrote as follows concerning the functioning of units other than conventional molecules in general biological processes: "When biochemistry went into bloom at the end of the last century the atom was an indivisible unit, molecules the aggregates of such units. Biochemistry was thus based on the rigid molecular concept. Later it was recognised that the atom is a whole universe and chemical reactions may be but the overall results of a series of subtler changes within these systems (e.g., polarization, intramolecular shift of electrons, etc.). . . . The subtler and more complex biological phenomena, linked to structures, may necessitate a further extension of our outlook, a fusion of the molecular with the sub- and supra-molecular."

The idea underlying these remarks appears to be equally relevant when applied to the more restricted field of genetics. The spectacular successes of classic genetics were achieved on the assumption that the gene, as observed in *Drosophila* and larger organisms, is an indivisible unit of crossing-over and of function. As a result of using smaller organisms for genetic experiments, the size of the gene has been progressively pared down, so that it now occupies only a few nucleotides (Benzer, 1957). There has been no new experimental evidence on the possible effects of units larger than genes. Even if they existed, they would not fit easily into the scheme of classic genetic experimentation, which depends mainly on localized positions of crossing-over. Consequently there has been a tendency to assume that all genetic effects which do not obey the accepted rules of crossing-over are due to some hypothetical genes, which are usually believed to exist in large numbers. It must be admitted that at present such an assumption is no more, and no less, likely than the alternative possibility that aggregates of genes, and perhaps whole chromosomes, exert a specific genetic effect.

The whole problem is particularly well illustrated by the behavior of the X-chromosome in man. This chromosome contains a large number of genes, whose behavior fits perfectly into accepted genetic theory. In addition, the X-chromosome has other effects, including the production of oocytes, which have so far eluded an explanation in genetic terms. The duality of its genetic behavior is paralleled by the dual cytological appearance of the X-chromosome and its timing of DNA synthesis. In both these aspects, the X-chromosome may either resemble autosomes, or it may assume the properties of heterochromatin. It seems certain that the new techniques which have become available within recent years will help to clarify the significance underlying this duality.

It will be remembered that the discovery of the sex chromosomes dates only from the beginning of the twentieth century. This discovery at last gave an answer to the age-old question as to the cause of sex differentiation. "Does sex arise, as was long believed, as a response of the organism to external stimuli? Or is it automatically ordered by internal factors, and if so, what is their nature (Wilson, 1909a)?" It is one of the triumphs of cytogenetics that these questions are no longer topical. However, now that the existence of sex chromosomes has become common knowledge, the problem of how they act remains to be tackled. Do the sex chromosomes determine sex through the action of individual genes, or do these chromosomes function also as larger units, which bring about the development of functional males and females? The answer to this question will represent another important step toward our understanding of sex determination and should, moreover, shed light on the wider problem of the role of the chromosomes in development.

BIBLIOGRAPHY

Adam, A., Sheba, C., Sanger, R., Race, R. R., Tippett, P., Hamper, J., Gavin, J., and Finney, D. J. (1963). Data for X-mapping calculations, Israeli families tested for Xg, g-6-pd and for colour vision. *Ann. Human Genet.* **26**, 187–194.

Aggeler, P. M., White, S. G., Glendening, M. B., Page, E. W., Leake, T. B., and Bates, G. (1952). Plasma thromboplastin component deficiency: A new disease resembling hemophilia. *Proc. Soc. Exptl. Biol. Med.* **79**, 692–694.

Allen, C. E. (1917). A chromosome difference correlated with sex in *Sphaerocarpus*. *Science* **46**, 466–467.

Allen, C. E. (1940). The genotypic basis of sex-expression in angiosperms. *Botan. Rev.* **6**, 227–300.

Anders, G. (1948). Einwirkung eines geschlechtsumwandelden Faktors ('tra') auf den pleiotropen Effekt des Gens lozenge-clawless ("lz") bei *Drosophila melanogaster*. *Arch. Julius Klaus-Stift. Vererbungsforsch. Sozialanthropol. Rassenhyg.* **23**, 510–512.

Ashley, D. J. B. (1962). "Human Intersex." Livingstone, Edinburgh and London.

Ashley, D. J. B., and Jones, C. H. (1958). Discrepancies in the diagnosis of genetic sex by leucocyte morphology. *Lancet* **I**, 240–242.

Ashley, D. J. B., and Theiss, E. A. (1959). Nuclear sex in species showing male homogamety. *Anat. Record* **135**, 115–117.

Atkin, N. B. (1960). Sex chromatin and chromosomal variation in human tumours. *Acta, Unio Intern. Contra Cancrum* **16**, 41–46.

Atkin N. B., and Klinger, H. P. (1962). The superfemale mole. *Lancet* **II**, 727–728.

Atkins, L., and Gustavson, K. H. (1964). The pattern of DNA synthesis in human chromosomes in cells with an XXY sex chromosome constitution. *Hereditas* **51**, 135–145.

Atkins, L., Taft, P. D., and Dalal, K. P. (1962). Asynchronous DNA synthesis of sex chromatin in human interphase nuclei. *J. Cell Biol.* **15**, 390–393.

Atkins, L., Böök, J. A., Gustavson, K.-H., Hansson, O., and Hjelm, M. (1963). A case of XXXXY sex-chromosome anomaly with autoradiographic studies. *Cytogenetics (Basel)* **2**, 208–232.

Austin, C. R., and Amoroso, E. C. (1957). Sex chromatin in early cat embryos. *Exptl. Cell Res.* **13**, 419–421.

Awa, A., Sasaki, M., and Takayama, S. (1959). An *in vitro* study of the somatic chromosomes in several mammals. *Japan. J. Zool.* **12**, 257–266.

Baccarini, J. (1908). Sulle cinesi vegitative de *Cynomorium coccineum* L. *Nuovo Giorn. Botan. Ital.* **15**, 189–203.

Bacci, G. (1965). "Sex Determination." Pergamon Press. Oxford.

Bain, A. D., and Scott, J. S. (1965). Mixed gonadal dysgenesis with XX/XY mosaicism. *Lancet* **I**, 1035–1039.

Bain, A. D., Gauld, I. K., and Farqhar, J. W. (1965). A ring X chromosome in dwarfism. *Lancet* **I**, 820.

Baker, J. R., and Callan, H. G. (1950). Heterochromatin. *Nature* **166**, 227–228.

Baker, W. K., and Spofford, J. B. (1959). Heterochromatic control of variegation in *Drosophila melanogaster*. *Proc. 10th Intern. Congr. Genet., Montreal, 1958*. Vol. 2, pp. 11–12. Univ. of Toronto Press, Toronto.

Balbiani, F. G. (1881). Sur le structure du noyau des cellules salivaries chez les larves de Chironomus. *Zool. Anz.* **4**, 637–641.

247

Bamford, S. B., Cassin, C. M., and Mitchell, B. S. (1963). Sex chromatin determinations in selected cases of developmental sex abnormalities with an assessment of results. *Acta cytol.* **7**, 151–158.

Bamford, S. B., Cassin, C. M., Dilba, D. L., and Mitchell, G. W. (1964). Neutrophil appendages as indicators of sex chromosome aberrations. *Acta Cytol.* **8**, 323–331.

Barigozzi, G. (1951). The influence of the Y-chromosome on quantitative characters of *D. melanogaster. Heredity* **5**, 415–432.

Barr, M. L. (1951). The morphology of neuroglial nuclei in the cat, according to sex. *Exptl. Cell Res.* **2**, 288–290.

Barr, M. L. (1963). The sex chromatin. *In* "Intersexuality" (C. Overzier, ed.), pp. 48–71. Academic Press, New York.

Barr, M. L., and Bertram, E. G. (1949). A morphological distinction between neurones of the male and female, and the behaviour of the nucleolar satellite during accelerated nucleoprotein synthesis. *Nature* **163**, 676–677.

Barr, M. L., and Carr, D. H. (1960). Sex chromatin, sex chromosomes and sex anomalies. *Can. Med. Assoc. J.* **83**, 979–986.

Barr, M. L., Bertram, E. G., and Lindsay, H. A. (1950). The morphology of the nerve cell nucleus, according to sex. *Anat. Record* **107**, 283–297.

Barr, M. L., Shaver, E. L., Carr, D. H., and Plunkett, E. R. (1959). An unusual sex chromatin pattern in three mentally deficient subjects. *J. Mental Deficiency Res.* **3**, 78–87.

Barr, M. L., Shaver, E. L., Carr, D. H., and Plunkett, E. R. (1960). The chromatin positive Klinefelter syndrome among patients in mental deficiency hospitals. *J. Mental Deficiency Res.* **4**, 89–107.

Barr, M. L., Carr, D. H., Pozsonyi, J., Wilson, R. A., Dunn, H. G., Jacobson, T. S., and Miller, J. R. (1962). The XXXXY sex chromosome abnormality *Can. Med. Assoc. J.* **87**, 891–901.

Barr, M. L., Carr, D. H., Soltan, H. C., Wiens, R. G., and Plunkett, E. R. (1964). The XXYY variant of Klinefelter's syndrome. *Can. Med. Assoc. J.* **90**, 575–580.

Barton, D. E., David, F. N., and Merrington, M. (1963). Numerical analysis of chromosome patterns. *Ann. Human Genet.* **26**, 349–353.

Basrur, P. K., and Coubrough, R. I. (1964). Anatomical and cytological sex of a Saanen goat. *Cytogenetics (Basel)* **3**, 414–426.

Bateson, W. (1909). Heredity and variation in modern lights. *In* "Darwin and Modern Science" (A. C. Seward, ed.), pp. 85–101. Cambridge Univ. Press, London and New York.

Bateson, W., Saunders, E. R., and Punnett, R. C. (1908). Experimental studies in the physiology of heredity. *Rept. Evolution Comm. Roy. Soc.* **4**, 1–18.

Bauer, H. (1947). Karyologische Notizen. T. Über generative Polyploidie bei Dermapteren. *Z. Naturforsch.* **2b**, 63–66.

Baur, E. (1912). Ein Fall von geschlechtsbegrenzter Vererbung bei *Melandrium album. Z. Induktive Abstammungs-Vererbungslehre* **8**, 335–336.

Baylet, R., and Grattepanche, H. (1964). Etude chromosomique du singe Papio papio. *Compt. Rend.* **259**, 2913–2916.

Beadle, G. W., and Tatum, E. L. (1941). Genetic control of biochemical reactions. *Proc. natl. Acad. Sci. U.S.* **27**, 499–506.

Beatty, R. A. (1957). "Parthenogenesis and Polyploidy in Mammalian Development." Cambridge Univ. Press, London and New York.

Beçak, W., Beçak, M. L., and Nazareth, H. R. S. (1962). Karyotypic studies of two species of South American snakes (*Boa constrictor amarali* and *Bothrops jararaca*). *Cytogenetics* (*Basel*) 1, 305–313.

Beçak, W., Beçak, M. L., Nazareth, H. R. S., and Ohno, S. (1964). Close karyological kinship between the repitilian suborder Serpentes and the class Aves. *Chromosoma* 15, 606–617.

Beermann, W. (1955). Geschlechtsbestimmung und Evolution der genetischen Y-Chromosomen bei *Chironomus*. *Biol. Zentr.* 74, 525–544.

Beermann, W. (1961). Ein Balbiani-Ring als Locus einer Speicheldrüsen-mutation. *Chromosoma* 12, 1–25.

Bell, J., and Haldane, J. B. S. (1937). The linkage between the genes for colour-blindness and hemophilia in man. *Proc. Roy Soc.* B123, 119–150.

Bender, M. A., and Chu, E. H. Y. (1963). The chromosomes of primates. *In* "Evolutionary and Genetic Biology of the Primates" (J. Buettner-Janasch, ed.), Vol. 1, pp. 261–310. Academic Press, New York.

Bender, M. A., and Mettler, L. E. (1960). Chromosome studies of primates. II. *Callithrix, Leontocebus*, and *Callimico*. *Cytologia* 25, 400–404.

Benirschke, K. (1964). Corrigendum. *Chromosoma* 15, 300.

Benirschke, K., and Brownshill, L. F. (1962). Further observations on marrow chimerism in marmosets. *Cytogenetics* (*Basel*) 1, 245–257.

Benirschke, K., and Brownhill, L. E. (1963). Heterosexual cells in testes of chimeric marmoset monkeys. *Cytogenetics* (*Basel*) 2, 331–341.

Benirschke, K., Anderson, J. M., and Brownhill, L. E. (1962a). Marrow chimerism in marmosets. *Science* 138, 513–515.

Benirschke, K., Brownhill, L. E., and Beath, M. M. (1962b). Somatic chromosomes of the horse, the donkey and their hybrids, the mule and the hinny. *J. Reprod. Fertility* 4, 319–326.

Benirschke, K., Low, R. J., Brownhill, L. E., Caday, L. B., and de Venecia-Fernandez, J. (1964a). Chromosome studies of a donkey grevy zebra hybrid. *Chromosoma* 15, 1–13.

Benirschke, K., Low, R. J., Sullivan, M. M., and Carter, R. M. (1964b). Chromosome study of an alleged fertile mare mule. *J. Heredity* 55, 31–38.

Benzer, S. (1957). The elementary units in heredity. *In* "The Chemical Basis of Heredity" (W. D. McElroy and B. Glass, eds.), pp. 70–93. Johns Hopkins Press, Baltimore, Maryland.

Berenbaum, M. C. (1960). Determination of sex in granulopoietic cells of mice and rats. *Nature* 188, 603–604.

Bergemann, E. (1961). Geschlechtschromatinbestimmungen am Neugeborenen. *Schweiz. Med. Wochschr.* 91, 292–294.

Bergemann, E. (1962). Manifestation familiale du karyotype triple-X. Communication préliminaire. *J. Genet. Humaine* 10, 370–371.

Bertram, E. G., Bertram, L. F., and Lindsay, H. A. (1950). The nucleolus associated chromatin in cat and man. *Anat. Record* 106, Suppl., 299.

Beutler, E., Robson, M., and Buttenwieser, E. (1957). The glutathione instability of drug sensitive red cells. *J. Lab. Clin. Med.* 49, 84–95.

Beutler, E., Yeh, M., and Fairbanks, V. F. (1962). The normal human female as a mosaic of X-chromosome activity: studies using the gene for G-6-Pd deficiency as a marker. *Proc. Natl. Acad. Sci. U.S.* 48, 9–16.

Bierich, J. R. (1963). The adrenogenital syndrome *In* "Intersexuality" (C. Overzier, ed.), pp. 345–386. Academic Press, New York.

Biggs, R., Douglas, A. S., Macfarlane, R. G., Dacie, J. V., Pitney, W. R., and Merskey, C. (1952). Christmas disease. A condition previously mistaken for haemophilia. *Brit. Med. J.* **II**, 1378–1382.

Bishop, A., and Bishop, O. N. (1963). Analysis of tritium-labelled human chromosomes and sex chromatin. *Nature* **199**, 930–932.

Blackburn, K. B. (1923). Sex chromosomes in plants. *Nature* **112**, 687–688.

Blank, C. E., Bishop, A., and Caley, J. P. (1960). Example of XY/XO mosaicism. *Lancet* **II**, 1450.

Blank, C. E., Zachary, R. B., Bishop, A. M., Emery, J. L., Dewhurst, C. J., and Bond, J. H. (1964). Chromosome mosaicism in a hermaphrodite. *Brit. Med. J.* **II**, 90–93.

Böök, J. A., and Santesson, B. (1961). Nuclear sex in triploid XXY human cells. *Lancet* **II**, 318.

Borland, R. (1964). The chromosomes of domestic sheep. *J. Heredity* **55**, 61–64.

Boveri, T. (1890). Über das Verhalten der chromatischen Kernsubstanz bei der Bildung der Richtungskörper und bei der Befruchtung. *Jena Z. Naturwiss.* **17**, 314–401.

Boveri, T. (1891). Befruchtung. *Ergeb. Anat. Entwicklungsgech. Abt.* 2, **1**, 386–485.

Boveri, T. (1892). Die Entstehung des Gegensatzes zwischen den Geschlechtszellen und den somatischen Zellen bei *Ascaris*. *Sitzber. Ges. Morphol. Physiol. Müench.* **8**, 114–125.

Boveri, T. (1915). Über die Entstehung der Eugsterschen Zwitterbiene. *Arch. Entwicklungsmech. Organ.* **41**, 264–310.

Bovey, R. (1949). Les chromosomes des chiroptères et des insectivores. *Rev. Suisse Zool.* **56**, 371–460.

Boyes, J. W. (1954). Somatic chromosomes of higher Diptera. *Can. J. Zool.* **32**, 39–63.

Bradbury, J. T., Bunge, R. G., and Boccabella, R. A. (1956). Chromatin test in Klinefelter's syndrome. *J. Clin. Endocrinol. Metab.* **16**, 689.

Bray, P., and Sr. Josephine, Ann (1963). An XXXYY sex chromosome anomaly. *J. Am. Med. Assoc.* **184**, 179–182.

Bridges, C. B. (1913). Non-disjunction of the sex-chromosomes of *Drosophila*. *J. Exptl. Zool.* **15**, 587–606.

Bridges, C. B. (1914). Direct proof through non-disjunction that the sex-linked genes are borne on the X-chromosome. *Science* **40**, 107–109.

Bridges, C. B. (1916). Non-disjunction as proof of the chromosome theory of heredity. *Genetics* **1**, 1–52 and 107–163.

Bridges, C. B. (1917). Deficiency. *Genetics* **2**, 445–465.

Bridges, C. B. (1919). Duplications. *Anat. Record* **15**, 357–358.

Bridges, C. B. (1921). Triploid intersexes in *Drosophila melanogaster*. *Science* **54**, 252–254.

Bridges, C. B. (1925). Sex in relation to chromosomes and genes. *Am. Naturalist* **59**, 127.

Bridges, C. B. (1927). Constrictions in the chromosomes of *Drosophila melanogaster*. *Biol. Zentr.* **47**, 600–603.

Bridges, C. B. (1935). Salivary chromosome maps. *J. Heredity* **25**, 60–64.

Bridges, C. B. (1936). The Bar "gene" a duplication. *Science* **83**, 210–211.

Bridges, C. B. (1938). A revised map of the salivary gland X-chromosome of *Drosophila melanogaster*. *J. Heredity* **29**, 11–13.

Bridges, C. B. (1939). Cytological and genetic basis of sex. *In* "Sex and Internal Secretions" (E. Allen, ed.), 2nd ed., pp. 15–63. Baillière, London.

Bridges, C. B., and Brehme, K. S. (1944). The Mutants of *Drosophila melanogaster*. *Carnegie Inst. Wash. Publ.* **552**.

Briggs, D. K. (1958). The individuality of nuclear chromatin with particular reference to polymorphonuclear neutrophil leukocytes. *Blood* **13**, 986–1000.

Briggs, D. K. and Kupperman, H. S. (1956). Sex differentiation by leukocyte morphology. *J. Clin. Endocrinol. Metab.* **16**, 1163–1179.

Brøgger, A., and Aagenaes, Ö. (1965). The human Y-chromosome and the etiology of true hermaphroditism. With the report of a case with XX/XY sex chromosome mosaicism. *Hereditas* **53**, 231–246.

Bullock, W., and Fildes, P. (1912). Haemophilia. *Treasury Human Inheritance* **1**, 169–354.

Burns, R. K. (1942). The effect of male hormone on the differentiation of the urogenital sinus in young opossums. *Contrib. Embryol. Carnegie Inst.* **31**, 165–175.

Burns, R. K. (1961). Role of hormones in the differentiation of sex. *In* "Sex and Internal Secretions" (W. C. Young, ed.), 3rd ed. Vol. 1, pp. 76–158. Baillière, London.

Burton, M. (1962). "Systematic Dictionary of Mammals of the World." Museum Press, London.

Callan, H. G. (1941). The sex-determining mechanism of the earwig, *Forficula auricularia. J. Genet.* **41**, 349–374.

Caratzali, A. (1963). Sex appendages, *Arneth* formula and the menstrual cycle. *Cytogenetics (Basel)* **2**, 14–23.

Caratzali, A., and Phleps, A. (1958). Considérations sur le determinisme des corpuscules sexuels des leucocytes. *Compt. Rend. Soc. Biol.* **152**, 1114–1115.

Caratzali, A., Phleps, A., and Turpin, R. (1957). Variations quantitatives des corpuscules sexuels des granulocytes neutrophiles au cours du cycle menstrual. *Bull. Acad. Med. (Paris)* **141**, 496–501.

Carr, D. H. (1965). Chromosome studies in spontaneous abortions. *Obstet. Gynecol.* **26**, 308–326.

Carr, D. H., Barr, M. L., and Plunkett, E. R. (1961). An XXXX sex chromosome complex in two mentally defective females. *Can. Med. Assoc. J.* **84**, 131–137.

Carson, P., Flanagan, C. L., Ickes, C. E., and Alving, A. S. (1956). Enzymatic deficiency in primaquine-sensitive erythrocytes. *Science* **124**, 484–485.

Caspersson, T., and Schultz, J. (1938). Nucleic acid metabolism of the chromosomes in relation to gene reproduction. *Nature* **142**, 294–295.

Caspersson, T. and Santesson, L. (1942). Studies on protein metabolism in the cells of epithelial tumours. *Acta Radiol. Suppl.* **46**, 1–105.

Cattanach, B. M. (1961). XXY mice. *Genet. Res.* **2**, 156–158.

Cattanach, B. M. (1962). XO mice. *Genet. Res.* **3**, 487–490.

Chang, C. Y., and Witschi, E. (1956). Genic control and hormonal reversal of sex differentiation in *Xenopus. Proc. Soc. Exptl. Biol. Med.* **93**, 140–144.

Chiarelli, B. (1961). Chromosomes of the Orang-Utan (*Pongo pygmaeus*). *Nature* **192**, 285.

Chiarelli, B. (1962). Comparative morphometric analysis of primate chromosomes. I. The chromosomes of anthropoid apes and of man. *Caryologia* **15**, 99–121.

Chiarelli, B., and Barberis, L. (1964). The "drumstick" nei leucociti dei primati. *Caryologia* **17**, 567–573.

Childs, B., Zinkham, W., Browne, E. A., Kimbro, E. L., and Terbert, J. V. (1958).

A genetic study of a defect in glutathione metabolism of the erythrocyte. *Bull. Johns Hopkins Hosp.* **102**, 21–37.

Chu, E. H. Y., and Bender, M. A. (1961). Chromosome cytology and evolution in primates. *Science* **133**, 1399–1405.

Chu, E. H. Y., and Giles, N. H. (1957). A study of primate chromosome complements. *Am. Naturalist* **91**, 273-282.

Chu, E. H. Y., and Swomley, B. A. (1961). Chromosomes of lemurine lemurs. *Science* **133**, 1925–1926.

Chu, E. H. Y., Thuline, H. C., and Norby, D. E. (1964). Triploid-diploid chimerism in a male tortoiseshell cat. *Cytogenetics (Basel)* **3**, 1–18.

Clapham, A. R., Tutin, T. G., and Warburg, E. F. (1962). "Flora of the British Isles," 2nd ed. Cambridge Univ. Press, London and New York.

Clark, A. M., and Clark, E. G. (1963). X-ray induced non-disjunction of the X-chromosome in female *Drosophila melanogaster*. *Drosophila Inform. Serv.* **37**, 70.

Clark, J. I., Puite, R. H., Marozynski, R., and Mann, J. D. (1963). Evidence for the absence of detectable linkage between the genes for Duchenne muscular dystrophy and the Xg blood group. *Am. J. Human Genet.* **15**, 292–297.

Clarke, C. M. (1962). Techniques in the study of human chromosomes. *In* "Chromosomes in Medicine" (J. L. Hamerton, ed.), pp. 35–47. Heinemann, London.

Clausen, J. J., and Syverton, J. T. (1962). Comparative chromosomal study of 31 cultured mammalian cell lines. *J. Natl. Cancer Inst.* **28**, 117–145.

Clayman, C. B., Arnold, J., Hockwald, R. S., Yount, E. H., and Edgcomb, J. H. (1952). Toxicity of primaquine in Caucasians. *J. Am. Med. Assoc.* **149**, 1563–1568.

Close, H. G. (1963). Two apparently normal triple X females. *Lancet* **II**, 1358–1359.

Commoner, B. (1964). Roles of deoxyribonucleic acid in inheritance. *Nature* **202**, 960–968.

Cook, P. J. L. (1965). The Lutheran-Secretor recombination fraction in man: A possible sex difference. *Ann. Human Genet.* **28**, 393–401.

Cooper, K. W. (1959). Cytogenetic analysis of major heterochromatic elements (especially Xh and Y) in *Drosophila melanogaster*. *Chromosoma* **10**, 535–588.

Corner, G. W. (1947). "The Hormones in Human Reproduction." Princeton Univ. Press, Princeton, New Jersey.

Correns, C. (1900). G. Mendel's Regel über des Verhalten der Nachkommenschaft der Rassenbastarde. *Ber. Deut. Botan Ges.* **18**, 146–168.

Correns, C. (1907). "Die Bestimmung und Vererbung des Geschlechts, nach neuen Versuchen mit höheren Pflanzen." Borntraeger, Berlin.

Correns, C. (1928). "Bestimmung, Vererbung und Verteilung des Geschlechtes bei den höheren Pflanzen." Volume 2: "Handbuch der Vererbungswissenschaft" (E. Baur and M. Hartmann, eds.). Borntraeger, Berlin.

Court Brown, W. M., Harnden, D. G., Jacobs, P. A., Maclean, N., and Mantle, D. J. (1964). Abnormalities of the sex chromosome complement in man. *Med. Res. Council, Spec. Rept. Ser.* **305**.

Court Brown, W. M., Jacobs, P., and Brunton, M. (1965). Chromosome studies on randomly chosen men and women. *Lancet* **II**, 561–562.

Cox, E. K. (1926). The chromosomes of the house mouse. *J. Morphol.* **43**, 45–53.

Crew, F. A. E. (1965). "Sex-Determination." Methuen, London.

Crippa, M. (1964). The mouse karyotype in somatic cells cultured *in vitro*. *Chromosoma* **15**, 301–311.

Culling, C. F. A. (1966). Staining affinities and cytochemical properties of the sex chromatin. In "The Sex Chromatin." (K. L. Moore, ed.), pp. 91–112. Saunders, Philadelphia.

Dantschakoff, V. (1941). "Der Aufbau des Geschlechts bei höheren Wirbeltieren." Fischer, Jena.

Darlington, C. D. (1929). Chromosome behaviour and structural hybridity in the Tradescantiae. J. Genet. 21, 207–286.

Darlington, C. D. (1931). Meiosis. Biol. Rev. 6, 221–264.

Darlington, C. D. (1932). "Recent Advances in Cytology," 1st ed. Churchill, London.

Darlington, C. D. (1936). The external mechanics of the chromosomes. Proc. Roy. Soc. (London) Ser. B, 121, 264–273.

Darlington, C. D. (1937). "Recent Advances in Cytology," 2nd ed. Re-issued (1965) under title "Cytology." Churchill, London.

Darlington, C. D. (1939). Misdivision and the genetics of the centromere. J. Genet. 37, 341–364.

Darlington, C. D. (1940a). The genetical and mechanical properties of the sex chromosomes. V. Cimex and the Heteroptera. J. Genet. 39, 101–137.

Darlington, C. D. (1940b). The origin of iso-chromosomes. J. Genet. 39, 351–361.

Darlington, C. D. (1958). "The Evolution of Genetic Systems." Oliver & Boyd, Edinburgh and London.

Darlington, C. D., and Haque, A. (1955). Chromosomes of monkeys and men. Nature 175, 32.

Darlington, C. D., and La Cour, L. F. (1938). Differential reactivity of the chromosomes. Ann. Botany (London) [N.S.] 2, 615–625.

Darlington, C. D. and La Cour, L. F. (1940). Nucleic acid starvation in Trillium. J. Genet. 40, 185–213.

Darlington, C. D., and Thomas, P. T. (1941). Morbid mitosis and the activity of inert chromosomes in Sorghum. Proc. Roy. Soc. B130, 127–150.

Darlington, C. D., and Upcott, M. B. (1941). The activity of inert chromosomes in Zea mays. J. Genet. 41, 275–296.

Davidson, J. N. (1965). "The Biochemistry of Nucleic Acids," 5th ed. Methuen, London.

Davidson, R. G., Nitowsky, H. M., and Childs, B. (1963). Demonstration of two populations of cells in the human female heterozygous for glucose-6-phosphate dehydrogenase variants. Proc. Natl. Acad. Sci. U. S. 50, 481–485.

Davidson, W. M. (1966). Sexual dimorphism in nuclei of polymorphonuclear leukocytes in various animals. In "The Sex Chromatin" (K. L. Moore, ed.), pp. 59–75.

Davidson, W. M., and Smith, D. R. (1954). A morphological sex difference in the polymorphonuclear neutrophil leucocytes. Brit. Med. J. II, 6–7.

Davidson, W. M., and Smith, D. R. (1958). The neutrophil sex nodule in Klinefelter's syndrome. In "Symposium on Nuclear Sex" (D. R. Smith and W. M. Davidson, eds.), pp. 93–101. Heinemann, London.

Davidson, W. M., and Smith, D. R. (1963). The nuclear sex of leucocytes. In "Intersexuality" (C. Overzier, ed.), pp. 78–85. Academic Press, New York.

Davidson, W. M., and Winn, S. (1961). The relationship between the sex nodule and the sex chromosomes. In "Human Chromosomal Abnormalities" (W. M. Davidson and D. R. Smith, eds.), pp. 28–36. Staples Press, London.

Davies, S. H., Gavin, J., Goldsmith, K. L. G., Graham, J. B., Hamper, J., Hardisty, R. M., Harris, J. B., Holman, C. A., Ingram, G. I. C., Jones, T. G., McAffee, L. A., McKusick, V. A., O'Brien, J. R., Race, R. R., Sanger, R., and Tippett, P. (1963). The linkage relation of hemophilia A and hemophilia B (Christmas disease) to the Xg blood group system. *Am. J. Human Genet.* **15**, 481–492.

Davies, T. S. (1963). Buccal smear surveys for sex chromatin. *Brit. Med. J.* **I**, 1541–1542.

Day, R. W., Wright, S. W., Koons, A., and Quigley, M. (1963). XXX 21-trisomy and retinoblastoma. *Lancet* **II**, 154–155.

de Castro, N. M. (1963). Frequency variations of drumsticks of peripheral blood neutrophiles in the rabbit in different alimentary conditions. *Acta Anat.* **52**, 341–368.

de Grouchy, J., Lamy, M., Yaneva, H., Salomon, Y., and Netter, A. (1961). Further abnormalities of the X chromosome in primary amenorrhoea or in severe oligomenorrhoea. *Lancet* **II**, 777–778.

Josso, N., de Grouchy, J., Auvert, J., Nezelof, C., Jayle, M. F., Moullec, J., Frezal, J., de Cassaubon, A., and Lamy, M. (1965). True hermaphroditism with XX/XY mosaicism, probably due to double fertilization of the ovum. *J. Clin. Endocrinol. Metab.* **25**, 114–126.

de la Chapelle, A. (1962). Cytogenetical and clinical observations in female gonadal dysgenesis. *Acta Endocrinol.* **40**, Suppl. 65, 1–122.

de la Chapelle, A., Hortling, H., Edgren, J., and Kääriäinen, R. (1963). Evidence for the existence of heritable large Y chromosomes unassociated with developmental disorders. A cytogenetical and clinical study of 4 males with hypogonadism, one with mongolism and their relatives. *Hereditas* **50**, 351–360.

de la Chapelle, A., Hortling, H., Niemi, M., and Wennstrom, J. (1964a). XX sex chromosomes in a human male. First case. *Acta Med. Scand.* **175**, 25.

de la Chapelle, A., Hortling, H., Sanger, R., and Race, R. R. (1964b). Successive non-disjunction at first and second meiotic division of spermatogenesis, evidence of chromosomes and Xg. *Cytogenetics (Basel)* **3**, 334–341.

de Mars, R. (1962). Sex chromatin mass in living, cultivated human cells. *Science* **138**, 980–981.

de Mars, R. (1964). Sex chromatin formation during the interphase of human fibroblasts. *Science* **146**, 424.

Demerec, M. (1940). Genetic behaviour of euchromatic segments inserted into heterochromatin. *Genetics* **25**, 618–627.

Dening, K. (1935/1936). Untersuchungen über sexuellen Dimorphismus der Gametophyten bei heterothallischen Lebermoosen. *Flora (Jena)* **30**, 57–86.

Dent, T., and Edwards, J. H. (1963). Monozygotic twins of different sex. *In* "Genetics To-day" (S. J. Geerts, ed.), Vol. 1, p. 304. Pergamon Press, Oxford.

Denver Conference (1960). A proposed standard system of nomenclature of human mitotic chromosomes. *Lancet* **I**, 1063–1065.

de Vries, H. (1900). Das Spaltungsgesetz der Bastarde. *Ber. Deut. Botan. Ges.* **18**, 83–90.

Dobzhansky, T. (1932). Cytological map of the X-chromosome of *Drosophila melanogaster. Biol. Zentr.* **52**, 493–509.

Dobzhansky, T. (1935). *Drosophila miranda*, a new species. *Genetics* **20**, 377–391.

Dobzhansky, T. (1944). Distribution of heterochromatin in the chromosomes of *Drosophila pallidipennis. Am. Naturalist* **78**, 193–213.

Dobzhansky, T., and Schultz, J. (1934). The distribution of sex-factors in the X-chromosome of *Drosophila melanogaster*. *J. Genet*. **28**, 349–386.

Doncaster, L. (1914). "The Determination of Sex." Cambridge Univ. Press, London and New York.

Doncaster, L., and Raynor, G. H. (1906). On breeding experiments with Lepidoptera. *Proc. Zool. Soc. London*, 125–133.

Doniach, I., and Pelc, S. R. (1950). Autoradiograph technique. *Brit. J. Radiol*. **23**, 184–192.

Drescher, W. and Rothenbuhler, W. C. (1963). Gynandromorph production by egg chilling. *J. Heredity* **54**, 195–201.

Drescher, W., and Rothenbuhler, W. C. (1964). Sex determination in the honey bee. *J. Heredity* **55**, 91–96.

Dronamraju, K. R. (1960). Hypertrichosis of the pinna of the human ear, Y-linked pedigrees. *J. Genet*. **57**, 230–244.

Dronamraju, K. R. (1965). The function of the Y-chromosome in man, animals, and plants. *Advan. Genet*. **13**, 227–310.

Dubinin, N. P., and Heptner, M. A. (1935). A new phenotypic effect of the Y-chromosome in *Drosophila melanogaster*. *J. Genet*. **30**, 423–446.

Dunsford, I., Bowley, C. C., Hutchison, A. M., Thompson, J. S., Sanger, R., and Race, R. R. (1953). A human blood-group chimera. *Brit. Med. J*. **II**, 81.

Dzierzon, J. (1848). "Theorie und Praxis des neuen Bienenfreundes, oder: Neue Art der Bienenzucht." Published by author, Carlsmarkt, Silesia.

Ellis, J. R., and Janick, J. (1960). The chromosomes of *Spinacia oleracea*. *Am. J. Botany* **47**, 210–214.

Ellis, J. R., Miller, O. J., Penrose, L. S., and Scott, G. E. R. (1961). A male with XXYY chromosomes. *Ann. Human Genet*. **25**, 145–151.

Emerson, R. A. (1932). The present status of maize genetics. *Proc. 6th Intern. Congr. Genet., Ithaca, New York, 1932* Vol. 1, pp. 141–167.

Engel, E. (1964). La dysgénèse gonadique (syndrome de Turner): Une affection rare mais riche d'enseiguement. Etude chromosomique de 35 cas. *Schweiz. Med. Wochschr*. **94**, 906–914.

Ernst-Schwarzenbach, M. (1939). Zur Kenntuis des sexuellen Dimorphismus der Laubmoose. *Arch. Julius Klaus-Stift. Vererbungsforsch. Sozialanthropol. Rassenhyg*. **14**, 361–474.

Evans, E. P., Breckon, G., and Ford, C. E. (1964). An air-drying method for meiotic preparations from mammalian testes. *Cytogenetics (Basel)* **3**, 289–294.

Evans, H. J. (1964). Uptake of ^{3}H-thymidine and patterns of DNA replication in nuclei and chromosomes of *Vicia faba*. *Exptl. Cell Res*. **35**, 381–393.

Evans, H. J. (1965). A simple microtechnique for obtaining human chromosome preparations with some comments on DNA replication in sex chromosomes of the goat, cow and pig. *Exptl. Cell Res*. **38**, 511–516.

Evans, H. J., Ford, C. E., Lyon, M. F., and Gray, J. (1965). DNA replication and genetic expression in female mice with morphologically distinguishable X-chromosomes. *Nature* **206**, 900–903.

Fabergé, A. (1943). The concept of polygenes. *Nature* **151**, 643.

Farmer, J. B., and Moore, J. E. S. (1905). On the maiotic phase (reduction divisions) in animals and plants. *Quart. J. Microscop. Sci*. **48**, 489–557.

Fechheimer, N. S., Herschler, M. S., and Gilmore, L. O. (1965). Sex chromosome mosaicism in unlike sexed cattle twins. *Proc. 11th Intern. Congr. Genet., The Hague, 1963* Vol. 1, p. 265. Pergaman Press, Oxford.

Ferguson-Smith, M. A. (1964). The sites of nucleolus formation in human pachytene chromosomes. *Cytogenetics* (*Basel*) 3, 124–134.

Ferguson-Smith, M. A. (1965). Karyotype-phenotype correlations in gonadal dysgenesis and their bearing on the pathogenesis of malformations. *J. Med. Genet.* 2, 142–155.

Ferguson-Smith, M. A., Johnston, A. W., and Handmaker, S. D. (1960). Primary amentia and micro-orchidism associated with a XXXY sex-chromosome constitution. *Lancet* II, 184–187.

Ferguson-Smith, M. A., Mack, W. S., Ellis, P. M., Dickson, M., Sanger, R., and Race, R. R. (1964a). Parental age and the source of the X chromosomes in XXY Klinefelter's syndrome. *Lancet* I, 46.

Ferguson-Smith, M. A., Alexander, D. S., Bowen, P., Goodman, R. M., Kaufmann, B. N., Jones, H. W., and Heller, R. H. (1964b). Clinical and cytogenetical studies in female gonadal dysgenesis and their bearing on the cause of Turner's syndrome. *Cytogenetics* (*Basel*) 3, 355–383.

Ferrier, P. (1964). Le chromosome X. *Rev. Med. Suisse Romande* 84, 192–210.

Ferrier, P., Ferrier, S., Stalder, G., Bühler, E., Bamatter, F., and Klein, D. (1964). Congenital asymmetry associated with diploid/triploid mosaicism and large satellites. *Lancet* I, 80–82.

Feulgen, R., and Rossenbeck, H. (1924). Miroskopisch-chemischer Nachweis einer Nukleinsäure vom Typus der Thymonukleinsäure. *Physiol. Chem.* 135, 203–248.

Fialkow, P. J. (1964). Autoimmunity: A predisposing factor to chromosomal aberrations. *Lancet* I, 474–475.

Flemming, W. (1879). Beiträge zur Kenntniss der Zelle und ihrer Lebenserscheinungen. *Arch. Mikroskop. Anat. Entwicklnngsmech.* 16, 302–436.

Flemming, W. (1880). Beiträge zur Kenntniss der Zelle und ihrer Lebenserscheinungen Theil II. [Translated by L. Piternick in *J. Cell Biol.* 25, 3–69 (1965).] *Arch. Mikroskop. Anat. Entwicklungsmech.* 18, 151–259.

Flemming, W. (1882a). "Zellsubstanz, Kern und Zelltheilung." Vogel, Leipzig.

Flemming, W. (1882b). Beiträge zur Kenntniss der Zelle und ihrer Lebenserscheinungen. III. *Arch. Mikroskop. Anat. Entwicklungsmech.* 20, 1–86.

Forbes, T. R. (1961). Endocrinology of reproduction in cold-blooded vertebrates. *In* "Sex and Internal Secretions" (W. C. Young, ed.), 3rd ed., pp. 1035–1087. Baillière, London.

Ford, C. E. (1961). Human chromosome mosaics. *In* "Human Chromosomal Abnormalities" (W. M. Davidson and D. R. Smith, eds.), pp. 23–27. Staples Press, London.

Ford, C. E. (1963). The cytogenetics of human intersexuality. *In* "Intersexuality" (C. Overzier, ed.), pp. 86–117. Academic Press, New York.

Ford, C. E., and Hamerton, J. L. (1956a). A colchicine, hypotonic citrate squash sequence for mammalian chromosomes. *Stain Technol.* 31, 247–251.

Ford, C. E., and Hamerton, J. L. (1956b). The chromosomes of man. *Nature* 178, 1020–1023.

Ford, C. E., Hamerton, J. L., and Sharman, G. B. (1957). Chromosome polymorphism in the common shrew. *Nature* 180, 392–393.

Ford, C. E., Jones, K. W., Miller, O. J., Mittwoch, U., Penrose, L. S., Ridler, M., and Shapiro, A. (1959a). The chromosomes in a patient showing both mongolism and the Klinefelter syndrome. *Lancet* I, 709–710.

Ford, C. E., Jones, K. W., Polani, P. E., de Almeida, J. C., and Briggs, J. H. (1959b). A sex-chromosome anomaly in a case of gonadal dysgenesis (Turner's syndrome). *Lancet* I, 711–713.

Ford, C. E., Polani, P. E., Briggs, J. H., and Bishop, P. M. F. (1959c). A presumptive human XXY/XX mosaic. *Nature* 183, 1030–1032.

Ford, E. B. (1955). "Moths." Collins, London.

Ford, E. H. R., and Woollam, D. H. M. (1963). A study of the mitotic chromosomes of mice of the strong A line. *Exptl. Cell Res.* 32, 320–326.

Ford, E. H. R., and Woollam, D. H. M. (1964). Testicular chromosomes of *Gallus domesticus*. *Chromosoma* 15, 568–578.

Fraccaro, M., and Lindsten, J. (1959). Observations on the so-called "sex chromatin" in human somatic cells cultivated in vitro. *Exptl. Cell Res.* 17, 536–539.

Fraccaro, M., and Lindsten, J. (1960). A child with 49 chromosomes. *Lancet* II, 1303.

Fraccaro, M., and Lindsten, J. (1964). The nature, origin, and genetic implications of structural abnormalities of the sex chromosomes in man. *In* "Cytogenetics of Cells in Culture" (R. J. C. Harris, ed.), pp. 97–110. Academic Press, New York.

Fraccaro, M., Kaijser, K., and Lindsten, J. (1959). Chromosome complement in gonadal dysgenesis. *Lancet* I, 886.

Fraccaro, M., Ikkos, D., Lindsten, J., Luft, R., and Kaijser, K. (1960a). A new type of chromosomal abnormality in gonadal dysgenesis. *Lancet* II, 1144.

Fraccaro, M., Kaijser, K., and Lindsten, J. (1960b). A child with 49 chromosomes. *Lancet* II, 899–902.

Fraccaro, M., Taylor, A. I., Bodian, M., and Newns, G. H. (1962a). A human intersex ("true hermaphrodite") with XX/XXY/XXYYY sex chromosomes. *Cytogenetics (Basel)* 1, 104–112.

Fraccaro, M., Davies, P., Glen-Bott, M., and Schutt, W. (1962b). Mental deficiency and undescended testis in two males with XYY sex chromosomes. *Folia Hered. Pathol. (Pavia)* 11, 211–220.

Fraccaro, M., Klinger, H. P., and Schutt, W. (1962c). A male with XXXXY sex chromosomes. *Cytogenetics (Basel)* 1, 52–63.

Fraccaro, M., Lindsten, J., Mittwoch, U., and Zonta, L. (1964). Size of drumsticks in patients with abnormalities of the X-chromosome. *Lancet* II, 43–44.

Fraccaro, M., Hulten, M., Lindsten, J., and Tiepolo, L. (1965a). A late-duplicating chromosome in spermatogonial mitosis in the mouse. *Exptl. Cell Res.* 38, 676–677.

Fraccaro, M., Gustavsson, I., Hulten, M., Lindsten, J., Mannins, A., and Tiepolo, L. (1965b). DNA replication patterns of canine chromosomes in vivo and in vitro. *Hereditas* 52, 264–270.

Franchi, L. L., Mandl, A. M., and Zuckerman, S. (1962). The development of the ovary and the process of oogenesis. *In* "The Ovary" (S. Zuckerman, ed.), Vol. 1, pp. 1–88. Academic Press, New York.

Fraser, G. R. (1964). Partial monosomy 18. *Lancet* I, 664.

Fraser, G. R., Defaranas, B., Kattamis, C. A., Race, R. R., Sanger, R., and Stamatoyannopoulos, G. (1964). Glucose-6-phosphate dehydrogenase, colour vision and Xg blood groups in Greece. *Ann. Human Genet.* 27, 395–403.

Fraser, J. H., Campbell, J., MacGillivray, R. C., Boyd, E., and Lennox, B. (1960). The XXX syndrome. Frequency among mental defectives and fertility. *Lancet* II, 626–627.

Fréderic, J. (1961). Contribution a l'étude du caryotype chez le poulet. *Arch. Biol. (Paris)* 72, 185–209.

Fredga, K. (1964). Heterochromatic regions in mitotic and meiotic chromosomes of Bennett's wallaby (*Protemnodon rufogrisea*, Desmaret). *Exptl. Cell Res.* **36**, 696–699.

Fredga, K. (1965). A new sex determining mechanism in a mammal. Chromosomes of Indian mongoose (Herpestes auropunctatus). *Hereditas* **52**, 409–420.

Fredga, K., and Santesson, B. (1964). Male meiosis in the Syrian, Chinese and European hamsters. *Hereditas* **52**, 36–48.

Frenster, J. H., Allfrey, V. G., and Mirsky, A. E. (1963). Repressed and active chromatin isolated from interphase lymphoctyes. *Proc. natl. Acad. Sci. U.S.* **50**, 1026–1032.

Frizzi, G. (1948). L'eteropicnosi come indice di riconoscimento dei sessi in "Bombyx mori L." *Ric. Sci.* **18**, 119–123.

Frolowa, S. (1912). Idiochromosomen bei Ascaris megalocephala. *Arch. Zellforsch.* **9**, 149–167.

Frost, J. N. (1960). The occurrence of partially fertile triploid metafemales in *Drosophila melanogaster*. *Proc. Natl. Acad. Sci. U.S.* **46**, 47–51.

Gahan, P. B., and Chayen, J. (1965). Cytoplasmic deoxyribonucleic acid. *Intern. Rev. Cytol.* **18**, 223–247.

Galton, M., and Holt, S. F. (1964). DNA replication patterns of the sex chromosomes in somatic cells of the Syrian hamster. *Cytogenetics (Basel)* **3**, 97–111.

Galton, M., and Holt, S. F. (1965). Asynchronous replication of the mouse sex chromosomes. *Exptl. Cell Res.* **37**, 111–116.

Galton, M., Benirschke, K., and Ohno, S. (1965). Sex chromosomes of the Chinchilla: allocycly and duplication sequence in somatic cells and behaviour in meiosis. *Chromosoma* **16**, 668–680.

Gartler, S. M., and Burt, B. (1964). Replication patterns of bovine sex chromosomes in cell culture. *Cytogenetics (Basel)* **3**, 135–142.

Gartler, S. M., Waxman, S. H., and Giblett, E. (1962). An XX/XY human hermaphrodite resulting from double fertilization. *Proc. Natl. Acad. Sci. U.S.* **48**, 332–335.

Geitler, L. (1937). Die Analyse des Kernbaus und der Kernteilung der Wasserlaufer *Gerris lateralis* und *Gerris lacustris* (Hemiptera, Heteroptera) und die Somadifferenzierung. *Z. Zellforsch. Mikroskop. Anat.* **26**, 641–672.

Geitler, L. (1939). Die Entstehung der polyploiden Somakerne der Heteropteren durch Chromosomenteilung ohne Kernteilung. *Chromosoma* **1**, 1–22.

Geitler, L. (1953). "Endomitose und endomitotische Polyploidisierung." Volume VI, of "Protoplasmatologia, Handbuch der Protoplasmaforschung." Springer, Vienna.

German, J. L. (1962). DNA synthesis in human chromosomes. *Trans. N.Y. Acad. Sci.* [2] **24**, 395–407.

Geyer-Duszyńska, I. (1963). On the structure of the XY bivalent in *Mus musculus* L. *Chromosoma* **13**, 521–525.

Gianelli, F. (1963). The pattern of X-chromosome deoxyribonucleic acid synthesis in two women with abnormal sex-chromosome complements. *Lancet* **I**, 863–865.

Giblett, E. R., Gartler, S. M., and Waxman, S. H. (1963). Blood group studies of an XX/XY hermaphrodite with generalized tissue mosaicism. *Am. J. Human Genet.* **15**, 62–68.

Gilbert, C. W., Muldal, S., Lajtha, L. G., and Rowley, J. (1962). Time-sequence of human chromosome duplication. *Nature* **195**, 869–873.

Gilchrist, B. M., and Haldane, J. B. S. (1947). Sex linkage and sex determination in a mosquito, *Culex molestus*. *Hereditas* **33**, 175–190.

Glenister, T. W. (1956). Determination of sex in early human embryos. *Nature* **177**, 1135–1136.

Goldschmidt, E. (1953). Multiple sex-chromosome mechanisms and polyploidy in animals. *J. Gent.* **51**, 434–440.

Goldschmidt, R. B. (1934). *Lymantria. Bibliotheca Genet.* (*Leipzig*) **11**, 1–180.

Goldschmidt, R. B. (1953). Experiments with a homeotic mutant bearing on evolution. *J. Exptl. Zool.* **123**, 79–114.

Goldschmidt, R. B. (1955). "Theoretical Genetics." Univ. of California Press, Berkeley, California.

Goldschmidt, R. B., and Lin, T. P. (1947). Ever since Boveri. *Science* **105**, 619.

Goldschmidt, R. B., Hannah, A., and Piternick, L. (1951). The podoptera effect in *Drosophila melanogaster. Univ. Calif.* (*Berkeley*) *Publ. Zool.* **55**, 67–294.

Goodfellow, S. A., Strong, S. J., and Stewart, J. S. S. (1965). Bovine freemartins and true hermaphroditism. *Lancet* I, 1040–1041.

Gordon, M. (1946). Interchanging genetic mechanisms for sex determination in fishes under domestication. *J. Heredity* **37**, 307–320.

Gordon, M. (1947). Genetics of *Platypoecilus maculatus*. IV. The sex determining mechanism in two wild populations of the Mexican platyfish. *Genetics* **32**, 8–17.

Gorman, J. G., di Re, J., Treacy, A. M., and Cahan, A. (1963). The application of Xg[a] antiserum to the question of red cell mosaicism in female heterozygotes. *J. Lab. Clin. Med.* **61**, 642–649.

Gouw, W. L., Coenegracht, J. M., and Stalder, G. (1964). A very large metacentric chromosome in a woman with symptoms of Turner's syndrome. *Cytogenetics* (*Basel*) **3**, 427–440.

Gowen, J. W., and Gay, E. H. (1933). Eversporting as a function of the Y chromosome in *Drosphila melanogaster. Proc. Natl. Acad. Sci. U.S.* **19**, 122–126.

Gowen, J. W., and Gay, E. H. (1934). Chromosome constitution and behaviour in eversporting and mottling in *Drosophila melanogaster. Genetics* **19**, 189–208.

Graham, M. A. (1954a). Detection of the sex of cat embryos from nuclear morphology in the embryonic membrane. *Nature* **173**, 310–311.

Graham, M. A. (1954b). Sex chromatin in cell nuclei of the cat from the early embryo to maturity. *Anat. Record* **119**, 469–485.

Graham, M. A., and Barr, M. L. (1952). A sex difference in the morphology of metabolic nuclei in somatic cells of the cat. *Anat. Record* **112**, 709–718.

Greenblatt, R. B., Aydar, C. K., and Gibson, H. H. (1962). Discrepancies in the evaluation of sex chromatin in oral smears and peripheral blood specimens. *Acta Cytol.* **6**, 103–107.

Grüneberg, H. (1935). Inversion of the X-chromosome in *Drosophila melanogaster. J. Genet.* **31**, 163–184.

Grüneberg, H. (1937). The position effect proved by a spontaneous reinversion of the X-chromosome in *Drosophila melanogaster. J. Genet.* **34**, 169–189.

Grüneberg, H. (1952a). "The Genetics of the Mouse," 2nd ed. Nijhoff, The Hague.

Grüneberg, H. (1952b). Genetical studies on the skeleton of the mouse. IV. Quasi-continuous variation. *J. Genet.* **51**, 95–114.

Grumbach, M. M., and Barr, M. L. (1958). Cytologic tests of chromosomal sex in relation to sexual anomalies in man. *Recent Progr. Hormone Res.* **14**, 255–334.

Grumbach, M. M., and Morishima, A. (1962). Sex chromatin and the sex chromosomes: On the origin of sex chromatin from a single X chromosome. *Acta Cytol.* **6**, 46–60.

Grumbach, M. M., Morishima, A., and Chu, E. H. Y. (1960). On the sex chromatin and the sex chromosomes in sexual anomalies in man. Relation to origin of the sex chromatin. *Acta Endocrinol.* Suppl. **51**, 633.

Grumbach, M. M., Marks, P. A., and Morishima, A. (1962). Erythrocyte glucose-6-phosphate dehydrogenase activity and X-chromosome polysomy. *Lancet* **I**, 1330–1332.

Grumbach, M. M., Morishima, A., and Chu, E. H. Y. (1960). On the sex chromatin and the sex chromosomes in sexual anomalies in man. Relation to origin of the sex chromatin. *Acta Endocrinol.* Suppl. **51**, 633.

Grumbach, M. M., Morishima, A., and Taylor, J. H. (1963). Human sex chromosome abnormalities in relation to DNA replication and heterochromatinization. *Proc. Natl. Acad. Sci. U.S.* **49**, 581–589.

Gustavsson, I. (1964a). The chromosomes of the dog. *Hereditas* **51**, 187–189.

Gustavsson, I. (1964b). Karyotype of the fox. *Nature* **201**, 950–951.

Gutherz, S. (1907). Zur Kenntniss der Hetero-Chromosomen. *Arch. Mikroskop. Anat. Entwicklungsmech.* **69**, 491–514.

Guyer, M. F. (1910). Accessory chromosomes in man. *Biol. Bull.* **19**, 219–234.

Haldane, J. B. S. (1919). The combination of linkage values, and the calculation of distances between the loci of linked factors. *J. Genet.* **8**, 299–309.

Haldane, J. B. S. (1921). Linkage in poultry. *Science* **54**, 663.

Haldane, J. B. S. (1936). A search for incomplete sex linkage in man. *Ann. Eugenics (London)* **7**, 317–326.

Haldane, J. B. S., and Smith, C. A. B. (1947). A new estimate of the linkage between the genes for colour blindness and haemophilia in man. *Ann. Eugenics (London)* **14**, 10–31.

Hamerton, J. L. (1958). Mammalian sex chromosomes. *In* "Symposium on Nuclear Sex" (D. R. Smith and W. M. Davidson, eds.), pp. 25–30. Heinemann, London.

Hamerton, J. L., Fraccaro, M., de Carli, L., Nuzzo, F., Klinger, H. P., Hulliger, L., Taylor, A., and Long, E. M. (1961). Somatic chromosomes of the gorilla. *Nature* **192**, 225–228.

Hamerton, J. L., Jagiello, G. M., and Kirman, B. H. (1962). Sex-chromosome abnormalities in a population of mentally defective children. *Brit. Med. J.* **I**, 220–223.

Hamerton, J. L., Klinger, H. P., Mutton, D. E., and Lang, E. M. (1963). The somatic chromosomes of the Hominoidea. *Cytogenetics (Basel* **2**, 240–263.

Hamilton, W. J., Boyd, J. D., and Mossman, H. W. (1962). "Human Embryology," 3rd ed. Heffer, Cambridge.

Hanhart, E., Delhanty, J. D. A., and Penrose, L. S. (1961). Trisomy in mother and child. *Lancet* **I**, 403.

Hannah, A. (1951). Localization and function of heterochromatin in *Drosophila melanogaster*. *Advan. Genet.* **4**, 87–125.

Hansen-Melander, E. (1965). The relation sex chromosomes to chromocenters in somatic cells of *Microtus agrestis* (L.). *Hereditas* **52**, 357–366.

Harnden, D. G. (1961). Nuclear sex in triploid XXY human cells. *Lancet* **II**, 488.

Harnden, D. G., and Armstrong, C. N. (1959). The chromosomes of a true hermaphrodite. *Brit. Med. J.* **II**, 1287–1288.

Harnden, D. G., and Jacobs, P. A. (1961). Cytogenetics of abnormal sexual development in man. *Brit. Med. Bull.* **17**, 206–212.

Harnden, D. G., and Stewart, J. S. S. (1959). The chromosomes in a case of pure gonadal dysgenesis. *Brit. Med. J.* **II**, 1285–1287.

Harris, H. (1962). "Human Biochemical Genetics." Cambridge Univ. Press, London and New York.

Harris, H., Hopkinson, D. A., Spencer, N., Court Brown, W. M., and Mantle, D. (1963). Red cell glucose-6-phosphate dehydrogenase activity in individuals with abnormal numbers of X-chromosomes. *Ann. Human Genet.* **27**, 59–66.

Hauschka, T. S., Hasson, J. E., Goldstein, M. N., Koepf, G. F., and Sandberg, A. A. (1962). An XYY man with progeny indicating familial tendency to non-disjunction. *Am. J. Human Genet.* **14**, 22–30.

Hauschteck, E. (1961). Die Chromosomen von fünf Ameisenarten. *Rev. Suisse Zool.* **68**, 218–223.

Hauschteck, E. (1962). Die Cytologie der Pädogenese und der Geschlechtsbestimmung einer heterogonen Gallmücke. *Chromosoma* **13**, 163–182.

Hauser, G. A. (1963). Gonadal dysgenesis. *In* "Intersexuality" (C. Overzier, ed.), pp. 298–339. Academic Press, New York.

Hay, J. C. (1960). Further observations on the sex chromatin of mammalian cells. *Anat. Record* **136**, 315.

Hayward, M. D., and Cameron, A. H. (1961). Triple mosaicism of the sex chromosomes in Turner's syndrome and Hirschsprung's disease. *Lancet* **II**, 623–627.

Heilbronn, A. (1949). Über die Genetik von Monöcie und Getrenntgeschlechtlichkeit bei *Bryonia* Bastarden. *Proc. 8th Intern. Congr. Genet., Stockholm, 1948* pp. 590–591. Mendelian Soc., Sweden.

Heitz, E. (1927). Geschlechtschromosomen bei *Pellia Fabbroniana* (diöcisch) und *P. epiphylla* (monöcisch). *Ber. Deut. Botan. Ges.* **45**, 607–610.

Heitz, E. (1928). Das Heterochromatin der Moose I. *Jahrb. wiss. Botan.* **69**, 762–818.

Heitz, E. (1931). Die Ursache der gesetzmässigen Zahl, Lage, Form and Grösse der pflanzlichen Nukleolen. *Planta* **12**, 774–844.

Heitz, E. (1932). Nukleolen und Chromosomen in der Gattung *Vicia*. *Planta* **15**, 495–505.

Heitz, E. (1933). Die somatische Heteropyknose bei *Drosophila melanogaster* und ihre genetische Bedeutung. *Z. Zellforsch. Mikroskop. Anat.* **20**, 237–287.

Heitz, E. (1934). Über α-und β-Heterochromatin sowie Konstanz und Bau der Chromomeren bei *Drosophila*. *Biol. Zentr.* **54**, 588–609.

Heitz, E. (1935a). Chromosomenstruktur und Gene. *Z. Induktive Abstammungs-Vererbungslehre* **70**, 402–447.

Heitz, E. (1935b). Die Nukleal-Quetschmethode. *Ber. Deut. Botan. Ges.* **53**, 870–878.

Heitz, E. (1942). Über mutative Intersexualität und Geschlechtsumwandlung bei *Pellia Neesiana* and *Sphaerocarpus Donnellii*. *Naturwissenschaften* **30**, 751.

Heitz, E., and Bauer, H. (1933). Beweise für die Chromosomennatur der Kernschleifen in den Knäuelkernen von *Bibio hortulanus*. *Z. Zellforsch. Mikroskop. Anat.* **17**, 67–82.

Hemsworth, B. N., and Jackson, H. (1963a). Effect of Busulphan on the developing ovary in the rat. *J. Reprod. Fertility* **6**, 229–233.

Hemsworth, B. N., and Jackson, H. (1963b). Effect on Busulphan on the developing gonad of the male rat. *J. Reprod. Fertility* **5**, 187–194.

Henking, H. (1891). Untersuchungen über die ersten Entwicklungsvorgänge in den Eiern der Insekten. II. Über Spermatogenese und deren Beziehung zur Entwicklung bei *Pyrrhocoris apterus*. *Z. Wiss. Zool., Abt. A* **51**, 685–736.

Hertwig, O. (1876). Beiträge zur Kenntnis der Bildung, Befruchtung und Theilung des thierischen Eies. *Morphol. Jahrb.* **1**, 341–343.

Hertwig, O. (1885). Das Problem der Befruchtung und der Isotropie des Eies, eine Theorie der Vererbung. *Jena. Z. Naturw.* **18**, 276–318.

Heuser, E. (1884). Beobachtungen über Zellkerntheilung. *Botan. Zentr.* **17**, 27–32 and 85–95.

Hinrichsen, K., and Gothe, H.-D. (1958). Morphologische und statistische Untersuchungen an Zellkernen von Ratten und Mäusen zur Frage einer cytologischen Geschlechtsdiagnostik. *Z. Zellforsch. Mikroskop. Anat.* **48**, 429–449.

Hirschhorn, K., Decker, W. H., and Cooper, H. L. (1960). Human intersex with chromosome mosaicism of type XY/XO. Report of a case. *New Engl. J. Med.* **263**, 1044–1048.

Hockwald, R. S., Arnold, J., Clayman, C. B., and Alving, A. S. (1952). Toxicity of primaquine in negroes. *J. Am. Med. Assoc.* **149**, 1568–1570.

Horner, J. F. (1876). Quoted by Kalmus (1965).

Howard, A., and Pelc, S. R. (1953). Synthesis of deoxyribonucleic acid in normal and irradiated cells and its relation to chromosome breakage. *Heredity* **6**, Suppl., 261–274.

Hsu, T. C. (1952). Mammalian chromosomes in vitro. X. The karyotype of man. *J. Heredity* **43**, 167–172.

Hsu, T. C. (1962). Differential rate in RNA synthesis between euchromatin and heterochromatin. *Exptl. Cell Res.* **27**, 332–334.

Hsu, T. C., and Rearden, H. (1965). Further karyological studies on Felidae, *Chromosoma* **16**, 365–371.

Hsu, T. C., Rearden, H. H., and Luquette, G. F. (1963). Karyological studies of nine species of Felidae. *Am. Naturalist* **97**, 225–235.

Hsu, T. C., Schmid, W., and Stubblefield, E. (1964). DNA replication sequences in higher animals. *In* "The Role of Chromosomes in Development" (M. Locke, ed.), pp. 83–112. Academic Press, New York.

Huang, R. C., and Bonner, J. (1962). Histone, a suppressor of chromosomal RNA synthesis. *Proc. Natl. Acad. Sci. U.S.* **48**, 1216–1222.

Hughes, A. (1952a). "The Mitotic Cycle." Butterworth, London and Washington, D.C.

Hughes, A. (1952b). Some effects of abnormal tonicity on dividing cells in chick tissue cultures. *Quart. J. Microscop. Sci.* **93**, 207.

Hughes, A. (1959). "A History of Cytology." Abelard-Schuman, London and New York.

Hughes-Schrader, S. (1948). Cytology of coccids (Coccoidea, Homoptera). *Advan. Genet.* **21**, 127–203.

Hughes-Schrader, S. (1950). The chromosomes of mantids (*Orthoptera: Manteidae*) in relation to taxonomy. *Chromosoma* **4**, 1–55.

Hughes-Schrader, S. (1953). Supplementary notes on the cyto-taxonomy of mantids (*Orthoptera: Mantoidea*). *Chromosoma* **6**, 79–90.

Hughes-Schrader, S. (1958). The DNA content of the nucleus as a tool in the cytotaxonomic study of insects. *Proc. 10th Intern. Congr. Entomol., Montreal, 1956.* Vol. 2, pp. 935–944. Intern. Congr. Entomol., Ottawa, Canada.

Hughes-Schrader, S., and Ris, H. (1941). The diffuse spindle attachment of coccids, verified by the mitotic behavior of induced chromosome fragments. *J. Exptl. Zool.* **87**, 429–451.

Hulliger, L., Klinger, H. P., and Allgöwer, M. (1963). Sex chromatin as a marker in some rabbit cells. *Experientia* **19**, 240–243.

Hungerford, D. A., Donnelly, A. J., Nowell, P. C., and Beck, S. (1959). The chromosome constitution of a human phenotypic intersex. *Am. J. Human Genet.* **11**, 215–236.

Hunter, W. F., and Lennox, B. (1954). The sex of teratomata. *Lancet* **II**, 633–634.

Hustinx, T. W. J., and Stoelinga, G. B. A. (1964). A ring-X-chromosome in part of the somatic cells of a patient with some characteristics of the Turner syndrome. *Genetics* **35**, 1–14.

Hustinx, T. W. J., Eberle, P., Geerts, S. J., Brink, J., and Woltring, L. M. (1961). Mongoloid twins with 48 chromosomes ($AA + A_{21}$ XXY). *Ann. Human Genet.* **25**, 111–115.

Hutt, F. B. (1949). "Genetics of the Fowl." McGraw-Hill, New York.

Iizuka, M., and Janick, J. (1963). Cytogenetic analysis of sex determination in spinach. *Genetics* **48**, 273–292.

Ishihara, S. (1944). "The Series of Plates Designed as Tests for Colour-Blindness," 9th ed. Lewis, London.

Ishizaki, H., and Kosin, I. L. (1960). Sex chromatin in early chick embryos. *Exptl. Cell Res.* **21**, 197–200.

Israelsohn, W. J., and Taylor, A. I. (1961). Chromatin-positive presumed Klinefelter's syndrome. *Brit. Med. J.* **I**, 633–635.

Izakovič, V. (1960). Gonadal dysgenesis in two sisters with male nuclear sex pattern and female characteristics in polymorphonuclear leucocytes. *J. Clin. Endocrinol. Metab.* **20**, 1301–1303.

Jackson, C. E., Symon, W. E., and Mann, J. D. (1964). X chromosome mapping of genes for red-green colorblindness and Xg. *Am. J. Human Genet.* **16**, 403–409.

Jackson, W. P. U., Shapiro, B. G., Uys, C. J., and Hoffenberg, R. (1956). Primary male hypogonadism with female nuclear sex. *Lancet* **II**, 857–859.

Jacob, F., and Wollman, E. L. (1961). "Sexuality and the Genetics of Bacteria." Academic Press, New York.

Jacobs, P. A., and Strong, J. A. (1959). A case of human intersexuality having a possible XXY sex-determining mechanism. *Nature* **183**, 302–303.

Jacobs, P. A., Baikie, A. G., Court Brown, W. M., MacGregor, T. N., Maclean, N., and Harnden, D. G. (1959a). Evidence for the existence of the human "super-female." *Lancet* **II**, 423–425.

Jacobs, P. A., Baikie, A. G., Court Brown, W. M., Forrest, H., Roy, J. R., Stewart, J. S. S., and Lennox, B. (1959b). Chromosomal sex in the syndrome of testicular feminisation. *Lancet* **II**, 591–592.

Jacobs, P. A., Harnden, D. G., Court Brown, W. M., Goldstein, J., Close, H. G., MacGregor, T. N., Maclean, N., and Strong, J. A. (1960). Abnormalities involving the X chromosome in women. *Lancet* **I**, 1213–1216.

Jacobs, P. A., Harnden, D. G., Buckton, K. E., Court Brown, W. M., King, M. J., McBride, J. A., MacGregor, T. N., and Maclean, N. (1961). Cytogenetic studies in primary amenorrhoea. *Lancet* **I**, 1183–1188.

Jacobs, P. A., Brunton, M., and Court Brown, W. M. (1964). Cytogenetic studies in leucocytes on the general population: Subjects of ages 65 year and more. *Ann. Human Genet.* **27**, 353–365.

Jacobs, P. A., Brunton, M., Melville, M. M., Brittain, R. P., and McClemont, W. F. (1965). Aggressive behaviour, mental sub-normality and the XYY male. *Nature* **208**, 1351–1352.

Jacobsen, P. (1957). The sex chromosomes in Humulus. *Hereditas* **43**, 357–370.

James, J. (1960). Observations on the so-called sex chromatin. *Z. Zellforsch. Mikroskop. Anat.* **51**, 597–616.

Janssens, F. A. (1909). Spermatogénèse dans les Batraciens. V. La théorie de la chiasmatypie. Nouvelles interprétations des cineses de maturations. *Cellule* **25**, 387–411.

Johannsen, W. (1909). "Elemente der exakten Erblichkeitslehre." Fischer, Jena.

Johnston, A. W., Ferguson-Smith, M. A., Handmaker, S. D., Jones, H. W., and Jones, C. S. (1961). The triple-X syndrome. *Brit. Med. J.* **II**, 1046–1052.

Jones, D. F. (1932). The interaction of specific genes determining sex in dioecious maize. *Proc. 6th Intern. Con. Genet., Ithaca, New York, 1932* Vol. 2, pp. 104–107.

Jones, D. F. (1934). Unisexual maize plants and their bearing on sex differentiation in other plants and animals. *Genetics* **19**, 552–567.

Jost, A. (1947). Recherches sur la différenciation sexuelle de l'embryon de lapin III. Rôle des gonades foetales dans la différenciation sexuelle somatique. *Arch. Anat. Microscop. Morphol. Exptl.* **36**, 271–315.

Jost, A. (1960). Hormonal influence in the sex development of bird and mammalian embryos. *In* "Sex Differentiation and Development" (C. R. Austin, ed.), pp. 49–61. Cambridge Univ. Press, London and New York.

Jude, A. C., and Searle, A. G. (1957). A fertile tortoiseshell tomcat. *Nature* **179**, 1087–1088.

Kalmus, H. (1962). Distance and sequence of the loci for protan and deutan defects and for glucose-6-phosphate dehydrogenase deficiency. *Nature* **194**, 215.

Kalmus, H. (1965). "Diagnosis and Genetics of Defective Colour Vision." Pergamon Press, Oxford.

Kaufmann, B. P. (1934). Somatic mitoses of *Drosophila melanogaster*. *J. Morphol.* **56**, 125–155.

Kawaguchi, E. (1928). Zytologische Untersuchungen am Seidenspinner und seinen Verwandten. *Z. Zellforsch.* **7**, 519–552.

Kawaguchi, E. (1933). Die Heteropyknose der Geschlechts-Chromosomen bei Lepidopteren. *Cytologia* **4**, 339–354.

Kelsall, P. J. (1961). Non-disjunction of the sex-chromosomes in the male of *D. melanogaster*. *Nature* **190**, 1035–1036.

Kelsall, P. J. (1963). Non-disjunction and maternal age in *Drosophila melanogaster*. *Genet. Res.* **4**, 284–289.

Kenney, J. D., and Mittwoch, U. (1965). Barr bodies in the mouse. *Nature* **208**, 93–94.

Kerr, C. B., Wells, R. S., and Sanger, R. (1964). X-linked ichthyosis and the Xg groups. *Lancet* **II**, 1369–1370.

Kerr, W. E. (1951). Sex-chromosomes in honeybee. *Evolution* **5**, 80–81.

Kesaree, N., and Woolley, P. V. (1963). A phenotypic female with 49 chromosomes, presumably XXXXX. *J. Pediat.* **63**, 1099–1103.

Kihara, H. (1929). Quoted by Westergaard (1958).

Kihara, H. (1930). Karyologische Studien an *Fvagaria* mit besonderer Berücksichtigung der Geschechtschromosomen. *Cytologia* **1**, 345–357.

Kihara, H., and Ono, T. (1923). Cytological studies on *Rumex* L. *Botan. Mag.* (*Tokyo*) **37**, 84–90.

Kindred, B. M. (1961). Abnormal inheritance of the sex-linked tabby gene. *Australian J. Biol. Sci.* **14**, 415–418.

Klinefelter, H. F., Jr., Reifenstein, E. C., Jr., and Albright, F. (1942). Syndrome characterised by gynecomastia, aspermatogenesis without aleydigism, and increased excretion of follicle stimulating hormone. *J. Clin. Endocrinol. Metab.* **2**, 615–627.

Klinger, H. P. (1957). The sex chromatin body in fetal and maternal portions in the human placenta. *Acta Anat.* **30**, 371–397.

Klinger, H. P. (1963). The somatic chromosomes of some primates—(*Tupaia glis, Nycticebus coucang, Tarsius bancanus, Cercocebus aterrimus, Symphalangus syndactylus*). *Cytogenetics (Basel)* **2**, 140–151.

Klinger, H. P., and Ludwig, K. S. (1957). A universal stain for the sex chromatin body. *Stain Technol.* **32**, 235–244.

Klinger, H. P., and Schwarzacher, H. G. (1960). The sex chromatin and heterochromatic bodies in human diploid and polyploid nuclei. *J. Biophys. Biochem. Cytol.* **8**, 345–364.

Klinger, H. P., and Schwarzacher, H. G. (1962). XY/XXY and sex chromatin positive cell distribution in a 60 mm human fetus. *Cytogenetics (Basel)* **1**, 266–290.

Klinger, H. P., Hamerton, J. L., Mutton, D. E., and Lang, E. M. (1963). The chromosomes of the Hominoidea. *Publs. Anthrop. Viking Fund* **37**, 235–242.

Klinger, H. P., Lindsten, J., Fraccaro, M., Barrai, I., and Dolinar, Z. J. (1965). DNA content and area of sex chromatin in subjects with structural and numerical aberrations of the X chromosome. *Cytogenetics (Basel)* **4**, 96–116.

Knapp, E. (1936). Heteroploidy in Sphaerocarpus. *Ber. Deut. Botan. Ges.* **54**, 346–361.

Knapp, E., and Hoffmann, I. (1939). Geschlechtsumwandlung bei *Sphaerocarpus* durch Verlust eins Stückes des X-Chromosomes. *Chromosoma* **1**, 130–146.

Kobel, H. R. (1962). Heterochromosomen bei *Vipera berus* L. (*Viperidae, Serpentes*). *Experientia* **18**, 173–174.

Kobel, H. R. (1963). Verleich der Chromosomensätze von *Vipera berus* L. und *Vipera aspis* L. (*Viperidae, Serpentes*). *Arch. Julius Klaus-Stift. Vererbungsforsch. Sozialanthropol. Rassenhyg.* **38**, 234–241.

Köhler, D. (1964). Geschlechtsbestimmung bei Blütenpflanzen. *Ergeb. Biol.* **27**, 88–115.

Koller, P. C. (1936). The genetical and mechanical properties of sex chromosomes. II. Marsupials. *J. Genet.* **32**, 451–472.

Koller, P. C. (1937). The genetical and mechanical properties of sex chromosomes. III. Man. *Proc. Roy. Soc. Edinburgh* **57**, 194–214.

Koller, P. C. (1938). The genetical and mechanical properties of sex chromosomes. IV. The golden Hamster. *J. Genet.* **36**, 177–195.

Koller, P. C. (1939). The structure of the sex-determining mechanism in the Field-Mouse. *J. Genet.* **37**, (2)–(3).

Koller, P. C. (1941a). The genetical and mechanical properties of sex chromosomes. VII. *Apodemus sylvaticus* and *A. hebridensis. J. Genet.* **41**, 375–389.

Koller, P. C. (1941b). The genetical and mechanical properties of sex chromosomes. VIII. The cat (*Felis domestica*). *Proc. Roy. Soc. Edinburgh* **B61**, 78–94.

Koller, P. C. (1943). Origin of malignant tumour cells. *Nature* **151**, 244–246.

Koller, P. C., and Darlington, C. D. (1934). The genetical and mechanical properties of sex-chromosomes. I. *Rattus norvegicus.* ♂. *J. Genet.* **29**, 159–173.

Kosambi, D. D. (1944). The estimation of map distances from recombination values. *Ann. Eugenics (London)* **12**, 172–175.

Kosenow, W. (1957). Abweichende Ergebnisse bei der Geschlechtsbestimmung an Leukocyten und Mundepithel-Kernen. *Klin. Wochschr.* **35,** 75–76.

Kosenow, W., and Scupin, R. (1956). Die Bestimmung des Geschlechts mit Hilfe einer Kernanhangsformel der Leukocyten. *Acta Haematol.* **15,** 349–363.

Kosin, I. L., and Ishizaki, H. (1959). Incidence of sex chromatin in *Gallus domesticus*. *Science* **130,** 43–44.

Kostoff, F. (1930). Discoid structure of the spireme and irregular cell division in *Drosophila melanogaster*. *J. Heredity* **21,** 323–324.

Krallinger, H. F. (1927). Über die Chromosomenzahl beim Rinde sowie einige allgemeine Bemerkungen über die Chromosomenforschung in der Säugetierklasse. *Verhandl. Anat. Ges., Anat. Anz.* **63,** Suppl., 209–214.

Kurita, M. (1937). Geschlechtschromosomen und Chromosomenzahl bei einigen Laubmoosen. *Z. Induktive Abstammungs- Vererbungslehre* **74,** 24–29.

Lawler, S. D. (1964). Localisation of autosomal genes in man. *Human Biol.* **36,** 146–156.

Lemli, L. and Smith, D. W. (1963). The XO syndrome: A study of the differentiated phenotype in 25 patients. *J. Pediat.* **63,** 577–588.

Lennox, B. (1963). Sex chromatin in tumours. *In* "Intersexuality" (C. Overzier, ed.), pp. 462–478. Academic Press, New York.

Lenz, W. (1964). Krankheiten des Urogenitalsystems. *In* "Humangenetik" (P. E. Becker, ed.), pp. 253–410. Thieme, Stuttgart.

Lenz, W., Novakowski, H., Prader, A., and Schirran, C. (1959). Die Ätiologie des Klinefelter-Syndroms. *Schweiz. Med. Wochschr.* **89,** 727–731.

Levan, A. (1946). Heterochromaty in chromosomes during their contraction phase. *Hereditas* **32,** 449–468.

Levan, A., Hsu, T. C., and Stich, H. F. (1962). The idiogram of the mouse. *Hereditas* **47,** 677–687.

Levan, A., Fredga, K., and Sandberg, A. A. (1964). Nomenclature for centromeric position on chromosomes. *Hereditas* **52,** 201–220.

Lewis, D. (1942). The evolution of sex in flowering plants. *Biol. Rev.* **17,** 46–67.

Lewis, D. (1954). Comparative incompatibility in Angiosperms and fungi. *Advan. Genet.* **6,** 235–285.

Lewis, E. B. (1950). The phenomenon of position effect. *Advan. Genet.* **3,** 73–115.

Lewis, F. J. W., Frøland, A., Sanger, R., and Race, R. R. (1964). Source of the X chromosomes in two XXXXY males. *Lancet* **II,** 589.

Lewis, K. R., and John, B. (1963). "Chromosome Marker." Churchill, London.

Lillie, F. R. (1917). The free-martin: A study of the action of sex hormones in the foetal life of cattle. *J. Exptl. Zool.* **23,** 371–452.

Lima-de-Faria, A. (1956). The role of the kinetochore in chromosome organization. *Hereditas* **42,** 85–160.

Lima-de-Faria, A. (1959). Differential uptake of tritiated thymidine into hetero- and euchromatin in *Melanoplus* and *Secale*. *J. Biophys. Biochem. Cytol.* **6,** 457–466.

Lima-de-Faria, A., Reitalu, J., and O'Sullivan, M. A. (1965). Replication of autosomal heterochromatin in man. *Chromosoma* **16,** 152–161.

Lindsay, H. A., and Barr, M. L. (1955). Further observations on the behaviour of nuclear structures during depletion and restoration of Nissl material. *J. Anat.* **89,** 47–62.

Lindsten, J. (1963). "The Nature and Origin of X Chromosome Aberrations in Turner's Syndrome." Almqvist & Wiksell, Uppsala.

Lindsten, J., and Tillinger, K. G. (1962). Self-perpetuating ring chromosome in a patient with gonadal dysgenesis. *Lancet* **I**, 593–594.

Lindsten, J., Fraccaro, M., Ikkos, D., Kaijser, K., Klinger, H. P., and Luft, R. (1963a). Presumptive iso-chromosomes for the long arm of the X in man. Analysis of five families. *Ann. Human Genet.* **26**, 383–405.

Lindsten, J., Bowen, P., Lee, C. S. N., McKusick, V. A., Polani, P. E., Wingate, M., Edwards, J. H., Hamper, J., Tippett, P., Sanger, R., and Race. R. R. (1963b). Source of the X in XO females: The evidence of Xg. *Lancet* **I**, 558–559.

Lindsten, J., Fraccaro, M., Polani, P. E., Hamerton, J. L., Sayer, R., and Race, R. R. (1963c). Evidence that the Xg blood group genes are on the short arm of the X chromosome. *Nature* **197**, 648–649.

Löve, A. (1943). Cytogenetic studies on *Rumex* subgenus *Acetosella. Hereditas* **30**, 1–136.

Löve, A., and Sarkar, N. (1956). Cytotaxonomy and sex determination in *Rumex paucifolius. Can. J. Botany* **34**, 261–268.

Löve, D. (1944). Cytogenetic studies on dioecious *Melandrium. Botan. Notiser* **97**, 125–213.

London Conference (1964). The normal human karyotype. *Ann. Human Genet.* **27**, 295–298.

London, D. R., Kemp, N. H., Ellis, J. R., and Mittwoch, U. (1964). Turner's syndrome with secondary amenorrhoea and sex chromosome mosaicism. *Acta Endocrinol.* **46**, 341–351.

Lorbeer, G. (1927). Untersuchungen über Reduktionsteilung und Geschlechts-bestimmung bei Lebermoosen. *Z. induktive Abstammungs-Vererbungslehre,* **44**, 1–109.

Lorbeer, G. (1936). Die Umwandlung eines haploiden, genotypical weiblichen Gametophyten von *Sphaerocarpus donnellii* in einen männlichen mit Hilfe von Röntgenstrahlen. *Planta* **25**, 70–83.

Lorbeer, G. (1938). Über das Vorkommen von drei verschiedenen Geschlechts-realisatoren bei den Lebermoosen. *Planta* **27**, 708–717.

Low, R. J., Benirschke, K., Grimmer, J. L., and Schneider, T. G. (1964). The chromosomes of three bears. Personal communication.

Lüers, T. (1956). Vergleichende Untersuchungen über Geschlechtsunterschiede der neutrophilen Leukozytenkerne bei Mensch und Kaninchen. *Blut* **2**, 81–88.

Lüers, T., and Petzel, G. (1958). Zellkernmorphologische Geschlechtsdiagnose bei Pelger-Anomalie der Blutkörperchen. *Blut* **4**, 168–189.

Lüers, T., Struck, E., and Nevinny-Stickel, J. (1963). Self-perpetuating ring chromosome in gonadal dysgenesis. *Lancet* **II**, 887.

Lyon, M. F. (1961). Gene action in the X-chromosome of the mouse (*Mus musculus* L.). *Nature* **190**, 372–373.

Lyon, M. F. (1962). Sex chromatin and gene action in the mammalian X-chromosome. *Am. J. Human Genet.* **14**, 135–148.

Lyon, M. F. (1963). Attempts to test the inactive-X theory of dosage compensation in mammals. *Genet. Res.* **4**, 93–103.

Lyon, M. F., Searle, A. G., Ford, C. E., and Ohno, S. (1964). A mouse translocation suppressing sex-linked variegation. *Cytogenetics* (*Basel*) **3**, 306–333.

McClintock, B. (1933). The association of non-homologous parts of chromosomes in the mid-prophase of meiosis in *Zea Mays. Z. Zellforsch. Mikroskop. Anat.* **21**, 294–328.

McClintock, B. (1938). The production of homozygous deficient tissues with mutant characteristics by means of the aberrant mitotic behavior of ring-shaped chromosomes. *Genetics* **23**, 542–571.

McClung, C. E. (1901). Notes on the accessory chromosome. *Anat. Anz.* **20**, 220–226.

Mackensen, O. (1951). Viability and sex determination in the honeybee (*Apis mellifera* L.). *Genetics* **36**, 500–509.

McKusick, V. A. (1964). "On the X Chromosome of Man." Am. Inst. Biol. Sci., Washington, D.C.

Maclean, N. (1962). The drumsticks of polymorphonuclear leucocytes in sex-chromosome abnormalities. *Lancet* **I**, 1154–1158.

Maclean, N. (1966). Sex chromatin surveys of newborn babies. *In* "The Sex Chromatin" (K. L. Moore, ed.), pp. 202–210. Saunders, Philadelphia.

Maclean, N., Mitchell, J. M., Harnden, D. G., Williams, J., Jacobs, P. A., Buckton, K. A., Baikie, A. G., Court Brown, W. M., McBride, J. A., Strong, J. A., Close, H. G., and Jones, D. C. (1962). A survey of sex-chromosome abnormalities among 4514 mental defectives. *Lancet* **I**, 293–296.

Maclean, N., Harnden, D. G., Court Brown, W. M., Bond, J., and Mantle, D. J. (1964). Sex-chromosome abnormalities in newborn babies. *Lancet* **I**, 286–290.

Mainx, F. (1957). Ein Fall von doppelter Befruchtung bei *Drosophila ambigua* (Po.) Z. *Induktive Abstammungs- Vererbungslehre* **88**, 289–290.

Mainx, F. (1962). Ein neuer Modus der genotypischen Geschlechtsbestimmung. *Biol. Zentr.* **81**, 335–340.

Mainx, F. (1964). Mosaikbildungen bei *Megasalia scalaris* durch doppelte Befruchtung. Z. *Vererbungslehre* **95**, 222–225.

Makino, S. (1941). Cytological investigations of mice included in the genus *Mus. J. Fac. Sci. Hokkaido Univ. Ser. VI* **7**, 305–380.

Makino, S. (1943). The chromosomes of the horse (*Equus caballus*). Chromosome studies in domestic mammals, I. *Cytologia* **13**, 26–38.

Makino, S. (1951). Studies on the murine chromosomes. V. A study of the chromosomes of *Apodemus*, especially with reference to the sex chromosomes in meiosis. *J. Morphol.* **88**, 93–126.

Mann, J. D., Cahan, A., Gelb., A. G., Fisher, N., Hamper, J., Tippett, P., Sanger, R., and Race, R. R. (1962). A sex-linked blood group. *Lancet* **I**, 8–10.

Manning, F. J. (1952). Sex determination in the honey bee. *Evolution* **6**, 443.

Marberger, E., Boccabella, R. A., and Nelson, W. O. (1955). Oral smear as a method of chromosomal sex detection. *Proc. Soc. Exptl. Biol.* New York, **89**, 488–489.

Marchal, E., and Marchal, E. (1907). Aposporie et sexualité chez les mousses. I. *Bull. Acad. Belg. Classe Sci.* pp. 765–789.

Marchal, E., and Marchal, E. (1909). Aposporie et sexualité chez les mousses. II. *Bull. Acad. Belg. Classe Sci.* pp. 1249–2388.

Marchal, E., and Marchal, E. (1911). Aposporie et sexualité chez les mousses. III. *Bull. Acad. Belg. Classe Sci.* pp. 750–778.

Marks, P. A. (1958). Red cell glucose-6-phosphate and 6 phosphogluconic dehydrogenases and nucleoside phosphorylase. *Science* **127**, 1338–1339.

Mather, K. (1943a). Polygenic inheritance and natural selection. *Biol. Rev.* **18**, 32–64.

Mather, K. (1943b). Polygenes in development. *Nature* **151**, 560.

Mather, K. (1944). The genetical activity of heterochromatin. *Proc. Roy. Soc.* **B132**, 309-332.

Mather, K., and Wigan, L. G. (1942). The selection of invisible mutations. *Proc. Roy. Soc.* **B131**, 50–64.

Matthey, R. (1936). La formule chromosomiale et les hétérochromosomes chez les Apodemus européens. *Z. Zellforsch. Mikroskop. Anat.* **25**, 501–515.

Matthey, R. (1947). Encore les hétérochromosomes des Apodemus. *Arch. Julius Klaus-Stift. Vererbungsforsch. Sozialanthropol. Rassenhyg.* **22**, 85–92.

Matthey, R. (1949). "Les Chromosomes des Vertébrés." Rouge, Lausanne.

Matthey, R. (1950). Les chromosomes sexuels géants de *Microtus agrestis*. *Cellule* **53**, 163–184.

Matthey, R. (1952a). Chromosomes de *Muridae* (*Microtinae* et *Cricetinae*). *Chromosoma* **5**, 113–138.

Matthey, R. (1952b). Chromosomes sexuels multiples chez un Rougeur (*Gerbillus pyramidum* Geoffrey). *Arch. Julius Klaus-Stift. Vererbungsforsch. Sozialanthropol. Rassenhyg.* **27**, 163–166.

Matthey, R. (1953). La formule chromosomique et la problème de la détermination sexuelle chez *Ellobius lutescens*. *Arch. Julius Klaus-Stift Vererbungsforsch. Sozialanthropol. Rassenhyg.* **28**, 271–279.

Matthey, R. (1954). Un cas nouveau de chromosomes sexuels multiples dans le genre *Gerbillus* (Rodentia-Muridae-Gerbillinea). *Experientia* **10**, 464–5.

Matthey, R. (1955). Les chromosomes de *Galago senegalensis* Geoffrey (Prosimii-Lorisidae-Galaginae). *Rev. Suisse Zool.* **62**, Suppl., 190–197.

Matthey, R. (1956). La formule chromosomique de quelques Murinae (Murida-Rodentia-Mammalia). *Arch. Julius Klaus-Stift. Vererbungsforsch. Sozialanthropol. Rassenhyg.* **31**, 294–306.

Matthey, R. (1958a). Les chromosomes des mammifères euthérien. Liste critique et essai sur l'évolution chromosomique. *Arch. Julius Klaus-Stift Vererbungsforsch. Sozialanthropol. Rassenhyg.* **33**, 253–297.

Matthey, R. (1958b). Un nouveau type de détermination chromosomique du sexe chez les mammifères *Ellobius lutescens*. Th. et *Microtus* (*Chilotus*) *oregoni* Bachm. (Muridés-Microtinae). *Experientia* **14**, 240–241.

Matthey, R. (1961). Cytologie comparée des Cricetinae paléarctiques et américains. *Rev. Suisse Zool.* **68**, 41–61.

Matthey, R. (1963a). Polymorphisme chromosomique intraspécifique chez un Mammifère *Leggada minutoides* Smith (Rodentia-Muridae). *Rev. Suisse Zool.* **70**, 173–190.

Matthey, R. (1963b). Polymorphisme chromosomique intraspecifique et intraindividuel chez *Acomys minous* Bate (Mammalia-Rodentia-Muridae) Etude cytologique des hybrides *Acomys minous* ♂ × *Acomys cahirinus* ♀. Le mécanisme des fusions centriques. *Chromosoma* **14**, 468–497.

Matthey, R. (1964a). Evolution chromosomique et spéciation chez les Mus du sous-genre *Leggada* Gray 1837. *Experientia* **20**, 657–665.

Matthey, R. (1964b). Etudes sur les chromosomes d'*Ellobius lutescens* (Mammalia-Muridae-Microtinae). II Informations complémentaires sur les divisions meiotiques. *Rev. Suisse Zool.* **71**, 401–410.

Matthey, R. (1965a). Un type nouveau de chromosomes sexuels multiples chez une souris africaine du groupe *Mus* (*Leggada*) *minutoides* (Mammalia-Rodentia) Male: X_1X_2Y. Femelle: X_1X_2/X_1X_2. *Chromosoma* **16**, 351–364.

Matthey, R. (1965b). Le problème de la détermination du sexe chez *Acomys selousi* de Winton. Cytogénétique du genre Acomys (Rodentia Murinae). *Rev. Suisse Zool.* **72**, 120–144.

Matthey, R. (1966). Présence dans une population Congolaise de *Mus* (*Leggada*) *triton* Th. de femelles hétérozygotes pour une délétion caractérisée par la suppression du bras court de l'un des chromosomes X métacentriques. *Z. Vererbungslehre* **97**, 361–369.

Matthey, R., and Meylan, A. (1961). Le polymorphisme chromosomique de *Sorex araneus* L. (Mamm. Insectivora). Etude de deux portées de 5 et 9 petits. *Rev. Suisse Zool.* **68**, 223–227.

Matthey, R., and van Brink, J. (1956). La question des hétérochromosomes chez les Sauropsides. I. Reptiles. *Experientia* **12**, 53–55.

Mavor, J. W. (1921). On the elimination of the X-chromosome from the egg of *Drosophila melanogaster* by X-rays. *Science* **54**, 277–279.

Myers, L. B., O'Leary, J. L., and Fox, R. R. (1964). Classification of chromosomes in normal and ataxic rabbits. *Neurology* **14**, 1058–1065.

Mazia, D. (1961). Mitosis and the physiology of cell division. *In* "The Cell" (J. Brachet and A. E. Mirsky, eds.), Vol. 3, pp. 80–412. Academic Press, New York.

Melander, Y. (1958). The mitotic chromosomes of some cavicorn mammals (*Boa taurus* L., *Bison bonasus* L. and *Ovis aries* L.). *Hereditas* **45**, 64–664.

Melander, Y. (1962). Chromosomal behavior during the origin of sex chromatin in the rabbit. *Hereditas* **48**, 645–661.

Mendel, G. (1866). Versuche über Pflanzenhybride. Reprinted in *Flora* **89**, 364–403 (1901).

Merriam, J. R., and Frost, J. N. (1964). Exchange and nondisjunction of the X-chromosomes in female *Drosophila melanogaster*. *Genetics* **49**, 109–122.

Merriam, R. W., and Ris, H. (1954). Size and DNA content of nuclei in various tissues of male, female and worker honeybees. *Chromosoma* **6**, 522–538.

Merrington, M., and Penrose, L. S. (1964). Distances which involve satellited chromosomes in metaphase preparations. *Ann. Human Genet.* **27**, 257–259.

Metz, C. W. (1914). Chromosome studies in the Diptera. I. A preliminary survey of five different types of chromosome groups in the genus Drosophila. *J. Exptl. Zool.* **17**, 45–59.

Miles, C. P. (1959). Sex chromatin in cultured human tissues. *Nature* **184**, 477–478.

Miles, C. P. (1960). Sex chromatin in cultured cells. *Exptl. Cell Res.* **20**, 325–337.

Miles, C. P. (1961). Peripheral position of sex chromatin. *Nature* **191**, 626–627.

Miles, C. P., and Storey, S. D. (1962). Nuclear chromocenters of cultured chicken cells. *Exptl. Cell Res.* **27**, 377–381.

Miller, O. J. (1964). The sex chromosome anomalies. *Am. J. Obstet. Gynecol.* **90**, 1078–1139.

Miller, O. J., Breg, W. R., Schmickel, R. D., and Tretter, W. (1961). A family with an XXXXY male, a leukaemic male and two 21-trisomic mongoloid females. *Lancet* **II**, 78–79.

Minouchi, O. (1928a). Spermatogenesis of the albino rat (*Mus norvegicus albus*). *Japan. J. Zool.* **I**, 235–254.

Minouchi, O. (1928b). The spermatogenesis of the dog, with special reference to meiosis. *Japan. J. Zool.* **1**, 255–268.

Minouchi, O., and Ohta, T. (1934a). On the chromosome number and sex chromosomes in the germ cells of male and female cats. *Cytologia* **5**, 355–362.

Minouchi, O., and Ohta, T. (1934b). On the number of chromosomes and the type of sex-chromosomes in man. *Cytologia* **5**, 472–490.

Mittwoch, U. (1957). Some observations on the leucocytes in mongolism. *J. Mental Deficiency Res.* **1**, 26–32.

Mittwoch, U. (1961). Nuclear sex and chromosome structure in mongolism and the Klinefelter syndrome. *In* "Human Chromosomal Abnormalities" (W. M. Davidson and D. R. Smith, eds.), pp. 97–105. Staples Press, London.

Mittwoch, U. (1963a). Sex differences in cells. *Sci. Am.* **161**, 54–62.

Mittwoch, U. (1963b). The incidence of drumsticks in patients with three X chromosomes. *Cytogenetics* (*Basel*) **2**, 24–33.

Mittwoch, U. (1964a). Frequency of drumsticks in normal women and in patients with chromosomal abnormalities. *Nature* **201**, 317–319.

Mittwoch, U. (1964b). Barr bodies and their relation to nuclear size. *Cytogenetics,* (*Basel*) **3**, 62–74.

Mittwoch, U. (1964c). Sex Chromatin. *J. Med. Genet.* **1**, 50–76.

Mittwoch, U., and Delhanty, J. D. A. (1961). Nuclear sex in triploid XXY human cells. *Lancet* **II**, 552.

Mittwoch, U., Atkin, N. B., and Ellis, J. R. (1963). Barr bodies in triploid cells. *Cytogenetics,* (*Basel*) **2**, 323–330.

Mittwoch, U., Lele, K. P., and Webster, W. S. (1965). Relationship of Barr bodies, nuclear size and deoxyribonucleic acid value in cultured human cells. *Nature* L. **205**, 477–479.

Mittwoch, U., Kalmus, H., and Webster, W. S. (1966). Deoxyribonucleic acid values in dividing and non-dividing cells of male and female larvae of the honey bee. *Nature* **210**, 264–266.

Mohr, O. L. (1915). Sind die Heterochromosomen wahre Chromosomen? *Arch. Zellforsch.* **14**, 151–176.

Mohr, O. L. (1916). Studien über die Chromatinreifung der männlichen Geschlechtszellen bei *Locusta viridissima*. *Arch. Biol.* (*Paris*) **29**, 579–752.

Montgomery, T. H. (1904). Some observations and considerations upon the maturation phenomena of the germ cells. *Biol. Bull.* **6**, 137–158.

Montgomery, T. H. (1906). The terminology of aberrant chromosomes and their behavior in certain Hemiptera. *Science* **23**, 36–38.

Moore, K. L. (1959). Sex reversal in newborn babies. *Lancet* **I**, 217–219.

Moore, K. L. (1966). Sex chromatin patterns in various animals. *In* "The Sex Chromatin" (K. L. Moore, ed.), pp. 16–58. Saunders, Philadelphia.

Moore, K. L., and Barr, M. L. (1953). Morphology of the nerve cell nucleus in mammals, with special reference to the sex chromatin. *J. Comp. Neurol.* **98**, 213–231.

Moore, K. L., and Barr, M. L. (1954). Nuclear morphology, according to sex, in human tissues. *Acta anat.* **21**, 197–208.

Moore, K. L., and Barr, M. L. (1955). Smears from the oral mucosa in the detection of chromosomal sex. *Lancet* **II**, 57–58.

Moore, K. L., and Hay, J. C. (1961). Sexual dimorphism in intermitotic nuclei of birds. *Anat. Record* **139**, 315.

Moore, K. L., Graham, M. A., and Barr, M. L. (1957). The sex chromatin in the bovine freemartin. *J. Exptl. Zool.* **135**, 101–126.

Moore, R. C. (1965). A biometric analysis of the chromosomes of the marsupials– *Macropus major, Macropus rufus* and *Potorous tridactylis*. *Cytogenetics* (Basel) **44**, 145–156.

Moore, R. C., and Gregory, G. (1963). Biometrics of the karyotype of *Protemnoden bicolor*, with reference to the limitations in accuracy of identifying human chromosomes. *Nature* **200**, 234–237.

Moore, W., Jr., and Lambert, P. D. (1963). The chromosomes of the beagle dog. *J. Heredity* **54**, 273–276.

Moorhead, P. S., and Defendi, V. (1963). Asynchrony of DNA synthesis in chromosomes of human diploid cells. *J. Cell Biol.* **16**, 202–209.

Morgan, L. V. (1947). A variable phenotype associated with the fourth chromosome of *Drosophila melanogaster* and affected by heterochromatin. *Genetics* **32**, 200–219.

Morgan, T. H. (1910). Sex-limited inheritance in *Drosophila. Science* **32**, 120–122.

Morgan, T. H. (1912). Eight factors that show sex-limited inheritance in *Drosophila. Science* **35**, 472–473.

Morgan, T. H. (1916). The Eugster gynandromorph bee. *Am. Naturalist* **50**, 39–45.

Morgan, T. H. (1926). "The Theory of the Gene." Yale Univ. Press, New Haven, Connecticut. Reprinted (1964) by Hafner, New York.

Morgan, T. H., and Bridges, C. B. (1916). Sex-linked inheritance in Drosophila. *Carnegie Inst., Wash. Publ.* **237**, 1–87.

Morgan, T. H., and Bridges, C. B. (1919). The origin of gynandromorphs. *Carnegie Inst. Wash. Publ.* 278, 1–122.

Morgan, T. H., and Goodale, H. D. (1912). Sex-linked inheritance in poultry. *Ann. N.Y. Acad. Sci.* **22**, 113–133.

Morgan, T. H., Bridges, C. B., and Sturtevant, A. H. (1925). The genetics of Drosophila. *Bibliogr. Genet.* **2**, 1–262.

Morgan, W. P. (1928). A comparative study of the spermatogenesis in five species of earwigs. *J. Morphol.* **46**, 241–271.

Morishima, A., Grumbach, M. M., and Taylor, J. H. (1962). Asynchronous duplication of human chromosomes and the origin of sex chromatin. *Proc. Natl. Acad. Sci. U.S.* **48**, 756–763.

Morris, J., McL. (1953). The syndrome of testicular feminization in male pseudohermaphrodites (82 cases). *Am. J. Obstet. Gynecol.* **65**, 1192–1211.

Mosier, H. D., Scott, L. W., and Cotter, L. H. (1960). The frequency of the positive sex-chromatin pattern in males with mental deficiency. *Pediatrics* **25**, 291–297.

Motulsky, A. G., and Campbell-Kraut, J. M. (1961). Population genetics of glucose-6-phosphate dehydrogenase deficiency of the red cell. *In* "Proceedings of the Conference on Genetic Polymorphisms and Geographic Variations in Disease" (B. G. Blumberg, ed.), pp. 159–180. Grune & Stratton, New York.

Mukherjee, B. B., and Sinha, A. K. (1963). Further studies on the pattern of chromosome duplication in cultured mammalian leucocytes. *Can. J. Genet. Cytol.* **5**, 490–495.

Mukherjee, B. B., and Sinha, A. K. (1964). Single-active-X-hypothesis; cytological evidence for random inactivation of X-chromosomes in a female mule complement. *Proc. Natl. Acad. Sci. U.S.* **51**, 252–259.

Muldal, S., and Ockey, C. H. (1960). The "double male": A new chromosome constitution in Klinefelter's syndrome. *Lancet* **II**, 492–493.

Muldal, S., Gilbert, C. W., Lajtha, L. G., Lindsten, J., Rowley, J., and Fraccaro, M. (1963). Tritiated thymidine incorporation in an isochromosome for the long arm of the X chromosome in man. *Lancet* **I**, 861–863.

Muller, H. J. (1930). Types of visible variations induced by X-rays in *Drosophila. J. Genet.* **22**, 299–334.

Muller, H. J. (1932). Further studies on the nature and causes of gene mutation. *Proc. 6th Intern. Congr. Genet., Ithaca, New York, 1932* Vol. 1, pp. 213–255.

Muller, H. J., and Painter, T. S. (1932). The differentiation of the sex chromosomes of *Drosophila* into genetically active and inert regions. *Z. Induktive Abstammungs- Vererbungslehre* 62, 316–65.

Muller, H. J., and Prokofyeva, A. A. (1935). The individual gene in relation to the chromomere and the chromosome. *Proc. Natl. Acad. Sci. U.S.* 21, 16–26.

Mutton, D. E., King, J. M., and Hamerton, J. L. (1964). Chromosome studies in the genus *Equus*. Private communication.

Nachtsheim, H. (1913). Cytologische Studien über die Geschlechtsbestimmung der Honigbiene. *Arch. Zellforsch.* 11, 169–241.

Nadler, C. F. (1964). Chromosomes and evolution of the ground squirrel *Spermophilus richardsonii*. *Chromosoma* 15, 298–299.

Nadler, C. F. (1965). Chromosomes of the ground squirrel *Spermophilus beldingi* and report of an aberrant karyotype in a phenotypically normal female. *Cytogenetics (Basel)* 4, 37–44.

Nadler, C. F., and Block, M. H. (1962). The chromosome of some North American chipmunks (Sciuridae) belonging to the genera *Tamias* and *Eutamias*. *Chromosoma* 13, 1–15.

Nadler, C. F., and Sutton, D. A. (1962). Mitotic chromosomes of some North American Sciuridae. *Proc. Soc. Exptl. Biol. Med.* 110, 36–38.

Naik, S. N., and Shah, P. N. (1962). Sex chromatin anomalies in newborn babies in India. *Science* 136, 1116.

Nance, W. E., and Uchida, I. (1964). Turner's syndrome, twinning and an unusual variant of glucose-6-phosphate dehydrogenase. *Am. J. Human Genet.* 16, 380–390.

Nasse, C. F. (1820). Von einer erblichen Neigung zu tödtlichen Blutungen. *Arch. Med. Erfahrung Gebiet Prakt. Med. Staatsarzneikunde* 1, 385–434.

Nelson, W. O. (1956). Sex differences in human nuclei with particular reference to the "Klinefelter-Syndrome," gonadal agenesis and other types of hermaphroditism. *Acta Endocrinol.* 23, 227–245.

Neuhaus, M. J. (1939). A cytogenetic study of the Y-chromosome of *Drosophila melanogaster*. *J. Genet.* 37, 229–254.

Nichols, W. W., Levan, A., and Lawrence, W. C. (1962). Bovine chromosomes by the peripheral blood method. *Hereditas* 48, 536–538.

Nichols, W. W., Levan, A., Hansen-Melander, E., and Melander, Y. (1965). The idiogram of the rabbit. *Hereditas* 53, 63–76.

Noll, F. (1907). Versuche über Geschlechtsbestimmung bei diözischen Pflanzen. *Sber. niederrhein. Ges. Natur-u. Heilk.* 68–91.

Nordenskiöld, E. (1927). "The History of Biology." Tudor Publ., New York.

Oestergren, G .(1950). Considerations on some elementary features of mitosis. *Hereditas* 36, 1–18.

Oestergren, G. (1951). The mechanism of co-orientation in bivalents and multivalents. The theory of orientation by pulling. *Hereditas* 37, 85–156.

Oguma, K. (1934). A new type of the mammalian sex chromosomes found in the field mouse, *Apodemus speciosus*. *Cytologia* 5, 460–471.

Oguma, K., and Kihara, H. (1923). Etude des chromosomes chez l'homme. *Arch. Biol. (Paris)* 33, 493–516.

Ohno, S. (1961). Sex chromosomes and micro-chromosomes of *Gallus domesticus*. *Chromosoma* 11, 484–498.

Ohno, S., and Cattanach, B. M. (1962). Cytological study of an X-autosome translocation in *Mus musculus*. *Cytogenetics (Basel)* 1, 129–140.

Ohno, S., and Makino, S. (1961). The single X nature of sex chromatin in man. *Lancet* I, 78–79.

Ohno, S., and Weiler, C. (1962). Relationship between large Y-chromosome and side-by-side pairings of the XY-bivalent observed in the Chinese hamster, *Cricetus griseus*. *Chromosoma* 13, 106–110.

Ohno, S., Kaplan, W. D., and Kinosita, R. (1959a). On the end-to-end association of the X and Y chromosomes of *Mus musculus*. *Exptl. Cell Res.* 18, 282–290.

Ohno, S., Kaplan, W. D., and Kinosita, R. (1959b). Formation of the sex chromatin by a single X-chromosome in liver cells of *Rattus norvegicus*. *Exptl. Cell Res.* 18, 415–418.

Ohno, S., Kaplan, W. D., and Kinosita, R. (1959c). On the sex chromatin of *Gallus domesticus*. *Exptl. Cell Res.* 19, 180–183.

Ohno, S., Kaplan, W. D., and Kinosita, R. (1960). On isopycnotic behavior of the XX-bivalent in oocytes of *Rattus norvegicus*. *Exptl. Cell Res.* 19, 637–639.

Ohno, S., Kaplan, W. D., and Kinosita, R. (1961a). Female germ cells in man. *Exptl. Cell Res.* 24, 106–110.

Ohno, S., Trujillo, J. M., Kaplan, W. D., and Kinosita, R. (1961b). Nucleolus organisers of chromosomal anomalies in man. *Lancet* II, 123–126.

Ohno, S., Trujillo, J. M., Christian, L. C., and Teplitz, R. L. (1962). Possible germ cell chimeras among newborn dizygotic twin calves (*Bos taurus*). *Cytogenetics (Basel)* 1, 258–265.

Ohno, S., Jainchill, J., and Stenius, C. (1963). The creeping vole (*Microtus oregoni*) as a gonosomic mosaic. I. The OY/XY constitution in the male. *Cytogenetics (Basel)* 2, 232–239.

Ohno, S., Beçak, W., and Beçak, M. L. (1964). X-autosome ratio and the behaviour pattern of individual X-chromosomes in placental mammals. *Chromosoma* 15, 14–30.

Oikawa, K., and Blizzard, R. M. (1961). Chromosomal studies of patients with gonadal anomalies simulating those of gonadal aplasia. *New Engl. J. Med.* 264, 1009–1016.

Ono, T. (1939). Polyploidy and sex determination in *Melandrium*. *Botan. Mag. (Tokyo)* 54, 225–30.

Opitz, J. M., Stiles, F. C., Wise, D., Race, R. R., Sanger, R., von Gemmingen, G. R., Kirland, R. R., Cross, E. G., and de Groot, W. P. (1965). The genetics of angiokeratoma corporis diffusum (Fabry's disease) and its linkage relations with the Xg locus. *Am. J. Human Genet.* 17, 325–342.

Orsi, E. V., and Ritter, H. B. (1958). A report of sex chromatin in human tumor tissue culture. *Exptl. Cell Res.* 15, 244–246.

Overzier, C. (1958). Diskrepanz der Geschlechtsdiagnose. *Klin. Wochschr.* 36, 845–849.

Overzier, C., ed. (1963a). True hermaphroditism. *In* "Intersexuality," pp. 128–234. Academic Press, New York.

Overzier, C., ed. (1963b). Pseudo-hermaphroditism. *In* "Intersexuality," pp. 235–254. Academic Press, New York.

Overzier, C., ed. (1963c). The so-called true Klinefelter's syndrome. *In* "Intersexuality," pp. 277–279. Academic Press, New York.

Owen, J. J. T. (1965). Karyotype studies on *Gallus domesticus*. *Chromosoma* 16, 601–608.

Painter, T. S. (1921). The Y-chromosome in mammals. *Science* **53**, 503–504.

Painter, T. S. (1922a). Studies in mammalian spermatogenesis. I. The spermatogenesis of the opossum (*Didelphis virginiana*). *J. Exptl. Zool.* **35**, 13–38.

Painter, T. S. (1922b). The sex chromosomes of the monkey. *Science* **56**, 286–287.

Painter, T. S. (1924a). The sex chromosomes of man. *Am. Naturalist* **58**, 506–524.

Painter, T. S. (1924b). Studies in mammalian spermatogenesis. III. The fate of the chromatin-nucleolus in the opossum. *J. Exptl. Zool.* **39**, 197–227.

Painter, T. S. (1924c). Studies in mammalian spermatogenesis IV. The sex chromosomes of monkeys. *J. Exptl. Zool.* **39**, 433–460.

Painter, T. S. (1926). Studies in mammalian spermatogenesis. VI. The chromosomes of the rabbit. *J. Morphol.* **43**, 1–22.

Painter, T. S. (1931). A cytological map of the X-chromosome of *Drosophila melanogaster*. *Anat. Record* **51**, 111.

Painter, T. S. (1933). A new method for the study of chromosome rearrangements and the plotting of chromosome maps. *Science* **78**, 585–586.

Painter, T. S. (1934a). A new method for the study of chromosome aberrations and the plotting of chromosome maps in *Drosophila melanogaster*. *Genetics* **19**, 175–188.

Painter, T. S. (1934b). The morphology of the X-chromosome in salivary glands of *Drosophila melanogaster* and a new type of chromosome map for this element. *Genetics* **19**, 448–469.

Painter, T. S. (1934c). Salivary chromosomes and the attack on the gene. *J. Heredity* **25**, 465–476.

Panshin, I. B. (1935). New evidence for the position effect hypothesis. *Dokl. Akad. Nauk SSSR* **9**, 85–88.

Panshin, I. B. (1938). The cytogenetic nature of the position effect of the genes white (mottled) and cubitus interruptus. *Biol. Zh.* **7**, 837–868.

Park, W. W. (1957). The occurrence of sex chromatin in early human and macaque embryos. *J. Anat.* **91**, 369–373.

Passarge, E., and Thompson, J. B. (1964). Autoradiography in a boy with XXY karyotype. *Am. J. Diseases Children* **108**, 184–188.

Patau, K., and Swift, H. (1953). The DNA-content (Feulgen) of nuclei during mitosis in a root tip of onion. *Chromosoma* **6**, 149–169.

Patterson, J. T. (1931). The production of gynandromorphs in *Drosophila melanogaster* by X-rays. *J. Exptl. Zool.* **60**, 173–211.

Payne, F. (1909). Some new types of chromosome distribution and their relation to sex. *Biol. Bull.* **16**, 119–166.

Pearse, A. G. E. (1960). "Histochemistry," 2nd ed., Churchill, London.

Peiper, U., and Oehme, J. (1956). Die Abhängigkeit geschlechtsgebundener Leukocytenmerkmale bei Feten und Frühgeborenen vor der Reife. *Klin. Wochschr.* **34**, 1067–1068.

Penrose, L. S. (1961). Parental age and non-disjunction. *In* "Human Chromosomal Abnormalities" (W. M. Davidson and D. R. Smith, eds.), pp. 116–122. Staples Press, London.

Penrose, L. S. (1964). A note on the mean measurements of human chromosomes. *Ann. Human Genet.* **28**, 195–196.

Penrose, L. S., and Smith, G. F. (1966). "Down's Anomaly." Churchill, London.

Peremeschko (1879). Über die Theilung der thierischen Zellen. *Arch. Mikroskop. Anat. Entwicklungsmech.* **16**, 437–457.

Petterson, G., and Bonnier, G. (1937). Inherited sex mosaic in man. *Hereditas* **23**, 49–69.

Pfeiffer, R. A. (1964). Chromosome abnormalities in children with congenital malformations. Personal communication.

Pipkin, S. B. (1940). Multiple sex genes in the X-chromosome of *Drosophila melanogaster. Texas Univ. Publ.* **4032**, 126–156.

Pipkin, S. B. (1947). A search for sex genes in the second chromosome of *Drosophila melanogaster* using the triploid method. *Genetics* **32**, 592–607.

Pipkin, S. B. (1960). Sex balance in *Drosophila melanogaster:* Aneuploidy of long regions of chromosome 3, using the triploid method. *Genetics* **45**, 1205–1216.

Platt, L. I., and Kailin, E. W. (1964). Sex chromatin frequency. *J. Am. Med. Assoc.* **187**, 182–186.

Plaut, W. S., and Mazia, D. (1956). The distribution of newly synthesized DNA in mitotic division. *J. Biophys. Biochem. Cytol.* **2**, 573–588.

Plunkett, E. E., and Barr, M. L. (1956). Testicular dysgenesis. *Lancet* **II**, 853–856.

Polani, P. E. (1962). Sex chromosome anomalies in man. *In* "Chromosomes in Medicine" (J. L. Hamerton, ed.), pp. 74–139. Heinemann, London.

Polani, P. E. (1963). Cytogenetics of Down's syndrome. (Mongolism). *Pediat. Clin. North America* **10**, 423–448.

Polani, P. E., Hunter, W. F., and Lennox, B. (1954). Chromosomal sex in Turner's syndrome with coarctation of the aorta. *Lancet* **II**, 120–121.

Pontecorvo, G. (1958). "Trends in Genetic Analysis." Columbia Univ. Press, New York.

Porter, I. H., Schulze, J. and McKusick, V. A. (1962). Genetical linkage between the loci for glucose-6-phosphate dehydrogenase deficiency and colour-blindness in American Negroes. *Ann. Human Genet.* **26**, 107–122.

Poulson, D. F. (1945). Chromosomal control of embryogenesis in Drosophila. *Am. Naturalist* **79**, 340–363.

Priestley, J. (1777). An account of persons who could not distinguish colours. (Letters from J. Huddart.) *Phil. Trans. Ray. Soc., London* **67**, 260–265.

Prince, R. H., Graham, M. A., and Barr, M. L. (1955). Nuclear morphology, according to sex, in *Macacus rhesus. Anat. Record* **122**, 153–171.

Prokofyeva-Belgovskaya, A. A. (1935). The structure of the chromocenter. *Cytologia* **6**, 438–443.

Prokofyeva-Belgovskaya, A. A. (1947). Heterochomatization as a change of chromosome cycle. *J. Genet.* **48**, 80–98.

Punnett, R. C. (1940). Genetic studies in poultry. X. Linkage data for sex chromosome. *J. Genet.* **39**, 335–342.

Race, R. R. (1965). Identification of the origin of the X-chromosome(s) in sex chromosome aneuploidy. *Can. J. Genet. Cytol.* **7**, 214–222.

Race, R. R., and Sanger, R. (1964). The X-linked blood group system Xg. *Acta Haematol.* **31**, 205–213.

Randolph, L. F. (1928). Types of supernumerary chromosomes in maize, *Anat. Record* **41**, 102.

Rao, S. R. V., and Prasad, M. R. N. (1963). The nuclear sex in the Indian elephant, *Elephas maximus* L. *Naturwissenschaften* **50**, 313.

Reitalu, J. (1957). Observations on the so-called sex chromatin in man. *Acta Genet. Med. Gemellol.* **6**, 393–402.

Renwick, J. H., and Schulze, J. (1964). An analysis of some data on the linkage between Xg and colorblindness in man. *Am. J. Human Genet.* **16**, 410–418.

Renwick, J. H., and Schulze, J. (1965). Male and female recombination fractions for the ABO: Nail-patella linkage. *Ann. Human Genet.* **28**, 379–392.

Rhoades, M. M. (1961). Meiosis. *In* "The Cell" (J. Brachet and A. E. Mirksy, eds), Vol. 3, pp. 1–75. Academic Press, New York.

Ricci, N., and Borgatti, L. (1963). XXX 18-trisomy. *Lancet* **II**, 1276.

Ridler, M. A. C., Shapiro, A., and McKibbon, W. R. (1963). Sex chromatin abnormalities in female sub-normal patient. *Brit. J. Psychiat.* **109**, 390–394.

Riis, P., Johnson, S. G., and Mosbech, J. (1956). Nuclear sex in Klinefelter's syndrome. *Lancet* **I**, 962–963.

Ris, H., and Kerr, W. E. (1952). Sex determination in the honey-bee. *Evolution* **6**, 444–445.

Risler, H. (1954). Die somatische Polyploidie in der Entwicklung der Honigbiene (*Apis mellifica* L.) und die Wiederherstellung der Diploidie bei den Drohnen. *Z. Zellforsch. mikroskop. Anat.* **41**, 1–78.

Robinson, G. C., Miller, J. R., Dill, F. J., and Kamburoff, T. D. (1964). Klinefelter's syndrome with the XXYY-sex chromosome complex. *J. Pediat.* **65**, 226–232.

Robinson, R. (1959). Genetics of the domestic cat. *Bibliogr. Genet.* **18**, 273–358.

Romatowski, H., Tolksdorf, M., and Wiedemann, H.-R. (1958). Ergänzede Beobachtungen zur hämatomorphologischen Diagnose des Kerngeschlechts. *Monatsschr. Kinderheilk* **106**, 380–381.

Root, A. W., Bongiovanni, A. M., Briebert, S., and Mellman, W. J. (1964). Double aneuploidy: Trisomy 21 and XO/XX sex chromosome mosaicism. *J. Pediat.* **65**, 937–939.

Rosenberg, H. S., Clayton, G. W., and Hsu, T. C. (1963). Familial true hermaphrodism. *J. Clin. Endocrinol. Metab.* **23**, 203–206.

Rosenkranz, W. (1965). Klinefelter Syndrom bei Kindern von Frauen mit Geschlechtschromosomen-Anomalien. *Helv. Paediat. Acta* **20**, 359–368.

Rosenkranz, W., Falk, W., Pichler, A., and Wascher, H. (1964). Familiäres Vorkommen von Chromosomenaberrationen. *Helv. Paediat. Acta* **19**, 444–457.

Ross, A. (1962). The demonstration of sex chromatin in cultured cells. *J. Med. Lab. Technol.* **19**, 112–113.

Rothenbuhler, W. C. (1958). Genetics and breeding of the honey bee. *Ann. Rev. Entomol.* **3**, 161–180.

Rothfels, K. H., and Siminovitch, L. (1958). The chromosome complement of the rhesus monkey (*Macaca mulatta*) determined in kidney cells cultivated in *vitro*. *Chromosoma* **9**, 163–175.

Rothfels, K. H., Axelrod, A. A., Siminovitch, L., McCalloch, E. A., and Parker, R. C. (1959). The origin of altered cell lines from mouse, monkey and man, as indicated by chromosome and transplantation studies. *Proc. Can. Cancer Res. Conf.* **3**, 189–214.

Rothfels, K. H., Aspden, M., and Mollison, M. (1963). The W-chromosome of the budgerigar, *Melopsittacus undulatus*. *Chromosoma* **14**, 459–467.

Rothschild, Lord (1960). X and Y spermatozoa. *Nature* **187**, 253–254.

Rowley, J., Muldal, S., Gilbert, C. W., Lajtha, L. G., Lindsten, J., Fraccaro, M., and Kajser, K. (1963). Synthesis of deoxyribonucleic acid on X-chromosomes of an XXXXY male. *Nature* **197**, 251–252.

Russell, L. B. (1961). Genetics of mammalian sex chromosomes. *Science* **133**, 1795–1803.

Russell, L. B. (1962). Chromosome aberrations in experimental mammals. *In* "Progress in Medical Genetics" (A. G. Steinberg and A. G. Bearn, eds.), Vol. 2, pp. 230–294. Grune & Stratton, New York.

Russell, L. B. (1963). Mammalian X-chromosome action: Inactivation limited in spread and in region of origin. *Science* **140**, 976–978.

Russell, L. B. (1964). Another look at the single-active-X hypothesis. *Trans. N.Y. Acad. Sci.* [2] **26**, 726–736.

Russell, L. B., and Chu, E. H. Y. (1961). An XXY male in the mouse. *Proc. Natl. Acad. Sci. U.S.* **47**, 571–575.

Russell, L. B., and Saylors, C. L. (1961). Spontaneous and induced abnormal sex-chromosome number in the mouse. *Genetics* **46**, 894.

Sachs, L. (1953). The giant sex chromosomes in the mammal *Microtus agrestis*. *Heredity* **7**, 227–238.

Sachs, L. (1954). Sex linkage and the sex chromosomes in man. *Ann. Eugenics* (*London*) **18**, 255–261.

Sachs, L. (1955). The possibilities of crossing-over between the sex chromosomes of the house mouse. *Genetics* **27**, 309–322.

Sandberg, A. A., Koepf, G. F., Grosswhite, L. H., and Hauschka, T. S. (1960). The chromosome constitution of human marrow in various developmental and blood disorders. *Am. J. Human Genet.* **12**, 231–249.

Sanderson, A. R., and Hall, D. W. (1948). The cytology of the honeybee, *Apis mellifica* L. *Nature* **162**, 34–35.

Sanderson, A. R., and Stewart, J. S. S. (1961). Nuclear sexing with acetoorcein. *Brit. Med. J.* **II**, 1065–1067.

Sanger, R. (1965). Genes on the X-chromosome. *Can. J. Gent. Cytol.* **7**, 179–188.

Santos, J. K. (1923). Differentiation among chromosomes in Elodea. *Botan. Gaz.* **77**, 353–376.

Sasaki, M., and Veomett, R. (1963). The chromosomes of the elephant, *Elephas indicus*. Personal communication.

Scherz, R. G., and Roeckel, I. E. (1963). The XXXXY syndrome. *J. Pediat.* **63**, 1093–1098.

Schleicher, W. (1879). Die Knorpelzelltheilung. *Arch. Mikroskop. Anat. Entwicklungsmech.* **16**, 248–300.

Schleiden, M. J. (1838). Beiträge zur Phytogenesis. *Arch. Anat. Physiol.* (*Leipzig*) [Translation by H. Smith in *Sydenham Soc.* (London, 1847)] **13**, pp. 231–268.

Schmid, W. (1962). DNA replication patterns of the heterochromosomes in *Gallus domesticus*. *Cytogenetics* (*Basel*) **1**, 344–352.

Schmid, W. (1963). DNA replication patterns of human chromosomes. *Cytogenetics* (*Basel*) **2**, 175–193.

Schnedl, W. (1964). Untersuchungen über das Sex Chromatin in menschlichen Fibroblastenkulturen. *Acta Anat.* **57**, 52–65.

Schneider, A. (1873). Untersuchungen über Plathelhelminthen. *Jahrb. Oberhessischen Ges. Natur-u. Heilk.* **14**, 69–140.

Schneiderman, L. J., and Smith, C. A. B. (1962). Non-random distribution of certain homologous pairs of normal human chromosomes in metaphase. *Nature* **195**, 1229.

Schrader, F. (1928). "Die Geschlechtschromosomen." Borntraeger, Berlin.

Schrader, F. (1935). Notes on the mitotic behavior of long chromosomes. *Cytologia*, **6**, 422–430.

Schrader, F., and Hughes-Schrader, S. (1931). Haploidy in metazoa. *Quart. Rev. Biol.* 6, 411–438.

Schultz, J. (1936). Variegation in *Drosophila* and the inert chromosome regions. *Proc. Natl. Acad. Sci. U.S.* 22, 27–33.

Schultz, J. (1941). The function of heterochromatin. *Proc. 7th Intern. Congr. Genet.,* Edinburgh *1939 J. Genet.* Suppl., 257–262.

Schultz, J. (1956). The relation of the heterochromatic chromosome regions to the nucleic acids of the cell. *Cold Spring Harb. Symp. Quant. Biol.* 21, 307–328.

Schwann, T. (1839). Mikroscopische Untersuchungen über die Ubereinstimmung in der Struktur und dem Wachstum der Thiere und Pflanzen. Berlin. [Translation by H. Smith in *Sydenham Soc.,* (London, 1847)] 13, pp. 1–228.

Schwarzacher, H. G. (1963). Sex chromatin in living human cells *in vitro. Cytogenetics (Basel)* 2, 117–128.

Sears, E. R. (1952). Misdivision of univalents in common wheat. Chromosoma 4, 535–550.

Seiler, J. (1914). Das Verhalten der Geschlechtschromosomen bei Lepidopteren. *Arch. Zellforsch.* 13, 159–269.

Serr, D. M., Ferguson-Smith, M. A., Lennox, B., and Paul, J. (1958). Representation of the X chromosome in intermitotic nuclei in man. *Nature* 182, 124.

Serra, J. A. (1949). A cytophysiological theory of the gene, gene mutation and position effect. *Port. Acta. Biol. Ser. A.* Volume R. B. Goldschmidt, pp. 401–562.

Shah, P. N., Naik, S. N., Mahajan, D. K., Dave, M. J., and Paymaster, J. C. (1961). A new variant of human intersex with discussion on the developmental aspect. *Brit. Med. J.* II, 474–477.

Shantaveerappa, T. R., and Bourne, G. H. (1962). A perineural epithelium. *J. Cell Biol.* 14, 343–346.

Shapiro, A., and Ridler, M. A. C. (1960). The incidence of Klinefelter's syndrome in a mental deficiency hospital. *J. Mental Deficiency Res.* 4, 48–50.

Sharman, G. B. (1956). Chromosomes of the common shrew. *Nature* 177, 941–942.

Sharman, G. B. (1961). The mitotic chromosomes of marsupials and their bearing on taxonomy and phylogeny. *Australian J. Zool.* 9, 38–60.

Sharman, G. B., McIntosh, A. J., and Barber, H. N. (1950). Multiple sex-chromosomes in the marsupials. *Nature* 166, 996.

Shearman, R. P., Singh, S., Lee, C. W. G., Hudson, B., and Ilbery, P. L. T. (1964). Clinical, hormonal and cytogenetic findings in a true hermaphrodite. *J. Obstet. Gynaecol. Brit. Empire* [N.S.] 71, 627–633.

Sharp, L. W. (1934). "Introduction to Cytology." McGraw-Hill, New York and London.

Shaver, E. L. (1962). The chromosomes of the opossum, *Didelphis virginiana. Canad. J. Genet. Cytol.* 41, 62–68.

Shaw, M. W., and Krooth, R. S. (1964). The chromosomes of the Tasmanian rat-kangaroo (*Potorous tridactylis apicalis*). *Cytogenetics* 3, 19–33.

Shiwago, P. I. (1931). Karyotypische Studien an Ungulaten. I. Über die Chromosomenkomplexe der Schafe und Ziegen. *Z. Zellforsch. Mikroskop. Anat.* 13, 511–522.

Shull, G. H. (1914). Sex-limited inheritance in *Lychnis dioica* L. *Z. Induktive Abstammungs- Vererbungslehre* 12, 265–302.

Siebner, H., Klaus, D., and Heni, F. (1963). Ein Extrachromosom bei der Pelger-Hüetschen Kernanomalie. *Med. Welt* pp. 877–880.

Siniscalco, M. (1965). Localization of genes on human chromosomes. *Proc. 11th Intern. Congr. Genet., The Hague, 1963* pp. 851–869. Pergamon Press, Oxford.

Siniscalco, M., Filippi, G., and Latte, B. (1964). Recombination between protan and deutan genes: Data on their relative positions in respect to the G-6-Pd locus. *Nature* **204**, 1062–1064.

Smith, D. W., Marden, P. M., McDonald, M. J., and Speckhard, M. (1962). Lower incidence of sex chromatin in buccal smears of newborn females. *Pediatrics, Springfield* **70**, 707–711.

Smith, I. C., and Peacock, A. D. (1957). The cytology of Pharaoh's ant, *Monomorium pharaonis* (L.). *Proc. Roy. Soc. Edinburgh* **B66**, 235–261.

Smith, S. G. (1944). The diagnosis of sex by means of heteropycnosis. *McGill Med. J.* **13**, 451–456.

Smith, S. G. (1945a). Heteropycnosis as a means of diagnosing sex. *J. Heredity* **36**, 195–196.

Smith, S. G. (1945b). The diagnosis of sex by means of heteropycnosis. *Sci. Agr.* **25**, 566–571.

Smith, S. G. (1953). A pseudo-multiple sex-chromosome mechanism in a Indian gryllid. *Chromosoma* **5**, 555–573.

Smith, S. G. (1965). Heterochromatin, colchicine and karyotype. *Chromosoma* **16**, 162–165.

Sohval, A. R. (1963). Chromosomes and sex chromatin in normal and anomalous sexual development. *Physiol. Rev.* **43**, 306–356.

Sohval, A. R., and Casselman, W. G. B. (1961). Alteration in size of nuclear sex-chromatin mass (Barr body) induced by antibiotics. *Lancet* **II**, 1386–1388.

Sohval, A. R., Gabrilove, J. L., Gaines, J. A., and Soffer, L. J. (1956). Observations on the sex chromatin in testicular disorders. *J. Mt. Sinai Hosp., N.Y.* **23**, 647–652.

Sokolov, I. (1930). The chromosomes in spermatogenesis of the goat (*Capra hircus*). *Izv. Byuro Genet. i. Evgenike* **8**, 63–76.

Soloman, I. L., Hamin, C. W., and Green, O. C. (1964). Chromosome studies on testicular tissue cultures and blood leucocytes of a male previously reported to have no Y chromosome. *New Engl. J. Med.* **271**, 386–592.

Spillman, W. J. (1908). Spurious allelomorphism: Results of some recent investigations. *Am. Naturalist* **42**, 610–615.

Steffensen, D. M. (1963). Evidence for the apparent absence of DNA in the interbands of *Drosophila* salivary chromosomes. *Genetics* **48**, 1289–1301.

Stenius, C., Christian, L. C., and Ohno, S. (1963). Comparative cytological study of *Phasianus colchicus*, *Meleagris gallopava*, and *Gallus domesticus*. *Chromosoma* **13**, 515–525.

Stern, C. (1927). Ein genetischer und zytologischer Beweis für Vererbung im Y-Chromosom von *Drosophila melanogaster*. *Z. Induktive Abstammungs- Vererbungslehre* **44**, 187–231.

Stern, C. (1929). Untersuchungen über Aberrationen des Y-chromosoms von *Drosophila melanogaster*. *Z. Induktive Abstammungs- Vererbungslehre* **51**, 253-353.

Stern, C. (1957). The problem of complete Y-linkage in man. *Am. J. Human Genet.* **9**, 147–166.

Stern, C. (1959). Use of the term "superfemale." *Lancet* **II**, 1088.

Stern, C. (1960). Dosage compensation—development of a concept and new facts. *Can. J. Genet. Cytol.* **2**, 105–118.

Stern, C. (1963). The genetics of sex determination in man. *Am. J. Med.* **34**, 715–720.

Stern, C., and Hannah, A. (1950). The sex combs in gynanders of *Drosophila melanogaster*. *Port. Acta Biol. Ser. A* Volume R. B. Goldschmidt, pp. 798–812.

Stevens, N. M. (1905). Studies in spermatogenesis, with especial reference to the accessory chromosome. *Carnegie Inst., Wash. Publ.*, **36**, 1–32.

Stevens, N. M. (1908). A study of the germ-cells in certain Diptera, with reference to the heterochromosomes and the phenomena of synapsis. *J. Exptl. Zool.* **5**, 359–374.

Stewart, J. S. S. (1960a). Mechanisms of meiotic non-disjunction in man. *Nature* **187**, 804.

Stewart, J. S. S. (1960b). Genetic mechanisms in human intersexes. *Lancet* **I**, 825–826.

Stich, H. F., and Hsu, T. C. (1960). Cytological identification of male and female somatic cells in the mouse. *Exptl. Cell Res.* **20**, 248–250.

Strasburger, E. (1880). "Zellbildung und Zelltheilung," 3rd ed. Fischer, Jena.

Strasburger, E. (1884). Die Controversen der indirecten Kerntheilung. *Arch. Mikroskop. Anat.* **23**, 246–304.

Strasburger, E. (1888). "Über Kern—und Zelltheilung im Pflanzenreich, nebst einem Anhang über Befruchtung." *Histol. Beitr. Heft Jena* **1**.

Strasburger, E. (1894). The periodic reduction of the number of the chromosomes in the life history of living organisms. *Ann. Botany (London)* **8**, 281–316.

Strasburger, E. (1900). Versuche mit diöcischen Pflanzen in Rücksicht auf Geschlechtsverteilung. *Biol. Zentr.* **20**, 657–665, 689–698, 721–731, and 753–785.

Strasburger, E. (1908). Chromosomenzahlen, Plasmastrukturen und Reduktionsteilung. *Jahrb. Wiss. Botan.* **45**, 479–570.

Strasburger, E. (1909). Zeitpunkt der Bestimmung des Geschlechts, Apogamie, Parthenogenesis und Reduktionsteilung. *Histol. Beitr. Heft* **7**, Jena.

Strasburger, E. (1910). Über geschlechtsbestimmende Ursachen. *Jahrb. Wiss. Botan.* **49**, 427–520.

Sturtevant, A. H. (1913). The linear arrangement of six sex-linked factors in *Drosophila*, as shown by their mode of association. *J. Exptl. Zool.* **12**, 499–518.

Sturtevant, A. H. (1921). A case of rearrangement of genes in *Drosophila*. *Proc. Natl. Acad. Sci. U.S.* **7**, 235–237.

Sturtevant, A. H. (1925). The effects of unequal crossing over at the Barr locus in *Drosophila*. *Genetics* **10**, 117–147.

Sturtevant, A. H. (1945). A gene in *Drosophila melanogaster* that transforms females into males. *Genetics* **30**, 297–299.

Sturtevant, A. H. (1951). The relation of genes and chromosomes. *In* "Genetics in the 20th Century" (L. C. Dunn, ed.), pp. 101–110. Macmillan, New York.

Sturtevant, A. H., and Beadle, G. W. (1939). "An Introduction to Genetics." Saunders, New York. Re-issued (1962) Dover, New York.

Sullivan, M. M., and Benirschke, K. (1964). The sex chromatin of interphase nuclei in the nine-banded armadillo, *Dasypus novemcinctus*. *Cytologia* **29**, 207–213.

Sutton, W. S. (1902). On the morphology of the chromosome group in *Brachystola magna*. *Biol. Bull.* **4**, 24–39.

Swanson, C. P. (1958). "Cytology and Cytogenetics." Macmillan, New York.

Szeinberg, A., Sheba, C., and Adam, A. (1958). Selective occurrence of glutathione instability in red blood corpuscles of the various Jewish tribes. *Blood* **13**, 1043–1053.

Szent-Györgiy, A. (1961). The supra- and submolecular in biology. *J. Theoret. Biol.* **1**, 75–82.

Taft, P. D., Dalal, K. P., McArthur, J. W., and Worcester, J. (1965). Sex chromatin body size and its relation to X chromosome structure. *Cytogenetics (Basel)* **4**, 87–95.

Tanaka, Y. (1922). Sex-linkage in the silkworm. *J. Genet.* **12**, 163–178.

Tanaka, Y. (1953). Genetics of the silkworm, *Bombyx mori. Advan. Genet.* **5**, 239–317.

Tandler, J., and Keller, K. (1911). Über das Verhalten des Chorions bei verschieden-geschlechtlicher Zwillings-gravidität des Rindes und über die Morphologie des Genitales der weiblichen Tiere, welche einer solchen Gravidität entstammen. *Deut. Tieraerztl. Wochschr.* **19**. 148–153.

Tatuno, S. (1936). Geschlechtschromosomen bei einigen Lebermoosen. II. *J. Sci. Hiroshima Univ.,* Ser. B-II **3**, 1–9.

Tatuno, S. and Yano, K. (1953). Geschlechtschromosomen bei vier Arten von Laubmoosen. *Cytologia* **18**, 36–42.

Tavares, A. S. (1966). Sex chromatin tumors. *In* "The Sex Chromatin" (K. L. Moore, ed.), pp. 405–433. Saunders, Philadelphia.

Taylor, A. I. (1963a). Nuclear sex of embryonic tumours. *Brit. Med. J.* **I**, 377–378.

Taylor, A. I. (1963b). Sex chromatin in the newborn. *Lancet* **I**, 912.

Taylor, J. H. (1957). The time and mode of duplication of chromosomes. *Am. Naturalist* **91**, 209–221.

Taylor, J. H. (1960). Asynchronous duplication of chromosomes in cultured cells of Chinese hamster. *J. Biophys. Biochem. Cytol.* **7**, 455–464.

Taylor, J. H., Woods, P. S., and Hughes, W. L. (1957). The organization and duplication of chromosomes as revealed by autoradiographic studies using tritium-labeled thymidine. *Proc. Natl. Acad. Sci. U.S.* **43**, 122–128.

Tazima, Y. (1964). "The Genetics of the Silkworm." Logos Press, London.

Teplitz, R., and Ohno, S. (1963). Postnatal induction of ovogenesis in the rabbit (*Oryctolagus cuniculus*). *Exptl. Cell Res.* **31**, 183–189.

Therkelsen, A. J. (1964). Del Castillo syndrome with female karyotype. *Lancet* **I**, 884–885.

Therkelsen, A. J., and Petersen, G. B. (1962). Frequency of sex-chromatin positive cells in the logarithmic and post-logarithmic growth phase of human cells in tissue culture. *Exptl. Cell Res.* **28**, 588–590.

Therman, E., Patau, D. W., Smith, D. W., and de Mars, R. I. (1961). The D trisomy syndrome and XO gonadal dysgenesis in two sisters. *Am. J. Human Genet.* **13**, 193–204.

Thomas, P. T., and Revell, S. H. (1946). Secondary association and heterochromatic attraction I. *Cicer arietinum. Ann. Botany (London)* [N.S.] **10**, 159–164.

Thuline, H. C., and Norby, D. E. (1961). Spontaneous occurrence of chromosome abnormality in cats. *Science* **134**, 554–555.

Tjio, J. H., and Levan, A. (1956a). The chromosome number of man. *Hereditas* **42**, 1–6.

Tjio, J. H., and Levan, A. (1956b). Note on the sex chromosomes of the rat during male meiosis. *Anales Estac. Exptl. Aula Dei* **4**, 173–184.

Tjio, J. H., and Levan, A. (1956c). Comparative idiogram analysis of the rat and the Yoshida rat sarcoma. *Hereditas* **42**, 218–234.

Tjio, J. H., and Puck, T. T. (1958). Genetics of somatic mammalian cells. II. Chromosomal constitution of cells in tissue culture. *J. Exptl. Med.* **108**, 259–268.

Tonomura, A., Toyofuko, Y., and Matsunaga, E. (1962). The frequency of so-called drumsticks in the polymorphonuclear neutrophil leucocytes of Japanese females. *Japan. J. Human Genet.* **7**, 60–66.

Townes, P. L., Ziegler, N. A., and Lenhard, L. W. (1965). A patient with 48 chromosomes (XYYY). *Lancet* **I**, 1041–1043.

Trujillo, J. M., Stenius, C. H., Christian, L. C., and Ohno, S. (1962). Chromosomes of the horse, the donkey, and the mule. *Chromosoma* **13**, 243–248.

Tschermak, O. (1900). Über künstliche Kreuzung bei *Pisum sativum*. *Ber. Deut. Botan. Ges.* **18**, 232–239.

Turner, H. H. (1938). A syndrome of infantilism, congenital webbed neck and cubitus valgus. *Endocrinology* **23**, 566–574.

Turner, H. H., and Zanartu, J. (1962). Ovarian dysgenesis in identical twins: discrepancy between nuclear chromatin pattern in somatic cells and in blood cells. *J. Clin. Endocrinol. Metab.* **22**, 660–665.

Turpin, R., and Bernyer, G. (1947). De l'influence de l'hérédité sur la formule d'Arneth (cas particulier du mongolisme) *Rev. Hématol.* **2**, 189–206.

Turpin, R., and Lejeune, J. (1965). "Les Chromosomes Humains." Gauthier-Villars, Paris.

Turpin, R., Lejeune, J., Lafourcade, J., Chigot, P. L., and Salmon, C. (1961). Présomption de monozygotism en dépit d'un dimorphisma sexuel: Sujet masculin XY et sujet neutre haplo X. *Compt. Rend.* **252**, 2945.

Turpin, R., Thoyer-Rozat, J., Lafourcade, J., Lejeune, J., Caille, B., and Kesselar, A. (1964). Coincidence de mongolisme et de syndrome de Klinefelter chez l'une et l'autre jumeaux d'une paire monozygote. *Pédiatrie* **19**, 43–52.

Uchida, I. A., and Bowman, J. M. (1961). XXX 18-trisomy. *Lancet* **II**, 1094.

Uchida, I. A., Wang, H. C., and Ray, M. (1964). Dizygotic twins with XX/XY chimerism. *Nature* **204**, 191.

Ushijima, R. N., Shininger, F. S., and Grand, T. I. (1964). Chromosome complements of two species of primates: *Cynopithecus niger* and *Presbytis entellus*. *Science* **146**, 78–79.

van Beneden, E. (1883). Recherches sur le maturation de l'oeuf, la fécondation et la division cellulaire. *Arch. Biol. (Liege)* **4**, 265–640.

van Brink, J. M. (1959). L'expression morphologique de la digamétie chez les Sauropsidés et les Monotrèmes. *Chromosoma* **10**, 1–72.

Vandel, A. (1931). "La Parthenogénèse." Doin, Paris.

Vanderlyn, L. (1948). Somatic mitosis in the root tip of *Allium cepa*—a review and a reorientation. *Botan. Rev.* **14**, 270–318.

Vanderlyn, L. (1949). The heterochromatin problem in cytogenetics as related to other branches of investigation. *Botan. Rev.* **15**, 507–582.

Van Wijck, J. A. M., Blakenborg, G. J., and Stolte, L. A. M. (1964) XO/XX mosaicism and mongolism in the same person. *Lancet* **I**, 171.

Virchow, R. (1858). "Die Cellularpathologie." Hirschwald, Berlin.

Vogel, F. (1964). A preliminary estimate of the number of human genes. *Nature* **201**, 847.

von Harnack, G. A., and Strietzel, H. N. (1956). Die Altersabhängigkeit der geschlechtsbedingten Leukocytenmerkenale. *Klin. Wochschr.* **34**, 401–402.

von Siebold, C. T. (1864). Ueber Zwitterbienen. *Z. Wiss. Zool.* **14**, 73–80.

von Wettstein, F. (1924). Morphologie und Physiologie des Formwechsels der Moose auf genetischer Grundlage I. *Z. Induktive Abstammungs- Vererbungslehre* **33**, 1–236.

von Winiwarter, H. (1912). Etudes sur la spermatogénèse humaine. *Arch. Biol.* (*Paris*) **27**, 91–188.

von Winiwarter, H. (1921). La formule chromosomiale dans l'espèce humaine *Compt. Rend. Soc. Biol.* **85**, 266–267.

Waddington, C. H. (1943). Polygenes and oligogenes. *Nature* **151**, 394.

Waddington, C. H. (1961). "The Nature of Life." Allen & Unwin, London.

Wahrman, J., and O'Brien, R. (1956). Nuclear content of DNA in chromosomal polymorphism in the genus Ameles (Orthoptera: Mantoidea). *J. Morphol.* **99**, 259–270.

Wahrman, J., and Ritte, U. (1963). Crossing-over in the sex bivalent of male mammals. *Proc. 11th Intern. Congr. Genet., The Hague, 1963* Vol. 1, p. 125. Pergamon Press, Oxford.

Wahrman, J., and Zahavi, A. (1955). Cytological contributions to the phylogeny and classification of the rodent genus *Gerbillus*. *Nature* **175**, 600–602.

Waldeyer, W. (1888). Über Karyokinese und ihre Beziehungen zu den Befruchtungsvorgängen. *Arch. Mikroskop. Anat. Entwicklungsmech.* **32**, 1–122.

Walen, K. H., and Brown, S. W. (1962). Chromosomes in a marsupial (Potorous tridactylis) tissue culture. *Nature* **194**, 406.

Warmke, H. E. (1946). Sex determination and sex balance in *Melandrium*. *Am. J. Botan.* **33**, 648–660.

Warmke, H. E., and Blakeslee, A. F. (1940). The establishment of a 4n dioecious race in *Melandrium*. *Am. J. Botany* **27**, 751–762.

Weiler, C., and Ohno, S. (1962). Cytological confirmation of female heterogamety in the African water frog (*Xenopus laevis*). *Cytogenetics* (Basel) **1**, 217–223.

Weismann, A. (1887). On the number of polar bodies and their significance in heredity *In* "Essays upon Heredity and Kindred Problems." (authorized translation by E. B. Poulton, S. Schönland, and A. Shipley), 2nd ed. 1891, pp. 345–396. Oxford Univ. Press (Clarendon), London and New York.

Wells, L. J. (1962). Experimental studies on the role of the developing gonads in mammalian sex differentiation. *In* "The Ovary" (S. Zuckerman, ed.), Vol. 2, pp. 131–153, Academic Press, New York.

Welshons, W. J., and Russell, L. B. (1959). The Y-chromosome as the bearer of the male determining factors in the mouse. *Proc. Natl. Acad. Sci. U.S.* **45**, 560–566.

Westergaard, M. (1940). Studies on the cytology and sex determination in polyploid forms of *Melandrium album*. *Dansk Botan. Arklv* **10**, 1–131.

Westergaard, M. (1953). Über den Mechanismus der Geschlechtsbestimmung bei *Melandrium album*. *Naturwissenschaften* **40**, 253–260.

Westergaard, M. (1958). The mechanism of sex determination in dioecious flowering plants. *Advan. Genet.* **9**, 217–281.

Westergaard, M. (1964). Studies on the mechanism of crossing over. I. Theoretical considerations. *Compt. Rend. Trav. Lab. Carlsberg* **34**, 359–405.

White, M. J. D. (1935). The effect of X-rays on mitosis in the spermatogonial division in *Locusta migratoria* L. *Proc. Roy. Soc.* **B119**, 61–84.

White, M. J. D. (1936). Chromosome cycle of *Ascaris megalocephala*. *Nature* **137**, 783.

White, M. J. D. (1940a). The heteropycnosis of sex chromosomes and its interpretation in terms of spiral structure. *J. Genet.* **40**, 67–82.

White, M. J. D. (1940b). The origin and evolution of multiple sex chromosome mechanisms. *J. Genet.* **40**, 303–336.

White, M. J. D. (1941). The evolution of the sex-chromosomes. I. The XO and X₁X₂Y mechanisms in praying mantids. *J. Genet.* **42**, 143–170.

White, M. J. D. (1945). "Animal Cytology and Evolution," 1st ed. Cambridge Univ. Press, London and New York.

White, M. J. D. (1954). "Animal Cytology and Evolution," 2nd ed. Cambridge Univ. Press, London and New York.

White, M. J. D. (1957). An interpretation of the unique sex chromosome mechanism of the rodent, *Ellobius lutescens* Thomas. *Proc. Zool. Soc., Calcutta* Mookerjee Mem. Volume, pp. 113–114.

White, M. J. D. (1962). A unique type of sex chromosome mechanism in an Australian mantid. *Evolution* **16**, 75–85.

White, M. J. D. (1964). Cytogenetic mechanisms in insect reproduction. *In* "Insect Reproduction" (K. C. Highnam, ed.), Symp. No. 2, pp. 1–12, Roy. Entomol. Soc., London.

White, M. J. D. (1965). Sex chromosomes and meiotic mechanisms in some African and Australian mantids. *Chromosoma* **16**, 521–547.

Whitehouse, H. L. K. (1965). "Towards an Understanding of the Mechanism of Heredity." Arnold, London.

Whiting, P. W. (1943). Multiple alleles in complementary sex determination of *Habrobracon*. *Genetics* **28**, 365–382.

Whiting, P. W. (1945). The evolution of male haploidy. *Quart. Rev. Biol.* **20**, 231–260.

Whittaker, D. L., Copeland, D. L., and Graham, J. B. (1962). Linkage of color blindness to hemophilias A and B. *Am. J. Human. Genet.* **14**, 149–158.

Wiedemann, H.-R. (1958). The result of haematological determination of the genetic sex in disturbances of sexual development. *In* "Symposium on Nuclear Sex" (D. R. Smith and W. M. Davidson, eds.), p. 102. Heinemann, London.

Wiedemann, H. R., Romatowski, H., and Tolkadorf, M. (1956). Geschlechtsbestimmung aus dem Blutbilde. *Muench. Med. Woschchr.* **98**, 1090–1095 and 1108–1112.

Wilkins, L., and Fleischmann, W. (1944). Ovarian agenesis; pathology, associated clinical symptoms and the bearing on the theories of sex differentiation. *J. Clin. Endocrinol.* **4**, 357–375.

Wilkins, L., Grumbach, M. M., and van Wyk, J. J. (1954). Chromosomal sex in "ovarian agenesis." *J. Clin. Endocrinol.* **14**, 1270–1271.

Wilson, E. B. (1896). "The Cell in Development and Inheritance," 1st ed. Macmillan, New York.

Wilson, E. B. (1905). Studies on chromosomes. I. The behaviour of the idiochromosomes in Hemiptera. *J. Exptl. Zool.* **2**, 371–405.

Wilson, E. B. (1906). Studies on chromosomes. III. The sexual differences of the chromosomes—groups in Hemiptera, with some considerations on the determination and inheritance of sex. *J. Exptl. Zool.* **3**, 1–40.

Wilson, E. B. (1909a). Recent researches on the determination and heredity of sex. *Science* **29**, 53–70.

Wilson, E. B. (1909b). Studies on chromosomes. IV. The "accessory" chromosome in *Syromastes* and *Pyrrhocoris* with a comparative review of the types of sexual differences of the chromosome groups. *J. Exptl. Zool.* **6**, 69–99.

Wilson, E. B. (1909c). The female chromosome groups in *Syromastes* and *Pyrrhocoris*. *Biol. Bull.* **16**, 199–204.

Wilson, E. B. (1909d). Studies on chromosomes. V. The chromosomes of Metapodius. A contribution to the hypothesis of the genetic continuity of chromosomes. *J. Exptl. Zool.* **6**, 147–205.

Wilson, E. B. (1911). The sex chromosomes. *Arch. Mikroskop. Anat. Entwicklungsmech.* **77**, II. 249–271.

Wilson, E. B. (1925). "The Cell in Development and Heredity," 3rd ed. Macmillan, New York.

Winge, O. (1922). One-sided masculine and sex-linked inheritance in *Lebistes reticulatus. J. Genet.*, **12**, 145–162.

Winge, O. (1923a). On sex chromosomes, sex determination and preponderance of females in some dioecious plants. *Compt. Rend. Trav. Lab. Carlsberg* **15**, 1–26.

Winge, O. (1923b). Crossing over between the X- and the Y-chromosomes in *Lebistes. J. Genet.* **13**, 201–217.

Winge, O. (1927). The location of eighteen genes in *Lebistes reticulatus. J. Genet.* **18**, 1–43.

Winge, O. (1930). On the occurrence of XX males in *Lebistes*, with some remarks on Aida's so-called "non-disjunctional" males in *Aplocheilus. J. Genet.* **23**, 69–76.

Winge, O. (1932). The nature of sex chromosomes. *Proc. 6th Intern. Congr. Genet., Ithaca, New York 1932* Vol. 1, pp. 343–355.

Winge, O. (1934). The experimental alteration of sex chromosomes into autosomes and vice versa, as illustrated by Lebistes. *Compt. Rend Trav. Lab. Carlsberg* **21**, 1–49.

Winge, O. (1937). Goldschmidt's theory of sex determination in *Lymantria. J. Genet.* **34**, 81–89.

Wintrobe, M. M. (1961). "Clinical Haematology," 5th ed. Kimpton, London.

Witschi, E. (1929). Studies on sex differentiation and sex determination in Amphibians. III. Rudimentary hermaphroditism and Y-chromosome in *Rana temporaria. J. Exptl. Zool.* **54**, 157–223.

Witschi, E. (1931). Studies on sex differentiation and sex determination in amphibians. V. Range of the cortex-medulla antagonism in parabiotic twins of Ranidae and Hylidae. *J. Exptl. Zool.* **58**, 113–145.

Witschi, E. (1948). Migration of the germ cells of human embryos from the yolk sac to the primitive gonadal folds. *Contrib. Embryol. Carnegie Inst.* **32**, 67–80.

Witschi, E. (1957). The inductor theory of sex differentiation. *J. Fac. Sci., Hokkaido Univ., Ser. VI* **13**, 428–439.

Witschi, E., and Opitz, J. M. (1963). Fundamental aspects of X intersexuality. In "Intersexuality" (C. Overzier, ed.), pp. 16–34. Academic Press, New York.

Wolf, U., Flinspach, G., Böhm, R., and Ohno, S. (1965). DNA-Reduplikationsmuster bei den Riesengeschlechtschromosomen von *Microtus agrestis. Chromosoma* **16**, 609–617.

Wolff, E. (1962). Experimental modification of ovarian development. *In* "The Ovary" (S. Zuckerman, ed.), Vol. 2, pp. 81–129. Academic Press, New York.

Woodard, J., and Swift, H. (1964). The DNA content of cold-treated chromosomes. *Exptl. Cell Res.* **34**, 131–137.

Woyke, J. (1963). Drone larvae from fertilized eggs of the honeybee. *J. Apicult. Res.* **2**, 19–24.

Woyke, J. (1965a). Genetic proof of the origin of drones from fertilized eggs of the honeybee. *J. Apicult. Res.* **4**, 7–11.

Woyke, J. (1965b). Study on the comparative viability of diploid and haploid larval drone honeybees. *J. Apicult. Res.* **4**, 12–16.

Yamamoto, T. (1961). Progenies of sex reversal females mated with sex-reversal males in the medaka. *Oryzias latres. J. Exptl. Zool.* **146**, 163–180.

Yamamoto, T. (1963). Induction of reversal in sex differentiation of YY zygotes in the medaka, *Oryzias latipes. Genetics* **48**, 293–306.

Yeager, C. H., Painter, T. S., and Yerkes, R. M. (1940). The chromosomes of the chimpanzee. *Science* **91**, 74–75.

Yerganian, G. (1959). Chromosomes of the chinese hamster *Cricetulus griseus*. I. The normal complement and identification of sex chromosomes. *Cytologia* **24**, 66–75.

Young, W. J., Merz, T., Ferguson-Smith, M., and Johnston, A. W. (1960). Chromosome number of the chimpanzee, *Pan troglodytes. Science* **131**, 1672–1673.

Yunis, J. J. (1965). "Human Chromosome Methodology." Academic Press, New York.

Zander, J., and Henning, H. D. (1963). Hormones and intersexuality. *In* "Intersexuality" (C. Overzier, ed.), pp. 118–172. Academic Press, New York.

Zuckerman, S. (1960). Origin and development of oocytes in foetal and mature mammals. *In* "Sex Differentiation and Development." (Mem. Soc. Endocrinol. No. 7. C. R. Austin, ed.), pp. 63–70. Cambridge, Univ. Press, London and New York.

AUTHOR INDEX

Numbers in italics refer to pages on which the complete references are listed.

SUBJECT INDEX

A

Abraxas, 11–12, 71–74, 77, 96, 135
Acarina, 85
Acomys, 152
Acrocentric chromosomes, nomenclature, 23
Acynonyx jabatus, 163
African water frog, see Xenopus laevis
Allium, 220, 223
Allocycly, 8, 221, 226, see also Hetero-chromatin, Heteropycnosis
Amblystegnium serpens, 37–38
Androgens, 130, 233, 236, 237, 238, 240, 243
Angiokeratoma corporis diffusum, 139
Apis mellifera, 83–85
Apodemus, 152–153, 173
Armadillo, 206
Arrhenotoky, 83, 85
Autoradiography, 221, 224–226
  in Drosophila, 68
  in fowl, 209–210
  in mammals, 146, 154, 207–208, 214
  in man, 105, 119, 121, 188–192

B

Barr bodies, 180, 225, see also Sex chro-matin
  abnormal size of, 187–188
  general properties, 180–184
  in embryos, 183, 243
  in tumors, 183–185
  numbers per nucleus, 184–187
  origin of, 191
  polyploidy and, 184–187
  relationship to drumsticks, 203–205
  structurally abnormal X-chromosomes and, 187–189, 210–212
Bean, see Vicia faba
Bear, see Euarctos americanus
Bennett's wallaby, see Protemnodon ru-fogrisea
Bobcat, see Lynx rufus
Bombyx mori, 76–77, 208, 233
Boa constrictor, 95

Bos taurus, 165, 207, see also Freemar-tin
Brachystola magna, 6, 8
Bryonia, 9, 37, 40–41
Bryum caespiticum, 37
Buccal smear, 179, 182, 184, 185, 210–212
Budgerigar, see Melopsittacus undulatus
Bush baby, see Galago

C

Callithrix jacchus, 167, 169
Campion, see Silene
Canis familiaris, 157–158, 205, 208
Cannabis, 41
Capra hircus, 165–166, 205, 208
Cat, see Felis domesticus
Cattle, see Bos taurus
Cebus, 167
Cell culture(s), 103, 182, 184, 206
Centimorgans, see Map units
Centric fusion, 81
Centromere, 20–21, 62, 152, 173
  heterochromatin and, 68, 218, 220, 222
  misdivision of, 119
  position of, 59, 104, 171
Cercopithecus, 167
Cheetah, see Acynonyx jabatus
Chiasmata, 7, 26, 140
  between X- and T-chromosomes, 27–28, 102, 152, 154, 172–174
Chiasmatype, 7
Chilocorus, 222
Chimpanzee, see Pan troglodytes
Chinchilla lanigera, 145
Chinese hamster, see Cricetus griseus
Chipmunks, see Tamias, Eutamias
Chironomus, 68, 87
Choristoneura (Archips) fumiferana, 178, 208
Christmas disease, 136
Chromatids, 20, 28
Chromatin nucleolus, 102
Chromocenters, 68, 180–182, 194, 206, 214, 225, 226, 228